ArcView® GIS Exercise Book

Pat Hohl and Brad Mayo

ArcView® GIS Exercise Book

Pat Hohl and Brad Mayo

Published by:

OnWord Press
2530 Camino Entrada
Santa Fe, NM 87505-4835 USA

Second Edition, 1997

SAN 694-0269

10 9 8 7 6 5 4 3

Printed in the United States of America

Library of Congress Cataloging-in-Publication Data

Hohl, Pat, 1961-
ArcView GIS exercise book / Pat Hohl and Brad Mayo. – 2nd ed.
     p.   cm.
Includes index.
ISBN 1-56690-124-3
Geographic information systems. 2. ArcView GIS (computer program).
I. Mayo, Brad, 1964-   . II. Title.
G70.212.H64   1997
910' .285--dc21   96-52395
                                    CIP

Trademarks

ArcView and ARC/INFO are registered trademarks of Environmental Systems Research Institute, Inc. OnWord Press is a registered trademark of High Mountain Press, Inc. All other terms mentioned in this book that are known to be trademarks or service marks have been appropriately capitalized. OnWord Press cannot attest to the accuracy of this information. Use of a term in this book should not be regarded as affecting the validity of any trademark or service mark.

Warning and Disclaimer

This book is designed to provide information on the use of the ArcView program. Every effort has been made to make the book as complete, accurate, and up to date as possible; however, no warranty or fitness is implied.

The information is provided on an "as is" basis. The authors and OnWord Press shall have neither liability nor responsibility to any person or entity with respect to any loss or damages in connection with or arising from the information contained in this book.

About the Authors

Pat Hohl is a senior electric engineer with the City of Riverside, California, Public Utilities Department. Pat earned his B.S.E.E. from Drexel University in 1984. He has served as the City's CADME/GIS project manager, responsible for data conversion, software development, and implementation. Pat is an instructor for the University of California-Riverside UNEX Extension GIS certificate program, and uses ARC/INFO, Oracle, and ArcView to manage electric utility facilities in Riverside.

Brad Mayo is a senior programmer analyst with the City of Riverside, California, Information Systems Department. He earned his B.A. in geography from California State University-San Bernardino in 1986. Brad is the public utilities CADME database administrator and the lead programmer for utility applications. He is an instructor for the University of California-Riverside UNEX Extension GIS certificate program and uses ARC/INFO, Oracle, PL/SQL, and ArcView to manage the GIS at the City of Riverside.

Acknowledgments

I would like to thank several people who helped make this book possible. First, thanks to ESRI and OnWord Press for their excellent support and cooperation. I would also like to thank my partner for his long hours of hard work and relentless enthusiasm. Finally, special thanks to my lovely wife, Dena, for her unwavering support and encouragement.

Pat Hohl

I would also like to thank the people at OnWord Press and ESRI for their support and cooperation. Without the technical support staff at ESRI, some of the exercises in the book would not have been possible. I would like to thank my wife Geraldine, and my two boys, Aaron and Joshua. They are the ones who suffered and kept me going through this project. They kept me going especially in terms of late nights, with questions and comments such as "What's that?" "Are you done yet?" and "Get to work." I would also like to thank Pat because it was his idea to write the book.

Brad Mayo

OnWord Press...

OnWord Press is dedicated to the fine art of professional documentation. In addition to the authors who developed the material for this book, other members of the OnWord Press team contributed their skills to make the book a reality. Thanks to the following people and other members of the OnWord Press team who contributed to the production and distribution of this book.

Dan Raker, President and Publisher
David Talbott, Acquisitions Director
Barbara Kohl, Editorial Manager, Acquisitions Manager
Carol Leyba, Senior Production Manager
Daril Bentley, Senior Editor
Michelle Mann, Production Editor
Cynthia Welch, Production Editor
Lauri Hogan, Marketing Services Manager
Kristie Reilly, Assistant Editor
Lynne Egensteiner, Cover designer, Illustrator

Contents

Chapter 4: Symbology and Layouts 83

Chapter 5: Theme-on-Theme Selection 125

Chapter 9: Proximity Analysis   207

Chapter 10: Geocoding   229

Chapter 13: Application Deployment **295**

Chapter 14: Network Analyst Extension **327**

Introduction

This book is intended for the average computer user with little or no experience in ArcView GIS or other geographic information systems (GIS) software. After completing the exercises in the book, you will be able to comfortably use ArcView GIS to view, query, analyze, chart, and map your geographic data. In addition, you will learn valuable skills that will enable you to customize ArcView GIS for your specific needs. You will also be provided with an overview of the data offered by a select group of commercial data vendors to help jump-start your ArcView GIS applications.

Written to ArcView GIS, the *ArcView GIS Exercise Book* can be used as a standalone text or in tandem with *INSIDE ArcView GIS* (OnWord Press, 1997) by Scott Hutchinson and Larry Daniel. Exercises cover all major ArcView functionality clearly and concisely, and sophistication increases as you proceed through the book.

Early chapters focus on the basic tools and functions of the various ArcView document types. Subsequent chapters highlight more advanced analysis and functions in the context of real world applications.

A series of exercises culminates in the deployment of a custom, end user, real estate application complete with a custom user interface. Two exercises cover the fundamentals of the Network and Spatial Analyst extensions.

A glossary of terms specific to geographic information systems and ArcView, and an ArcView functionality quick reference follow Chapter 15. Finally, a detailed index appears at the end of the book.

The companion CD-ROM contains sample data and all files necessary to perform the exercises. Upon reading the *ArcView GIS Exercise Book*, you will see examples of how to use ArcView in real world applications, learn many useful tips, and use several handy scripts and extensions to make running ArcView easier.

If you have any comments, questions, or recommendations about the book, we encourage you to contact us at OnWord Press, 2530 Camino Entrada, Santa Fe NM 87505-4835 USA, or e-mail us at *readers@hmp.com*.

Typographical Conventions

The names of ArcView GIS functionality interface items—such as menus, windows, menu options, tool buttons, icons, and dialog box options—are capitalized. An example follows:

❐ Symbols are modified using the Legend Editor and the Symbol Palette.

User input—and names for files, directories, tables, fields, column names, and so on—are italicized. Examples follow:

❐ Navigate to the *$AVEXDS\avexer\project* directory and select the *chapt5.apr* project.

❏ In the Table Properties dialog box, remove the checks for visibility for the *Area, Perimeter, Parcels#, Parcels-id, Genplan, Landuse,* and *Zoning* fields.

❏ The additional data reside in another table, called *assessor.dat.*

Emphasis is indicated by italics.

❏ Symbols called *pens* symbolize linear data.

❏ An *update event* occurs when user action alters the state of the active document.

❏ The View Scale is the ratio of distance on the view or *interactive map* to distance on the ground.

General function and single keyboard keys appear enclosed in angle brackets.

❏ <Enter>

❏ <Shift>

❏ <P>

Key sequences—instructions to hold a key down while clicking the mouse or pressing another key—are linked with a plus sign.

❏ <Ctrl>+click

❏ <Ctrl>+<P>

Avenue code lines are shown in a monospaced typeface.

```
theDoc = av.GetProject.FindDoc("LockUp")  'Get this script
av.GetProject.RemoveDoc(theDoc)         'Remove this script
av.GetProject.Save     'Save the project, making it read only
```

For a discussion of views, see Chapter 3, "More About Views," page 61.

Pen Styles - Setting

References to *INSIDE ArcView GIS* by Scott Hutchinson and Larry Daniel (OnWord Press, 1997) appear in the margin as shown in the left margin.

ArcView GIS's on-line help system is an excellent resource you can access at any time. References to the on-line help system appear as shown in the left margin.

✓ **TIP:** *Tips on functionality usage, shortcuts, and other information aimed at saving you time and toil appear like this.*

⤙ **NOTE:** *Information on features and tasks that is not immediately obvious or intuitive appears in notes.*

☛ **WARNING:** *A handful of warnings appear in the book to help prevent you from committing yourself to outcomes you may not expect or desire.*

On Directories and Operating Systems

Screen pictures and references to accessing files and directories throughout this book are written for the Microsoft Windows 95 environment. However, you can perform the exercises regardless of your operating system. The project files were created for 800 x 600 screen resolution. If you have lower resolution than 800 x 600, cascade or resize the windows as necessary.

When you encounter a reference in the text to a directory, simply "convert" it to your operating system's syntax. For example, you are frequently directed to the *$AVEXDS\avexer* directory. In a UNIX environment you would convert this directory to *$AVEXDS/avexer.* If you are working in the Mac environment, the directory becomes *avexds:avexer.*

Because the installation location of ArcView GIS may vary by site and operating system, the ArcView GIS installation location is referred to as *$AVHOME.* When you see this reference, convert it to the location where ArcView GIS is installed.

In order to perform the exercises with the accompanying ArcView GIS project files, you need to set several environment variables on your system. If the *HOME* variable is not normally set on your operating system, it should be set to point to the *avlearn* directory. This directory is used by ArcView as the default read/write directory. The *AVEXDS* variable should be set to point to the location of the *avexer* directory. The *AVEXDATA* variable should be set to point to the location of the *avdata* directory. You will need write access to both the *HOME* and *AVEXDS* directories.

Installing Files from the CD-ROM

Please consult the *README.txt* file on the CD-ROM for additional notes. The companion CD-ROM contains data and project files used in the exercises prepared by the authors or supplied by commercial data providers.

↝ **NOTE:** *Exercise drectories on the CD-ROM are named* avexer *and* avdata.

The *avexer* directory contains several subdirectories containing project files and data. You must copy *avexer* to a hard drive where you have write access. The *dbf* subdirectory contains database tables. The *project* subdirectory contains ArcView GIS project files and other miscellaneous files. The *results* subdirectory is provided for reference. It contains data and the project files resulting from successful completion of each exercise. The *shape* subdirectory contains data you will edit during the exercises. The *scripts* subdirectory contains scripts and extensions. The *tempgrid* directory will be used to store temporary files for Spatial Analyst.

The *avdata* directory contains data used in the exercises. We *strongly* recommend that you copy *avdata* to a hard drive. If you do not have sufficient disk space to load *avdata* onto a hard drive, you can access it directly from the CD-ROM. However, accessing files from the CD drive will increase ArcView GIS processing time.

You must copy *avexer* from the CD-ROM. On some systems, a read-only flag will be set for files copied from the CD-ROM. In these cases, we have included a command to unset the flags.

The commands for accessing the CD-ROM files are operating system dependent. Refer to the ArcView GIS CD-ROM installation notes if necessary. These notes shipped with your ArcView GIS CD-ROM, and contain the precise commands for mounting the CD-ROM on your system. Guidelines for transferring files from the CD-ROM by operating system follow.

Hard Drive Space Requirements

CD-ROM	
avexer	37 Mb
avdata	76 Mb
CLARITAS	
Root directory files	114.73 Kb
DEMO	10.45 Mb
RESOURCE	3.33 Mb
SAMPLES	
BOUNDARY	763.5 Kb
HEALTH	20.1 Mb
HIGHWAY	136.1 Kb
LANDMARK	11 Kb
REALEST	17.21 Mb
RETAIL	16.59 Mb
SOLUTION	1.21 Mb

Windows 3.x, Windows 95, and Windows NT

1. Create a directory on your hard drive for your files. The recommended name for this directory is *avlearn*. From the Windows environment, access the File Manager or Explorer and create a directory called *avlearn*.

2. Insert the CD-ROM in your CD drive. Open two windows in your File Manager or Explorer so that you can view the *avlearn* directory and the contents of the CD-ROM.

3. Select the *avexer* directory from the CD-ROM and drag it into the *avlearn* directory. Follow the same procedure to copy the *avdata* directory.

4. From DOS or a DOS window, navigate to the *avlearn* directory and issue the following DOS command to remove the Read-Only flag.

```
ATTRIB   -R   /S
```

To access the data properly in the ArcView GIS projects, you need to set three environment variables. The setting of the variables is dependent on the Windows version you are using.

❐ For Windows 3.x and Windows 95, set the required environment variables to access the Arc-View projects and data by adding the following statements to your *AUTOEXEC.BAT* file. If you install the files in *c:\avlearn*, the commands would look like this:

```
SET HOME=c:\avlearn
SET AVEXDS=c:\avlearn
SET AVEXDATA=c:\avlearn
```

❐ In Windows NT, you need to access the System Control Panel to set environment variables.

The previous statements *must* reflect the actual location of where you placed the files on your system. If you did not use the recommended directory name, or are storing the files on a server, or choose to access *avdata* from the CD-ROM, you will have to modify the previous command syntax to reflect the actual location of the various files.

For all versions of Windows except NT, you will need to reboot your system for the environment variables to take effect. If you have any problems setting environment variables, refer to your Windows documentation.

Apple Macintosh

1. Create a folder on your system and name it *avlearn*.

2. Insert the CD-ROM.

3. Double-click on the CD-ROM icon.

4. Select the *avexer* folder on the CD-ROM and drag it to your *avlearn* folder. Repeat the same procedure for the *avdata* folder.

5. In order to perform the exercises with the accompanying ArcView GIS project files, you need to set several environment variables on your system. You will need to create a file called *startup* located in your preference folder under the system folder. Input the following lines and save as a normal text file. (Consult the on-line help system in ArcView GIS under the following heading: "Environment variables - setting.") If you installed the files in a drive named *pnb*, the commands would look like this:

```
System.SetEnvVar("HOME","pnb:avlearn")
System.SetEnvVar("AVEXDS","pnb:avlearn")
System.SetEnvVar("AVEXDATA","pnb:avlearn")
'

' For the initial test of this script, use the following lines.
' When you are sure that the script is working, remove these lines.
MsgBox.Info(System.GetEnvVar("HOME"),"HOME is set to...")
MsgBox.Info(System.GetEnvVar("AVEXDS"),"AVEXDS is set to...")
MsgBox.Info(System.GetEnvVar("AVEXDATA"),"AVEXDATA is set to...")
```

The previous statements *must* reflect the actual location of where you placed the files on your system. If you did not use the recommended folder name, or are storing the files on a server, or choose to access *avdata* from the CD-ROM, you will have to modify the previous command syntax to reflect the actual location of the various files.

UNIX

1. Mount the CD-ROM on your system.

2. Make a directory named *avlearn*.

3. Change your working directory to *avlearn*.

4. Transfer the files and directories from the CD-ROM to the *avlearn* directory. The following commands assume that the CD-ROM is mounted to */cdrom*. Substitute your own path for the CD-ROM if it differs from */cdrom*. These command lines also assume that you are located in the *avlearn* directory.

```
cp -rp /cdrom/avexer
cp -rp /cdrom/avdata
chmod -R u+w *
```

In order to perform the exercises with the accompanying ArcView GIS project files, you need to set several environment variables on your system. Setting environment variables is UNIX-shell specific.

1. If you are using the C shell, add the following commands to your *.cshrc* file. These statements must reflect the actual location on your system where you placed the files. If you did not use the recommended directory name, or choose to access *avdata* from the CD-ROM, you will have to modify the command syntax to reflect the actual location of the various files. If you installed the files in */home/bmayo/avlearn*, the commands would look like this:

```
setenv AVEXDS /home/bmayo/avlearn
setenv AVEXDATA /home/bmayo/avlearn
```

2. After you have edited the *.cshrc* file, type the following command line, open a new command window, or execute a new login to your system for the changes to take effect.

```
% cd
% source .cshrc
```

3. If you are using the Bourne or Korn shell, add the following commands to your *.profile* file to set the environment variables:

```
AVEXDS=/home/bmayo/avlearn
export AVEXDS
AVEXDATA=/home/bmayo/avlearn
export AVEXDATA
```

4. After you have edited the *.profile* file, type the following command line, open a new command window, or re-login to your system for the changes to take effect.

```
$ cd
$ .profile
```

Data Providers

Some of the data files used in the exercises were provided by commercial data vendors. For more information about the data files, sources, and availability, contact the vendors directly.

Environmental Systems Research Institute

ESRI provided some of the graphics and data files used in this book. The ESRI files as they appear on the companion CD follow:

❐ avdata\misc\house1.tif

❐ avdata\world

❐ avdata\namerica

❐ avdata\redwood

❐ avdata\oklahoma (base data)

❐ avdata\grids (several grids, base data)

For more information, call ESRI at 909-793-2853.

Equifax National Decision Systems, Inc.

Equifax National Decision Systems provides market information and target marketing solutions that can assist in market analysis, site evaluation, trade area definition, target marketing, and much more. Through data, software, and industry-specific applications expertise, Equifax National Decision Systems helps professionals improve decision-making capabilities.

With over 65 unique databases available, Equifax National Decision Systems can be a single source for market-level data for many GIS applications. Data are available by region, state, MSA, county, zip code, census tract, and block group.

For more information, call an Information Services Representative at 1-800-866-6510, ext. 1.

Geographic Data Technology, Inc.

Geographic Data Technology Inc. (GDT) develops and sells geographic digital street network and boundary databases, geocoding software, and custom geographic services. GDT continuously updates a nationwide street database producing a complete and comprehensive database for analysis and geocoding through addition of new streets and postal information. This nationwide internal database forms the foundation for a range of cartographic database products, including Dynamap/1000, Dynamap/2000, 5-digit ZIP Code boundaries, Address Geocoding Services, and Matchmaker/2000 for Windows geocoding software.

For more information, call GDT at 1-800-331-7881.

SPOT IMAGE, S.A.

SPOT is a leading provider of Earth observation satellite image data and geographic information. SPOT Image Corporation was established in 1982 to develop the U.S. market for image data acquired by the international SPOT satellite system. SPOT satellites acquire highly detailed imagery of the entire earth's surface. SPOT Image Corporation has made it a priority to keep pace with new software developments by offering image products that give GIS users direct access to the information contained in image data.

For more information, call 1-800-ASK-SPOT.

VISTA Information Solutions, Inc.

VISTA, based in San Diego, California, provides computerized geographic information solutions in the areas of compliance and risk management for the insurance, finance, real estate, marketing, and environmental engineering industries. Its subsidiary, VISTA Environmental Information, Inc., is the leading supplier of environmental information on contaminated and potentially contaminated commercial, industrial, and residential real estate in the United States.

For more information, call Vista at 619-450-6100.

Claritas Sample Software and Data Files

Claritas delivers solutions for precise, timely business decisions. Claritas data, software, support, and analytic expertise enable you to understand your customers and markets thoroughly to pinpoint your most profitable business opportunities. In addition, with specialized solutions and industry expertise in retail, healthcare, packaged goods, finance, telecommunications, real estate, and media, you will be working with seasoned experts who know your business.

The Claritas portfolio of GIS databases is among the most comprehensive in the world. It includes geographic, demographic, consumer, lifestyle, business, and industry specific information. The company's experience in compiling and integrating data, and its expertise in applying information and analytic techniques, means that you will receive effective solutions to the challenges you face. Databases are available for whatever geographic level you need, including census, political, postal, media, and telecommunications. All databases are available in a variety of media and formats to ensure plug-and-play usability.

Of course, the products you use are only as good as the company that supports them. Claritas's 25 years of experience, commitment to quality, premium value, and dedicated support for building your business are the reasons why over 97 percent of its clients say they would recommend Claritas to others.

Claritas can be reached at Claritas, Inc., 53 Brown Rd., Ithaca, NY 14850; (800) 234-5973; (607) 266-0425; http://www.claritas.com; or info@claritas.com.

Claritas Solutions

Success in business requires fast, accurate decisions. Those decisions depend on information and software tools that can quickly reveal the best opportunities and the most critical risks for your business.

Now Claritas offers you the **solution**series—precision-crafted packages of data and software specifically designed for your industry. This innovative product line brings together the power of the industry's leading demographic and retail data with sophisticated software tools from the Claritas Precision Marketing Suite. With the **solution**series, you'll have everything you need to profile America's neighborhoods, businesses, retailers, and consumers.

The **solution**series delivers the information and tools you need to tackle many challenges:

- ❐ Trade area analysis
- ❐ Cannibilization analysis
- ❐ Competitive analysis
- ❐ Environmental impact
- ❐ List selection
- ❐ Market share and penetration
- ❐ Merchandising
- ❐ Product demand
- ❐ Sales forecasting
- ❐ Sales management
- ❐ Segmentation
- ❐ Site location
- ❐ Strategic planning
- ❐ Target promotions

Rely on Some of the Best Names in the Business

In addition to Claritas's award-winning demographics, consumer expenditure estimates, and lifestyle segmentation data, the **solution**series integrates industry-specific data and software tools from many other top providers:

- ❐ American Business Information, Inc.
- ❐ American Medical Information, Inc.
- ❐ Business Location Research
- ❐ Geographic Data Technology
- ❐ HCIA
- ❐ National Research Burea
- ❐ U.S. Bureau of the Census

Claritas has tailored a **solution**series for the health-care, retail, and real estate industries. More industry versions are in the works. Within each **solution**series there are four levels of data and software. Each successive level delivers greater data diversity and detail, and more software functionality, as indicated in the following matrix.

	1	2	3	4
Attribute Data				
Demographics	x	x	x	x
Workplace profiles		x	x	x
Consumer expenditures	x	x	x	x
Business information		x	x	x
Data specific to your industry		x	x	x
Geographic Data				
Boundary files			x	x
Highways			x	x
City locations			x	x
Landmarks			x	x
Software				
Claritas Connect		x	x	x
Claritas Coder				x

For as little as $295, you can have accurate profiles of your retail markets. You can start with the complete **solution**series package immediately, or you can select just the components you need today and add on as your business grows. Choose the level that's right for you, and enjoy an unbeatable value.

Level 1: A generous demographic database customized for your industry.

Level 2: More comprehensive demographics and decision-critical data for your industry, such as business profiles, consumer spending estimates, workplace population, retail locations, traffic volumes, healthcare data, and more. Includes Claritas Connect for easy, 24-hour online access to all of the company's Precision Marketing databases and reports.

Level 3: Even more detailed data, plus boundary and landmark files for mapping.

Level 4: The ultimate in data detail and software functionality! You get rich, robust data, plus Claritas Connect, mapping files, and Claritas Coder for online geocoding and point coding.

Installing Claritas Demonstration Programs and Resource Files

The companion CD-ROM includes many resources to help you understand the **solution**series product line and to choose the level that best matches your needs and budget.

Install the **solution**series resources from the companion CD-ROM by taking following the steps.

For Windows 3.1 and NT:

1. Insert the CD in your CD-ROM drive.

2. In the Windows Program Manager, select Run from the File menu.

3. Type *D:\CLARITAS\SETUP* (where *D* is your CD-ROM drive).

4. Click on OK.

For Windows 95:

1. Insert the CD in your CD-ROM drive.

2. Click Start on the Windows 95 Task Bar and select Run.

3. Type *D:\CLARITAS\SETUP* (where *D* is your CD-ROM drive).

4. Click on OK.

Follow the instructions in the installation program and choose the options that best suit your needs.

Using Claritas Demonstration Programs and Resource Files

Once you have completed the installation, the following steps are recommended to fully appreciate the **solution**series files included on the companion CD-ROM.

1. Browse the **solution**series reference file. This simple help file is loaded with information on the benefits, content, and design of the **solution**-series. The help file also includes layouts of all of the sample **solution**series data files on the companion CD-ROM. You'll find that Claritas has done its homework in compiling these databases and tailoring them to your needs. The finest data sources and software have been integrated to deliver analytic power to build your business.

2. Run the **solution**series slide show installed with the companion CD. This Microsoft PowerPoint slide show illustrates how the **solution**series database and software components work together to tackle the tough business challenges you face.

3. Once you have inspected the contents of the **solution**series using the help file, take a look at the Claritas Connect demo, which installs with the CD. You'll see how Connect can reveal new perspectives on your markets by allowing you to tap into its complete online library of databases and reports 24 hours a day. Samples of all Claritas Connect reports are included in the RapiData Reports help file, also available on the companion CD.

4. Now you're ready to take **solution**series data and boundaries for a test drive. The sample files on the CD cover all four **solution**series levels for each of three industries: healthcare, retail, and real estate. Files are formatted for use with ArcView. You need an installed and licensed copy of ArcView in order to map the sample data. Consult the "How to" section of the **solution**series reference file for more information on using the sample data.

5. The CD contains a Dr. Know-It-All Census help file. Dr. Know-It-All is a glossary of census geographic and demographic terms. It is an ideal reference for understanding the many nuances of demographic tabulations. Also included is the RapiData Report Guide—another help file, which provides samples and pricing for all print reports available through Claritas Connect and the Claritas call-in service. View these files at your leisure for an overview of the many Precision Marketing resources available to you.

Claritas Connect

Claritas Connect, one of the software components in the **solution**series, can also be licensed separately. Claritas Connect is the perfect information resource to help you succeed in business today. It gives you access to the data you need to outpace your competition, take advantage of new opportunities, and perform critical business applications quickly and accurately. Claritas Connect can help you accomplish the following tasks:

- ❏ Conduct site and competitive analyses
- ❏ Identify market trends
- ❏ Define target markets
- ❏ Position products and services
- ❏ Develop merchandising and marketing strategies
- ❏ Assess acquisitions and consolidations, and more

Claritas Connect is High IQ software because it delivers "Information, *Quick*." You get immediate online access to all the marketing intelligence you need to get a grip on today's marketing and consumer data explosion: Demographics... Business & Retail... Consumer Expenditure... Healthcare... Media... Financial Services... and more. In addition to Claritas proprietary data, such as PRIZM segmentation and award-winning local-area demographics, Claritas also carries data from the country's leading suppliers.

Accessing Data Has Never Been So Easy

If you can use a mouse, you can use Claritas Connect. One click gives you access to the most current demographic, consumer, and business databases for every neighborhood and market in the United States. All data, reports, and geographic lists are logically grouped in on-screen folders, making it easy to explore Claritas Connect's entire database collection.

Every step is easy: defining markets and selecting and integrating data (point, click). Choose from over 100 online preformatted reports or create your own folders in minutes, with data selections and study area definitions you can re-use or modify later. You can even tailor the system's geography levels, default database formats, and more. When you're ready, Claritas Connect retrieves your data automatically online from the Claritas host. If you need it, help is always available through on-screen help and the Claritas technical assistance hotline.

From Reports to Maps, Data in the Form You Want

Whether you want printed reports, a database formatted for your favorite spreadsheet, or data and boundary files for your GIS mapping applications, Claritas Connect delivers. Data can be quickly exported to Lotus, Excel, Quattro, dBase, ASCII, or DBF formats. For mapping applications, both data and boundary files can be automatically integrated into a variety of GIS mapping packages, including ArcView. All standard geographic levels are available, including census, postal, media, and political geographic rosters. Claritas Connect also makes it simple to summarize information for study areas such as ring studies.

The Power of Online Access

Only Claritas Connect has the flexibility to deliver data online so that you can concentrate on how to use the data, not how to get it. Online, you harness the power of the Claritas host mainframe, which stores immense databases and processes your data requests and reports. Data are kept "fresh" through routine updates.

Data Access for the Budget-conscious

With Claritas Connect, you can choose to pay only for the data you use, or you can purchase an unlimited access license for data you use regularly. The license fee covers Claritas Connect software and basic upgrades, access to database updates, software and database documentation, and technical support. No other system is so flexible and so economical.

The companion CD-ROM includes a demonstration program for Claritas Connect. It will be automatically installed when you run *D:\CLARITAS\SETUP.EXE*. If you would rather run the demonstration from the CD-ROM, run *D:\CLARITAS\RESOURCE\CONNECT\CONNDEMO.EXE* (where *D* is your CD-ROM drive).

Information Resource Files

As the leading provider of Precision Marketing information, Claritas has developed many information resources for users. Two such files have been included on the companion CD-ROM.

Dr. Know-It-All's Help file

Dr. Know-It-All is a Windows help file that provides quick access to information about demographic and geographic terms. Did you know, for example, that census data for housing value are tabulated for "specified owner-occupied housing units" that only include one-family houses on fewer than 10 acres without a business or medical office on the property? That's why 1990 value data for Manhattan only totals 2,179 housing units, when there were actually over 785,000 housing units there in 1990. Drawing the right conclusion from demographic data requires that you understand the caveats inherent in the data. Dr. Know-It-All makes it much easier for you to do just that.

The companion CD-ROM includes a Dr. Know-It-All's help file. It will be automatically installed when you run *D:\CLARITAS\SETUP.EXE*. If you would rather run the demonstration from the CD-ROM, run *D:\CLARITAS\RESOURCE\DOCTOR\HELPFILE.HLP* (where *D* is your CD-ROM drive).

RapiData Report Guide

Although maps are an effective tool for analyzing data, sometimes you only need printed reports showing the data in an easy-to-read layout. This is not always easy to produce with mapping software. That's why Claritas offers a full line of standard reports covering dozens of databases. RapiData reports can be ordered simply by calling 1 800 234 5973, or accessed online using Claritas Connect.

Included on the companion CD-ROM is the Rapi-Data Report Guide. The RapiData Report Guide makes it easy to shop Clarita's portfolio of over 100 reports providing a wide variety of information about every American neighborhood. This Windows help file includes an introduction to each database, as well as a listing of the geographic levels for which they are available. All reports are also available for summarized study areas such as ring studies. Most importantly, the RapiData Report Guide provides sample reports for each database so that you can choose the ones that fit your needs before ordering or accessing online.

The RapiData Report Guide will be automatically installed when you run *D:\CLARITAS\SETUP.EXE*. If you would rather run the demonstration from the CD-ROM, run *D:\CLARITAS\RESOURCE\RAPIDATA\RAP-IDATA.HLP* (where *D* is your CD-ROM drive).

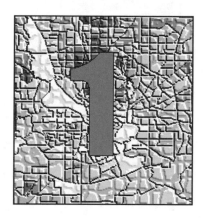

Exploring the ArcView Interface

This chapter examines the anatomy of ArcView GIS in order to highlight its capabilities. ArcView employs several components that permit you to visualize, tabulate, chart, and lay out geographic data, customize the graphical user interface (GUI), and extend Arc-View's basic functionality. The exercise will present each document type or component, examine how it works, and introduce you to the ArcView way of doing things.

Topics and Functions

❏   Starting ArcView

❏   Projects

❏   Views

❏   Tables

❏   Charts

❏   Layouts

❏   Scripts

❏   On-line help

Description

In this exercise, you will open each of the ArcView document types or components and observe their interactions. You will be introduced to each document and examine the graphical user interface (GUI). The exercise begins with opening an existing project and several existing components. The steps and topics in the exercise are summarized below:

❏   Start ArcView

❏   Open a project

❏   Examine the project window

❏   Open a view and examine the view user interface

❏   Open a table and examine the table user interface

❏   Open a chart and examine the chart user interface

❏   Open a layout and examine the layout user interface

❏   Open a script and examine the script user interface

❏   On-line help

For a complete explanation of the interface, see Chapter 1, "Windows, Icons, and Menus," page 13.

Start ArcView

Start ArcView. You will see the main ArcView application window containing a menu, button bar, and a subwindow named *Untitled.*

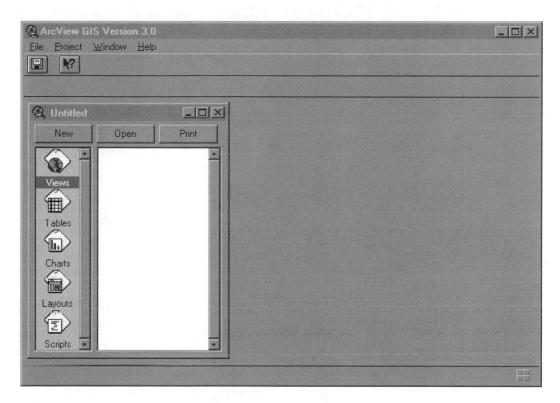

The main ArcView window showing the project window.

Open a Project

Access the File menu and select Open Project to access the Open Project dialog box. Navigate to the *$AVEXDS\avexer\project* directory. Select the *chapt1.apr* project and click the OK button. A moment will pass, the ArcView window will enlarge, and the title of the project window will change from

Untitled to *chapt1.apr.* All project components are accessible from the project window.

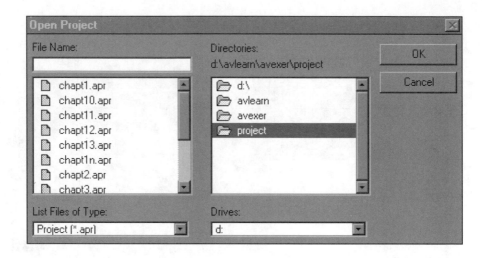

Open Project dialog box.

The project file, identified by the *.apr* extension, stores all parameters of an ArcView session. The project is the highest level of organization in ArcView. This master document is saved and reopened in subsequent sessions.

When you open a project, the project window contains previously defined components and provides an interface to list, add, open, or create new components for the project. The Project menu provides access to project properties and various project level functions. The properties and functions allow you to rename or remove components, open or save projects, control the subwindows in the main ArcView window, and access on-line help.

For a complete explanation of windows, see Chapter 1, "Navigating Windows in ArcView," page 9.

ArcView's various document types are selected with the icons to the left of the project window.

All document types are reviewed below, beginning with views.

Project window.

Views

Views are interactive "maps" that allow you to display, query, and analyze geographic data. A view consists of a set of *themes*. A theme represents a single feature class of a specific data set. In this project, one theme represents the boundaries of the United States, and another the interstate highways. In the next exercise, you will open a view and examine data.

For a complete explanation of views, see Chapter 3, "More About Views," page 61.

1. In the project window, select the View icon to list the view components.

2. In the scrolling list, highlight the *United States* view by clicking it, and then click on the Open button. The view depicting the United States opens.

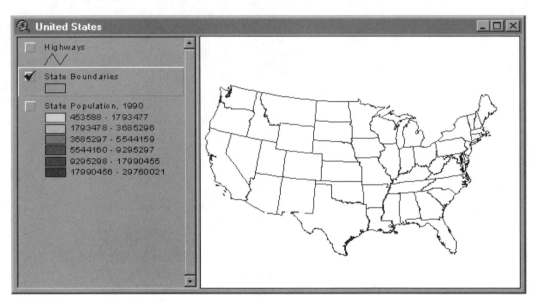

View depicting the United States.

Table of Contents

On the left side of the view window is the Table of Contents, which lists themes contained in the view, along with their symbology. You can change the draw state in the Table of Contents, which is controlled via check boxes for each theme.

For a complete explanation of themes, see Chapter 3, "More About Themes," page 59.

1. Click on the *Highways* theme check box. The screen will refresh and show highways and state boundaries.

2. Similarly, click on the *State Population, 1990* theme check box to display it.

View Controls

The ArcView interface has four control areas, which change to accommodate the active document type.

❑ The main menu bar controls nearly everything. Keyboard shortcuts for some menu items are listed on the menu.

❑ The upper button bar is a convenient shortcut to many of the menu functions. If you place the mouse pointer over one of the buttons, a tool tip will appear that provides help on the icon's purpose.

❑ The lower tool bar allows you to select the function of the pointer or mouse cursor. The pointer is used for many purposes, but performs only one at a time, depending on the tool bar setting. Tool tips will also appear on all tool icons.

❑ The status bar at the bottom of the ArcView window provides visual feedback on the current mouse action and updates on the status of a process, among other things.

❏ Right click on the view canvas (on Macintosh, click
    option key + mouse button), which opens a con-
    text-sensitive pop-up box. A selected action is per-
    formed where the pop-up menu is activated.

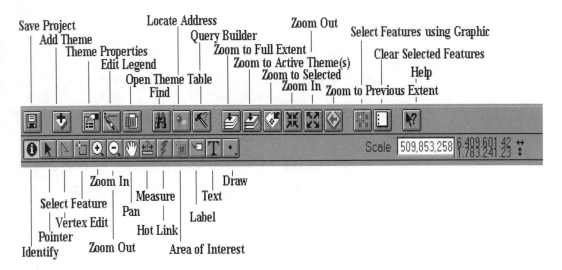

View button and tool bar.

When a view is the active document, the menu,
button, and tool bars perform actions on the view or
its individual themes. The controls on the button bar
immediately affect the view, while the tool bar
changes the pointer function. (The pointer function
remains the same until a new tool is chosen.) Try
experimenting with a few button and tool actions in
the following exercise.

1. Click on the Zoom In button to zoom in on the
center of the view.

2. Click on the Zoom In tool and move the cursor to an area on the view and click. Note that ArcView zoomed in on the view by centering the zoom on the spot you picked. The Zoom Out tool works the same way.

3. Click and drag a box on the view using the Zoom In tool. This action zooms in on the boxed area.

4. Click on the Pan tool to make it active. Click and drag on the view to slide the displayed area. Many ArcView users say Pan is among their favorite features.

5. Right click on the canvas to open the pop-up menu. Select Zoom Out. Repeat until you are satisfied with the geographic area depicted. You can also zoom out with the Zoom Out button or tool. Another means of navigation is to use the Zoom Previous button to step back through the last five view extents.

6. Click on the name text of the *State Population, 1990* theme so that it appears raised in the Table of Contents. Click on the Identify tool to make it active and click on several states in the display. This action activates the Identify window and displays the state's attributes. The Clear and Clear All buttons clear the current records and all records from the Identify window, respectively. Close the Identify window.

Identify window with attributes of the State Population, 1990 theme.

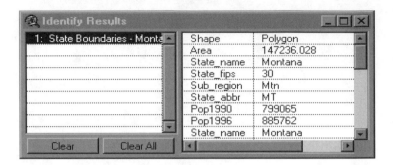

Tables

The table document type allows you to view and work with tabular data. Common examples of tabular data in ArcView are attributes of themes and tables of information related to themes.

1. Click on the project window to make it active. Optionally, you could activate the project window by accessing the Window menu and selecting *chapt1.apr*.

2. Click on the Table icon to list the table components of the project.

3. Highlight *Attributes of State* with a click, and then click on the Open button to open the table.

Project window with the Attributes of States table active.

Similar to the view component, the table user interface contains a menu. This menu controls table properties, and allows you to edit, build queries, search, and identify tabular data. The button and tool bars perform actions on the table and change the cursor state, respectively. By default, the table document does not have a pop-up menu.

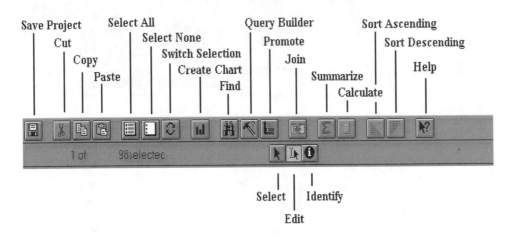

Table button bar and tool.

The table in the following illustration represents the attributes for the *State Population, 1990* theme. ArcView links the records in the table to graphics in the view, and highlights both the selected table record and associated graphic in the view.

Highlighted row (record) in the table and associated geographic feature.

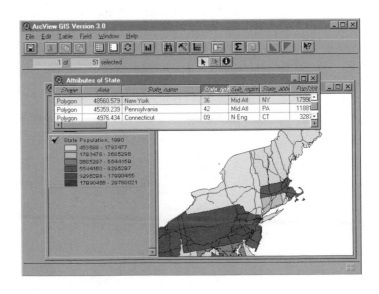

1. With the table active, click on the Select tool.

2. Click on a row in the table. Note that the state also highlights in the view. If you do not see a highlighted state, verify that the *State Population, 1990* theme is turned on via its check box. Zoom out if necessary.

3. To see more than one state highlighted, you can click on several records while holding the <Shift> key. This action will highlight several records at once.

4. Click the Unselect All Records button to clear the selected set of records.

◆ **NOTE:** *Records will also be highlighted in the table when you select states in the view.*

Charts

Charts provide a graphic presentation of tabular data. If a table is open, you can create a chart of the data in the table by clicking on the Chart button. You can also create or open a chart from the project window. Experiment with creating a chart by taking the following steps.

For a complete explanation of charts, see Chapter 7, "Charts," page 169.

1. Verify that the *Attributes of State* table is the active document.

2. Use the Select tool and <Shift>+click to highlight four records in the table.

3. Click on the Create Chart button to activate the Chart Properties dialog box.

↝ **NOTE:** *While in the Chart Properties dialog box, use the <F1> key to access context-sensitive help on the current environment. This shortcut will usually take you directly to the appropriate section of the on-line help system.*

Chart Properties dialog box.

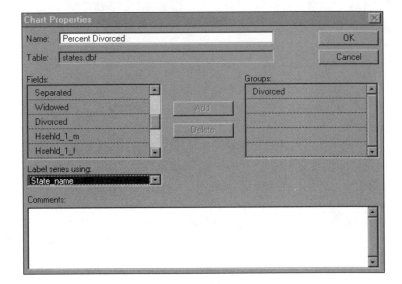

1. Change the chart name to *Percent Divorced.*

2. Move down the left scrolling list labeled Fields to select the fields to chart. Click the *Divorced* field.

3. The Add button will become active after a field is highlighted. Click on this button to add *Divorced* to the right scrolling list, titled Groups.

4. Access the Label series using the drop-down list and click on *State_name*.

5. Click on the OK button to execute the choices. This action will result in a chart depicting the selected data.

Chart of percent divorced by state.

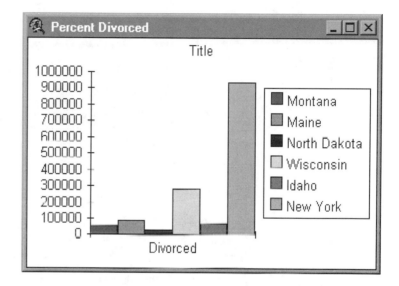

The chart user interface is fairly straightforward. Most of the buttons quickly change a chart's style and appearance. The chart represents values in a table, and you can perform an "identify" on the associated record directly from the chart. Of the selected states, which have the highest and lowest percentage of divorced people?

1. With the chart active, click on the Identify tool to make it active.

2. Click on the largest and smallest bars to identify the states in which the highest and lowest percentages of divorced people reside within your sample data set. Note how you have access to the values in the Identify window.

The Chart button bar and tool.

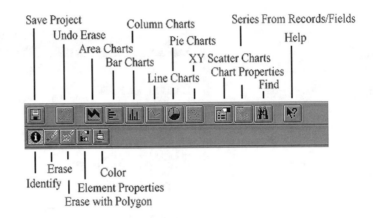

3. In some cases, you may want to remove data from a charted sample. You can accomplish this by changing the active tool to Erase data, and clicking on the bar to remove the data. Try it now, and then close the Chart and Identify windows.

Layouts

A *layout* represents a piece of paper on which you can arrange project components and create a presentation quality map. ArcView functions allow you to create standard maps easily. You also have the freedom to customize a map within a layout. You can change the size of each component, add or subtract individual project components, and add text or graphics to the map.

For a complete explanation of layouts, see Chapter 8, "Layouts," page 197.

1. Make the *United States* view the active document.

2. Access the View menu and select Layout.

3. Select the Landscape option in the Template Manager dialog box.

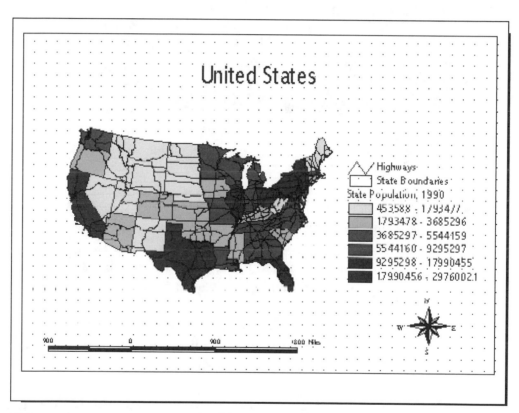

ArcView makes creating a standard layout easy.

The layout interface provides tools to control document frames, graphics, and text on the layout. In addition, the interface contains a context-sensitive pop-up menu and tools to control your view of the layout in the window.

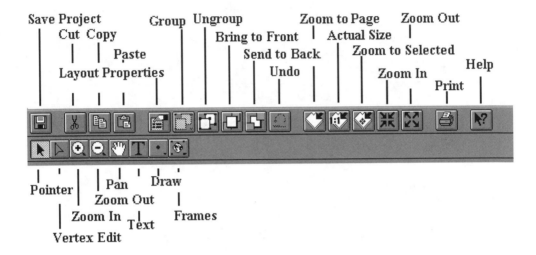

Layout button and tool bars.

1. Maximize the layout window for a good look at the map.

2. Click the Actual Size button to set the display to actual size. This allows you to see how the map will appear on paper.

3. Use the Pan tool to move around the display and inspect layout components.

4. Close the layout document.

Scripts

Scripts are written in Avenue, ArcView's powerful object-oriented scripting language. Scripts allow you to automate repetitive tasks, extend ArcView's base functionality, and customize the look and feel of the user interface. All existing ArcView functions are available as Avenue scripts.

For a discussion of scripts, see Chapter 14, "ArcView Customization," page 349.

You will use an Avenue script to create bar chart graphics for each state. The script will prompt the user for fields and colors to use for the charts.

1. Make the *United States* view active.

2. Verify that the *State Boundaries* theme is on and that the other themes are turned off. Zoom into a five- or six-state area.

3. Click on the name text of the *State Boundaries* theme to activate it.

4. Access the Theme menu and select Bar Chart Script. This script is a part of the default ArcView interface.

5. From the Bar Symbols dialog box, select the Small option. Click on the OK button.

6. Click on No to decline the use of gridlines.

7. Select the *Divorced* field and click the OK button.

8. Select the color blue for the *Divorced* bar.

9. Select the *Married* field and click the OK button.

10. Select the color magenta for the *Married* bar.

11. Click on the Cancel button to stop adding fields to the bar chart. The script will calculate the sizes and draw a bar chart for each state.

12. To repeat the script and set different values, you must first delete the chart graphics from the view. Choose the Select All Graphics option from the Edit menu and then hit the <Del> key. When you have experimented enough, close the view.

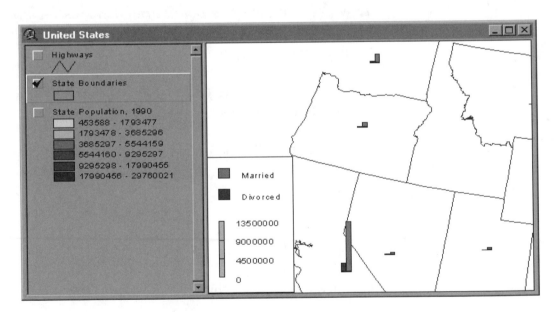

Custom charts created with a script.

Now that you have seen what the script can do, open the script and examine it.

1. Make the project window active.

2. Click on the Scripts icon to list the scripts in this project.

3. The *BarChartSpotSymbols* script is highlighted. Click the Open button to open it. This is the Avenue code that prompted you for bar chart information and then created the charts.

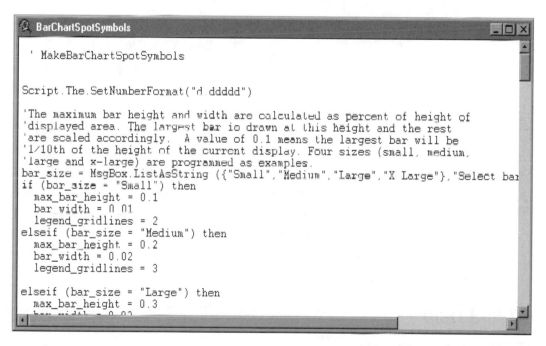

```
' MakeBarChartSpotSymbols


Script.The.SetNumberFormat("d.ddddd")

'The maximum bar height and width are calculated as percent of height of
'displayed area. The largest bar is drawn at this height and the rest
'are scaled accordingly.  A value of 0.1 means the largest bar will be
'1/10th of the height of the current display. Four sizes (small, medium,
'large and x-large) are programmed as examples.
bar_size = MsgBox.ListAsString ({"Small","Medium","Large","X Large"},"Select bar
if (bar_size = "Small") then
  max_bar_height = 0.1
  bar_width = 0.01
  legend_gridlines = 2
elseif (bar_size = "Medium") then
  max_bar_height = 0.2
  bar_width = 0.02
  legend_gridlines = 3

elseif (bar_size = "Large") then
  max_bar_height = 0.3
```

BarChartSpotSymbols script.

The script button bar contains functions to create, modify, and test scripts. There are no tool bar buttons for scripts. Similar to a word processing program, the pointer always acts as an insertion point.

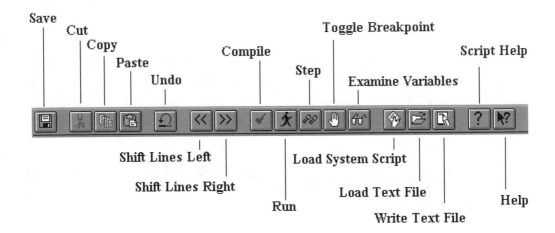

Script button bar.

Although ArcView is not completely written in Avenue, you can access most ArcView functions from Avenue and alter them. For example, you can modify the way the Identify tool works. You can also write your own scripts and link them to events such as the opening of a document.

On-line Help

Most of ArcView's documentation is on-line in the help system.

1. Access the Help menu and select Help Topics. Take a few moments to explore the contents. If you are stuck on the various options available in

one of the many dialog boxes within ArcView, you can get context-sensitive help by pressing <F1>.

2. Click on the Index tab. As you type in a keyword or keywords on the entry line, topics will appear in the window. When you find the topic you want, double-click on it, or click once and click on the Display button. Try finding help on *Views, adding themes.*

3. Remember that the status bar at the bottom of the main ArcView window provides a brief description of button and tool functions when the pointer is positioned over the button. The tool tips that appear when you leave the mouse positioned over a tool or button provide further clues as to the function of an icon.

Optional

If you are familiar with other Windows applications, you should have sufficient background to consider optional activities. Take the following steps to explore the help system and print a copy of the layout.

1. Start the on-line help. Under the Contents tab, click on the Introduction to ArcView book and go to the What Is ArcView section. Read the Introduction to ArcView and follow the hot links to the various ArcView document types.

2. Reopen the layout and use the Print Setup and Print selections in the File menu to print a hard copy of the layout.

Summary

This exercise presented an overview of ArcView document types. The document types are project, view, table, chart, layout, and script. You have now used several of the menus, buttons, and pointer tools. You have also observed the dynamic nature of ArcView controls, which change to accommodate the active document type, and then experimented with the on-line help system.

Discussion Topics

❐ Why is the concept of the active document type critical in ArcView?

❐ In this exercise, you focused on a very simple layout. In what situations would you consider including a chart or table in a layout?

❐ Even with limited exposure to ArcView, you can probably see the potential of scripts. Where else would they be useful?

Working with Views and Themes

The purpose of this exercise is to explore views and themes in depth. The view document type is the main graphic display window, which consists of themes. Think of a view as an "interactive map" that allows you to display and query geographic data. A working knowledge of views and themes is fundamental to the use of ArcView.

Topics and Functions

❑ Project properties
❑ View properties
❑ Theme properties
❑ Theme operations
❑ Theme management
❑ View pop-up menu

Description

This exercise focuses on views and themes and their respective properties and operations. You will open views and alter the display, as well as manipulate the themes component. The steps and topics in the exercise follow.

❑ Open the project
❑ Basic project properties
❑ Open and delete views
❑ View properties
❑ Theme operations
❑ Theme properties
❑ Add themes to a view
❑ Use the View pop-up menu

Open the Project

If ArcView is not currently running, start the program. Access the File menu and select Open Project. Navigate to the *$AVEXDS\avexer\project* directory to select the *chapt2.apr* project.

Basic Project Properties

Access the Project menu and select Properties. This window is used to view and modify project properties. If the default selection color of yellow is not to your liking, modify it by clicking the Selection Color button and altering the slider settings in the dialog box. Pick OK to save your changes and close the dialog box.

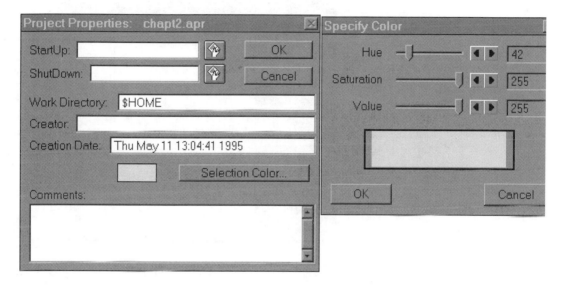

Project Properties and Specify Color dialog boxes.

Open and Delete Views

Note that the Views icon is highlighted at the left of the project window. From the project window, open the *Countries of the World* view by highlighting it and clicking the Open button, or by double-clicking its name. The view you just opened has become active, as evidenced by its highlighted title bar.

The project window is also the place from which you create a new view. To open a new view, make the project window active (by clicking in it), verify that the Views icon is highlighted, and click the New button.

Components listed in the project window.

ArcView controls are very dynamic and context sensitive. You can use the Project menu to rename or delete any individual component of a project. To rename or delete a project component, simply highlight the appropriate icon on the left, select the individual component on the right, and select Rename or Delete from the Project menu.

You will not need a second view for this exercise. Delete the new view by making the project window active, clicking on the view name (which by default is *View1*), accessing the Project menu, and selecting Delete *View1*.

✓ **TIP:** *A project component can also be deleted with the <Del> key after highlighting it in the project window.*

View Properties

Make the *Countries of the World* view active by clicking in it or selecting it from the Windows menu. Now that a view is active, ArcView has set the menus, tool bar, and button bar to work with views and themes. Access the View menu and select Properties. You can view and set properties of the view in the View Properties dialog box. These properties affect each theme in the view.

For a discussion of views, see Chapter 3, "More About Views," page 61.

1. Take this opportunity to change the view name to *Countries*, and enter your name as the creator.

2. Examine the pull-downs for Map Units and Distance Units, but leave them set to Meters and Miles, respectively. You can also store comment notes for the view.

   Map units are the coordinate units of the data with which you are working. The default for Map Units is Unknown. If you know the units for the data at hand, set them. If you do not, retain the default setting.

   Distance units are the units ArcView uses when displaying distances and taking user input. It is always best to set your preference for distance units rather than accept the Unknown default. If you set the distance units, ArcView distance numbers—such as those from the Measure tool—will make much more sense.

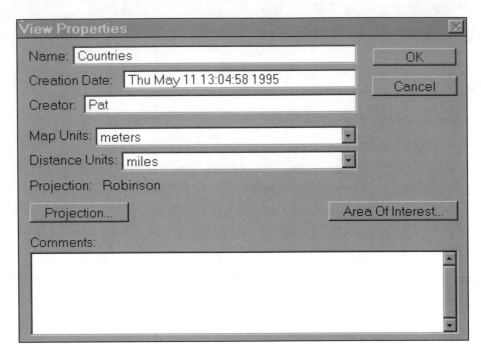

View Properties window.

3. The map projection is also set as a view property. Click the Projection button and observe that the Robinson projection has been selected from the standard set of Projections of the World. ArcView supports a wide range of projections, and each has strengths and weaknesses. The Robinson projection is useful for thematic maps of the world. Select OK to close the Projection Properties dialog box.

4. An area of interest (AOI) can be specified to greatly accelerate ArcView project startup time and the display of themes based on ARC/INFO Librarian or ArcStorm data. By setting an AOI you limit the quantity of data ArcView must process.

This property of the view controls all library-based themes in the view. Select OK to close the View Properties dialog box.

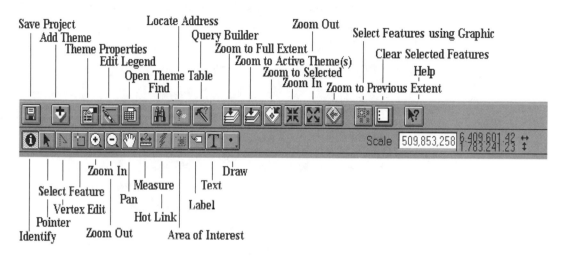

View button and tool bars.

Theme Operations

Active Themes

When the active document is a view, you can act either on the view or on its component themes. Most of the theme functions can be accessed from the button and tool bars in addition to the pull-down menus. ArcView carries out your commands on the *active* theme or themes. A theme is active when it appears raised in the view Table of Contents.

In the view now titled *Countries*, the *Countries '92* theme is the only one active. It appears raised, standing out above the others.

*For a discussion
of themes, see
Chapter 3, "More
About Themes,"
page 59.*

↝ ***NOTE:*** *ArcView functions that only act on an active
theme will be grayed out when no themes are active.*

Clicking a theme name in the Table of Contents
will change it to the active theme. Clicking in the box
to the left of the theme name will turn the theme on
and off in the display. Try clicking themes on and off,
and making various themes active.

✓ ***TIP:*** *Several themes can be made active at once by
employing ArcView's <Shift>+click method. If you
hold down the <Shift> key you can activate or
deactivate individual themes, without clearing
previously active themes, by clicking them. This is
a very useful shortcut when you want to act on
several themes simultaneously. This method also
applies to most selected sets in ArcView.*

*Active Countries '92
theme in the Countries
view Table of
Contents.*

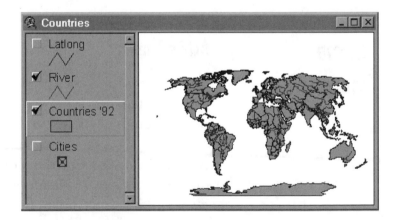

✓ ***TIP:*** *When a view is the active document, all
themes can be turned off with the <Esc> key.*

Setting the Display to Extent of Themes

In addition to the Pan and Zoom tools discussed in Chapter 1, ArcView provides some handy functions to set the area of the view display.

With the *Countries '92* theme active, zoom in and click the Zoom to Active Themes button. The display will zoom out to include all features of the active theme or themes. The Zoom to Full Extent button will set the display to the spatial extent necessary to include all features of all themes, regardless of their state.

➤ **NOTE:** *The Zoom to Full Extent and Zoom to Active Themes buttons will set the display extent whether the themes are on or off. If you do not see a theme, make sure it is turned on.*

Theme Drawing Order

Take a closer look at the theme Table of Contents in the *Countries* view, and at ArcView's drawing order.

1. Click off the theme check boxes until the *Countries '92* theme is the only drawn theme.

2. Zoom in to display only the South American continent.

3. Turn on the *Cities* theme. Note that the *Cities* points appear to be peeking out from under the shaded *Countries '92* polygons. ArcView draws themes in a specific order: from bottom to top per the Table of Contents. Therefore, shaded polygon themes should normally be placed at the bottom of the list, allowing other themes with points, lines, and text to be drawn over them.

Cities points are partially hidden by the Countries '92 polygons.

4. Drag the *Countries '92* theme to the bottom of the list. Now you can see all points in the *Cities* theme.

➦ **NOTE:** *When the reordering of themes alters the display, ArcView will automatically redraw the view.*

Theme Legends

Each theme has a small legend below the theme name. In the *Countries* view, these legends are currently visible. As you add themes to a view, the Table of Contents may become crowded and thus prevent you from seeing all themes at once. When this happens, you can use the scroll bar to scroll up and down to access the themes.

ArcView provides the option of turning the theme legends on and off. To toggle between hiding and showing the legend, access the Theme menu and select Hide/Show Legend. This function works on active themes only.

1. Practice activating themes and using the Hide/ Show Legend function.

2. Turn the legends off for all four themes.

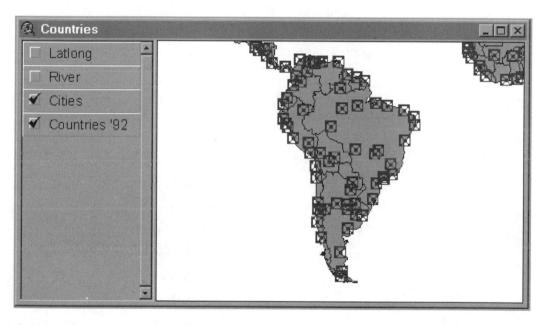

All theme legends turned off.

Copy/Paste Themes

It is often convenient to copy a theme rather than create a new one from scratch. First, make more room in the view Table of Contents by deleting a theme.

1. Make the *Latlong* theme active, access the Edit menu, and select Delete Themes.

2. Now create a new theme of the Amazon river system by copying and modifying the *River* theme. Make the *River* theme active, access the Edit menu, and select Copy Theme.

3. Access the Edit menu and select Paste.

   Note that ArcView added a duplicate *River* theme to the top of the Table of Contents and that both are now active. You can use the Edit menu to cut, copy, and paste themes in the same or different views.

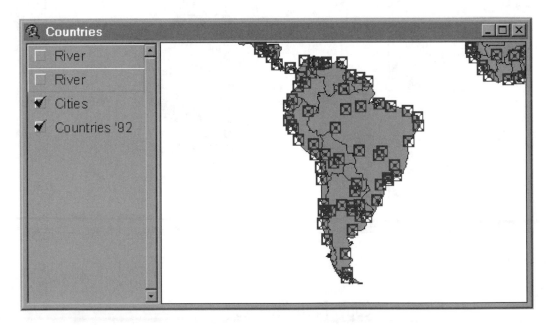

A duplicate River theme pasted into the view.

Theme Properties

Like views, themes have properties. To view and modify theme properties, access the Theme menu and select Properties, or click the Theme Properties button.

↝ **NOTE:** *If several themes are active when you edit theme properties, ArcView will display the Properties dialog box for each theme in descending order as seen in the Table of Contents. As one is closed, the next is brought up until you have seen the properties for every active theme.*

1. Examine the properties of the new *River* theme you copied by making it active, accessing the Theme menu, and selecting Properties (or clicking the Theme Properties button).

2. Theme properties are divided into seven logical categories: Definition, Text Labels, Geocoding, Display, Hot Link, Locking, and Editing. The desired category is selected at the left of the Theme Properties dialog box. Hot Linking, Geocoding and Editing (the last applies only to shapefile themes) will be discussed in later exercises.

3. In the definition category, change the theme name to *Amazon System*.

Definition

The Query Builder and Clear buttons affect theme definition. The Query Builder button contains a hammer and a question mark.

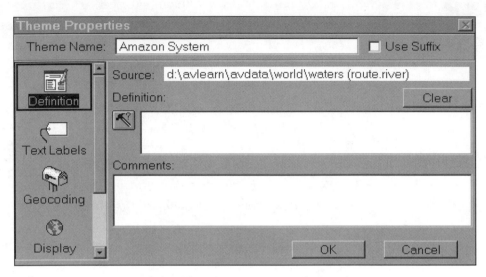

Definition category of the Theme Properties dialog box.

1. Click the Query Builder button under Definition to access a query builder for the theme data. Arc-View will define a subset of a larger data set when you specify a query. The Clear button removes the query from the properties.

2. In addition to the standard fields _Shape_, _River#_, and _River-id_, the _route.rivers_ of the _Water_ data source has two descriptive fields: _Name_ and _System_. For the _Amazon System_ theme, select only features whose _System_ field is equal to _Amazon_. Under Fields, double-click _System_ and note that it is inserted into the Expression box. Because the Update Values box is checked, the values for the _System_ field appear under Values. Click the Equals (=) button, and double-click the _Amazon_ value. ArcView builds the entire expression for you in the box.

✓ *TIP: When Query Builder initially appears, parentheses enclose the query. If you make a mistake and choose to delete all text in the text box, you may need to manually add parentheses around the expression.*

3. Close the dialog box. Add a few notes in the Comments box for future reference, and close the Theme Properties dialog box.

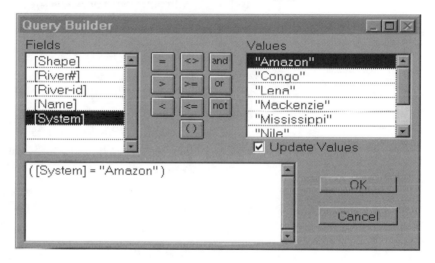

Query Builder for theme definition.

4. Turn off the *Cities* theme and turn on the *Amazon System* theme.

5. Zoom out enough to see other continents and confirm that the *Amazon System* theme contains only the subset of world rivers.

6. Make the *Amazon System* theme active and zoom to its extent using one of the methods presented earlier.

7. Access the *Amazon System* theme properties again to prepare for labeling the rivers that constitute the Amazon River system.

Text Labels

Every theme has properties that control its default labeling of features; to utilize ArcView's labeling function, a theme's draw state must be on. In the following, you will examine relevant theme properties.

For a complete explanation of labeling features, see Chapter 5, "Labeling Features," page 118.

1. Select the Text Labels category of the theme properties for the *Amazon System* theme.

2. Set the Label Field to Name, turn On the Alignment Relative to Line, and set the Alignment Along Length to Midway. Leave the Scale Labels check box checked so that ArcView will automatically change the size of the text as you zoom in and out. This will keep the text the same size in real-world coordinates, just like regular theme features. If the Scale Labels check box is off, the text will remain the same size on the screen at all times. ArcView labels features with the field and parameters set in the theme properties. Several other options are available to customize the placement of the labels relative to the feature. Close the dialog box.

✓ **TIP:** *Once the labels are placed, the scale property of the text cannot be changed. To change from Scale to Unscaled, you would need to delete and re-add the text labels.*

3. Set the pointer to the Label tool, and click on a river.

4. Note the small boxes or handles on the name text, indicating it is selected. Change the pointer to the Pointer tool.

5. Position the pointer over the text and move it by dragging.

6. Try positioning the pointer over one of the handles and resizing the text. You can manually adjust any selected text.

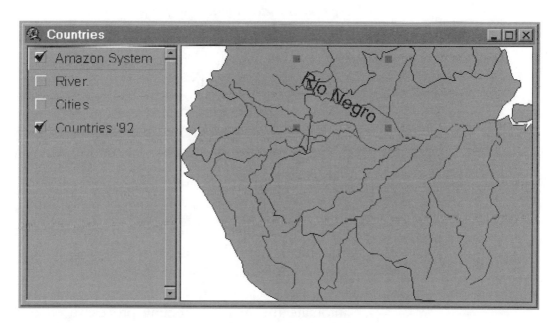

Selected text labels with handles.

7. With the Label tool, click on another river to label it. Now the new label is selected.

8. Access the Edit menu and select Delete Graphics. The selected label is deleted.

9. Try zooming in and out and observe the effect of the Scale Labels setting. Add a few unscaled labels and observe the difference in the way they work.

10. To remove all labels, access the Edit menu, click on Select All Graphics, and select Delete Graphics or press the <Del> key.

➥ ***NOTE:*** *Graphics can be individually selected with the Pointer tool, or all at once with the Edit menu. By holding down the <Shift> key you can add or remove individual graphics from a selected set by clicking on them.*

Next, let's label some features.

1. Prepare to automatically label the Amazon rivers by zooming to the extent of the *Amazon System* theme. Then access the Theme menu and select Auto-Label.

2. Verify that the Label field drop-down list box is set to use the *Name* field for the text to be added. Auto-label has two modes of operation: Use Theme's Text Label Placement Property and Find Best Label Placement. The first mode is used to automate the manual labeling process used earlier. Use the second mode to have ArcView select the optimal positions for labels.

*Auto-label
dialog box.*

NOTE: *In Auto-label, the Label, Field and Scale Labels settings default to the current settings of the theme's Text Label property.*

3. Select the Use Theme's Text Label Placement Property mode and notice that the central box of options becomes grayed out. In this mode, the only optional settings are Scale Labels and Label Only Features in View Extent. If you select Label Only Features in View Extent, ArcView will limit the labeling to features visible in the view. This is a handy feature, because labeling everything in a theme with many features can be very time-consuming. Choose the Scale Labels check box to place scaled labels and close the dialog box.

NOTE: *If multiple themes are active when Auto-label is initiated, ArcView will label the theme that appears highest in the Table of Contents.*

4. ArcView accurately labeled all rivers of the Amazon system, but it can do better. Delete all the labels you just added, and reinitiate Auto-label. This time select the Find Best Label Placement mode. In this mode, ArcView will evaluate each feature and the space around it in an attempt to find the optimal location for each label. The ArcView help system explains the process used for each feature class in detail. Select Allow Overlapping Labels, because disallowing overlapping labels may result in some features not getting labeled due to a conflict with other labels. Select Remove Duplicates and choose to place line labels On the Line and close the dialog box. These settings result in better-looking labels. Labels that conflict with others are drawn in green, thereby identifying which ones would be eliminated if you disallowed overlapping labels.

*Auto-Label
Dialog Box*

↝ **NOTE:** *Remove Duplicates is only available for line themes. This is provided to deal with challenging situations such as labeling streets with names. Several lines may connect to form one street, and each section should not necessarily be labeled independently. ArcView will remove duplicates for contiguous line features with the same value in the Label field. Best results for line themes are usually obtained by selecting both Remove Duplicates and Allow Overlapping Labels.*

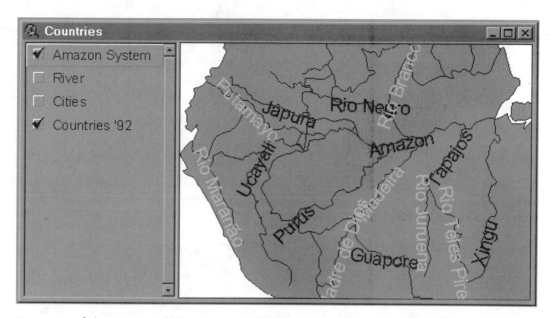

Features of the Amazon System auto-labeled by name.

Selecting Theme Features

It is often necessary to select a subset of theme features on which to perform an operation. One way to select features is with the Select Feature tool. With this tool you can drag a box to select features in the active theme or themes, or click on them one at a time. You can also employ ArcView's <Shift>+click methodology to add or remove features from the selected set, as explained earlier. Selected features will be drawn in the selection color set as a property of the project.

1. Delete the labels added previously, and use the Select Feature tool to drag a box over several of the Amazon rivers. Hold down the <Shift> key and click on an additional river to add it to the selected set. Use the same method to remove a river from the selected set.

2. Auto-label operates on the currently selected set of features. If no features are selected when you initiate Auto-label, ArcView will automatically label all features in the theme. Use Auto-label to place names on selected rivers, and experiment to find optimal settings.

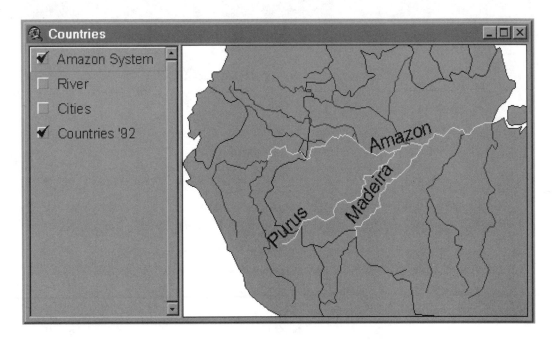

Labels placed on a selected set of Amazon System features.

3. Clear the selected set by accessing the Theme menu and picking Clear Selected Features. Alternatively, you could use the Clear Selected Features button.

Text and Color Palettes

You can alter the appearance of inserted or selected text with the Symbol Palette. The Palettes also control other symbology, which is covered in a later Chapter. Access the Window menu and select Show Symbol Palette. Resize the view if necessary and position the palette next to it. The Symbol Palette consists of Fill, Pen, Marker, Font, Color, and Manager palettes or modes. The palette mode is set with the option button bar across the top of the Symbol Palette.

1. Select the Font palette by clicking the Font button.

2. Select a few labels with the Pointer tool either by clicking or dragging a box. Try several combinations of font, size, and style to create a pleasing and legible display. For labels created under the Auto-Label command, a change to any single label is executed on all labels.

3. Next, select the Color button at the top of the Symbol Palette.

4. Select the Text option under the Color drop-down list.

5. Click a color that will contrast with the rest of the view and emphasize your labels.

6. Close the Symbol Palette.

↝ **NOTE:** *ArcView provides many tools to customize the visual presentation of data. Powerful analysis*

*is only as good as the ability to effectively commu-
nicate results, and as such, you should carefully
consider the visual impact of a final product.*

*Font Palette and
Color Palette.*

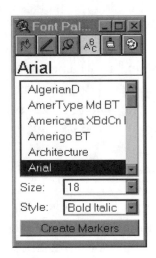 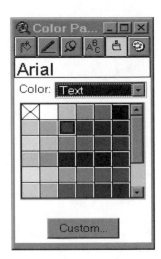

➥ **NOTE:** *The Font and Color palettes do not show
changes to standard font size and style. Thus,
although the user selected Arial 18 pt., and bold
and italic styles, the palettes do not demonstrate
the chosen size and styles.*

Display and Scale

View scale is the ratio of distance on the view to distance on the ground. As such, the view scale will vary
with the size of the view window and the geographic
extent shown in the view.

1. Set the display to the extent of all themes.

2. Turn off the *Amazon System* theme and turn on the *River* theme. Make a note of the scale of the display shown on the View tool bar. When zoomed out to view the entire planet, the scale should be a big number.

3. At this scale, the lines representing the rivers are difficult to distinguish from one another. To remedy the situation, you will set them to draw only at a scale of less than 1:100,000,000. To view this scale, manually set the display to this exact scale. Use the cursor to highlight the number in the scale box, key in *100,000,000*, and press the <Enter> key. The display will remain centered on the same point but will zoom to a scale of 1:100,000,000.

4. Make the *River* theme active, and access its Properties dialog box.

5. Select the Display category, set Maximum Scale at *1 to 100,000,000*, and close the dialog box. A minimum scale can also be set. The combination of the two settings effectively allows you to control the range of scales at which ArcView draws themes.

6. Zoom in and out while observing the scale. Verify that ArcView draws the River theme only in the correct scale range.

Display category of the Theme Properties dialog box.

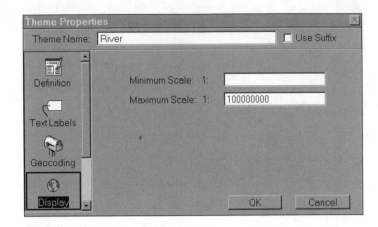

Locking Themes

Each theme's properties can be locked with a password to prevent other users from making unauthorized modifications. This feature can be very useful in a multi-user environment to ensure that standard themes remain intact for everyone's use.

1. Select the Locking category of the *River* theme's properties.

2. Check the Locked box, click the Set Password button, and enter your choice of password.

3. Close the Properties dialog box. ArcView will now prompt for the password prior to displaying the Properties dialog box for this theme.

4. Try modifying the *River* theme properties and test the lock.

Locking category of the Theme Properties dialog box.

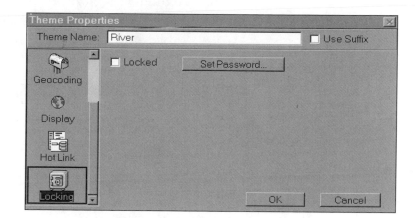

NOTE: *You can turn off the lock applied to theme properties at any time by removing the check from the Locked box. Remember that attribute data and shapefiles can be edited when the Locked box is checked.*

Adding Themes to a View

Finally, you will explore how to add a theme to a view.

1. With the *Countries* view as the active document, click the Add Theme button, or access the View menu and select Add Theme.

2. Navigate to the *$AVEXDATA\avdata\world* directory and click once on the small, yellow *Waters* data set folder to open it. You will see a variety of available feature classes, including *regions.lakes, route.drain, route.river, polygon, arc,* and *labelpoint.*

3. Highlight *regions.lakes* and click OK. ArcView will add a theme called *Lakes* to the top of the Table of Contents. Turn the new *Lakes* theme on.

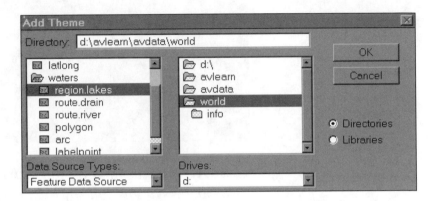

Add Theme dialog box.

❧ **NOTE:** *In the Add Theme dialog box, you must be careful to click on the small, yellow folder representing a data set. Clicking will open it and allow you to select from the available feature classes. Clicking it a second time will close the folder. When a data set does not have a folder, it contains a single feature class and can be selected directly.*

✓ **TIP:** *You can simultaneously add multiple themes by highlighting several data sources using the <Shift>+click method: hold down the <Shift> Key while clicking on each source you would like to add.*

Using the View Pop-up Menu

A shortcut to several commonly used functions is provided in the form of a pop-up menu on the display area of the view document. This menu is accessed by right clicking the mouse in the display area. On the Macintosh, use the <Option>+mouse click.

↠ **NOTE:** *The pop-up menu is customizable through the Customize dialog box. Access the view pop-up menu in the* Countries *view and try each of the functions.*

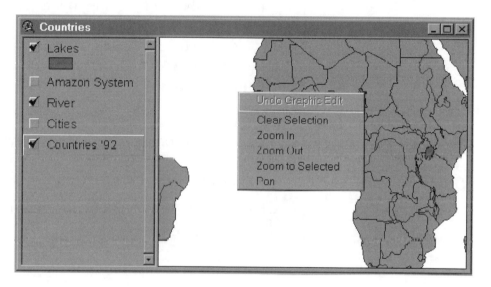

Default view pop-up menu.

Optional

Practice your theme manipulation skills by performing the following additional steps.

1. Navigate to the *$AVEXDATA\avdata\world* direc-
   tory and add the *Latlong* theme to the *Countries*
   view.

2. Display the new *Latlong* theme.

3. Label a selected set of features in the new theme
   with text for the *Value* field.

Summary

In this exercise, you opened a view and modified its
properties and those of its component themes. You
also performed several basic theme operations.
Finally, you added new themes to the view by copying an existing theme, and you brought a theme in
from a new data source.

Discussion Topics

❏ How could you optimize ArcView's redraw performance by setting theme display properties? What
are the trade-offs?

❏ When would theme locking be useful in your
intended ArcView application?

Working with Tables and Charts

The purpose of this chapter is to explore tables and charts in depth. The table document type is the main "window" into tabular data. This display of tabular data is not the table itself, but a means of viewing data. In ArcView, you can create and simultaneously use multiple, differing table documents on the same data. Charts are a flexible, visual way to graphically display selected tabular data. Like the table document, you can create and manipulate several charts on the same data at once.

Topics and Functions

❏ Table properties

❏ Modifying tables

❏ Table queries

❏ Table summaries

❏ Chart properties

❏ Modifying charts

Description

In the following exercise, you will investigate tables and charts and their respective properties and operations. You will open tables, modify them, alter their display, and chart them. You will also customize the resulting charts. The steps and topics in the exercise follow.

❏ Open the project

❏ Basic table properties and operations

❏ Edit tables

❏ Index fields

❏ Make a summary table

❏ Create a chart from a table

❏ Find function

❏ Build a new table

❏ Advanced charting

Open the Project

If ArcView is not currently running, start the program. Access the File menu and select Open Project. Navigate to the *$AVEXDS\avexer\project* directory and select the *chapt3.apr* project.

Basic Table Properties and Operations

The ArcView table document enables you to view, query, analyze, edit, and chart a variety of tabular data sources. These data sources can be attributes of spatial data, delimited text files, or dBASE, INFO, or RDBMS tables. The table document type is a dynamic reference to the data source, or a "window" into the tabular data. Therefore, you can alter the way the data are displayed in the ArcView table document without making a permanent change to the data. You can also open several table documents on the same table at once. Each time the project is opened, it accesses the current source data.

For a discussion of tables, see Chapter 6, "Basic Table Operations," page 133.

1. Open the Attributes of *Countries '92* table from the project window by highlighting the Tables icon and clicking the Open button. This table contains the tabular data for the *Countries '92* theme in the *Countries of the World* view. From the project window you can also add existing tables to the project with the Add button, or define a new table with the New button.

2. With the table active, access the Table menu and select Properties. Tables have the now familiar properties of Title, Creator, and Comments. Add your name, and key in comments if you wish.

3. ArcView allows you to alter the appearance of tables in several ways. This table contains ARC/INFO fields that are not important in this exercise, as well as duplicate fields (the result of a prior join), so clean up the display. Under Visible, click to remove the check boxes for the *Shape, Area,*

Perimeter, Yr92#, Yr92-id, Abbrevname, Fips_ code, and *Wb_cntry* fields to hide them from view. When Visible shows a check mark for a field, it means you will see it in the table document in Identify results, or in dialog boxes displaying the fields.

4. When listing the field values, you can change the displayed field names. For example, you might replace a cryptic field name with a descriptive name that makes more sense. The new alias name will then be used instead of the original field name everywhere the field name is referenced. Add aliases for several fields. Set *Tot_pop* to *Pop Total*, *Pr_pop2000* to *Pop 2000*, and *Life_exp* to *Life Expect*. Close the dialog box. Note how the column, or field labels, have changed to the alias values.

Table Properties dialog box.

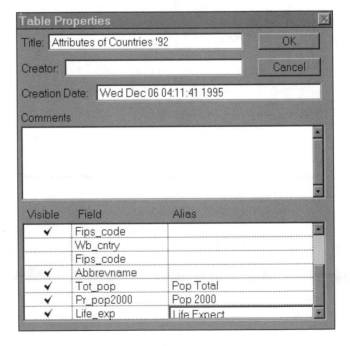

5. The display width for the field marked *Life Expect* is not wide enough. Resize it by positioning the cursor on the right edge of the box that contains the *Life Expect* column name. When the cursor changes to a horizontal double arrow, drag it to the right to make the box wider.

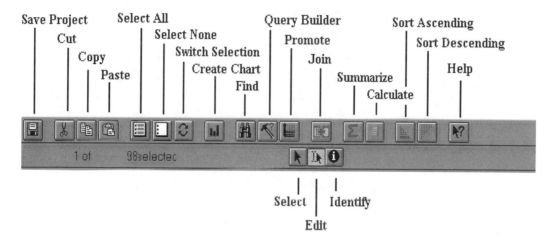

Table button and tool bars.

6. Open the *Countries of the World* view and position it so that you can see both the view and the table.

7. Click on the Name column label of the table to make it the active field. Note that the active field is darker and appears depressed. Click the Sort Ascending button to sort the records by the active field. Because Name is a character field, it sorts alphabetically. The sort function recognizes the active field's type, and sorts accordingly.

8. Use the Select tool to select the record for Argentina by clicking on it in the table. Both the view graphic and the table record are highlighted because they are internally linked by ArcView.

9. If a table is not wide enough to display all columns at once, you can use the Identify tool as an alternative method to see all of the fields. Use the Table Identify tool to examine several table records by clicking on them. This works just as if you had identified the related graphic feature in the view. Next, try using the View Identify tool to identify a country in the view. ArcView will place the identify results in the existing Identify window. Identify will only show the fields marked as visible in the Table Properties. Remember, the *Countries '92* theme must be active to identify it. When finished, close the Identify window.

➡ **NOTE:** *Identify does not affect the selected set.*

10. The Sort Descending button works in the same way as the Sort Ascending button. Make the table active and try a descending sort on the Name field. These sorting functions can also be accessed from the Field menu.

11. With the table sorted in descending order, you have lost track of the selected record for Argentina. Click the Promote button to bring the selected record or records to the top of the table display. You can perform the same function by accessing the Table menu and selecting Promote.

12. If you have a printer available, access the File menu and select Print to make a hard copy of the table.

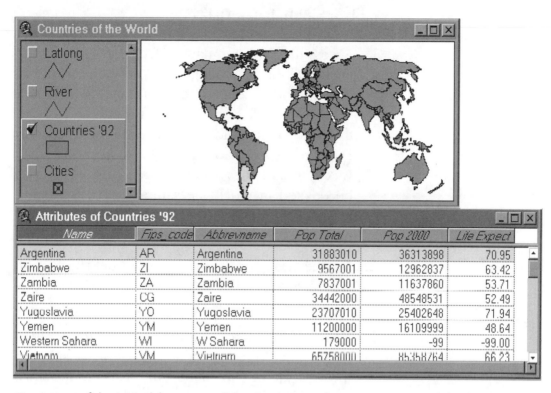

Countries of the World view and the Attributes of Countries '92 table showing the selected Argentina graphic and related tabular record.

Edit Tables

Tables can also be edited in ArcView in a variety of ways. You can add or delete fields, add records, and edit the contents of existing record fields. Enable editing of the table by accessing the Table menu and selecting Start Editing.

➜ **NOTE:** *Table column names are normally italicized, but when you begin editing they change to a non-italic font. Fields that remain italicized cannot be edited.*

Adding and Deleting Fields

1. Access the Edit menu and select Add Field. In the Field Definition dialog box, set the Name to *grp_id*, and accept the default Type of Number. Set the Width to *2* and Decimal Places to *0*. Close the dialog box. Field types of String, Boolean, and Date are also available in the Type drop-down list. By default, the new field will be active. Fields can be deleted in much the same way by activating them and selecting Delete Field from the Edit menu.

2. Set the alias for the new *grp_id* field to *Group Number* in the table properties, and resize the column name.

3. You will be referencing the *Group Number* field frequently. For convenience, move its position in the table all the way to the left. To accomplish this, first click the column name to deactivate it, and then drag it to the far left. ArcView will leave this field active after the repositioning.

Group Number	Name	Fips_code	Abbrevname	Pop Total	Pop 2000	Life Expect
	Argentina	AR	Argentina	31883010	36313898	70.95
	Iceland	IC	Iceland	252000	287333	77.82
	Estonia	EN	Estonia	1600000	-99	-99.00
	Latvia	LG	Latvia	2700000	-99	-99.00
	Lithuania	LH	Lithuania	3751000	-99	-99.00
	United Kingdom	UK	UK	57270000	59188515	75.58
	Ireland	EI	Ireland	3537000	3525345	74.26
	Mongolia	MG	Mongolia	2128000	2858753	61.96

New Group Number field has been added, aliased, and repositioned in the Attributes of Countries '92 table.

Calculating Field Values

In the view, use the Select Features tool to select two or three South American countries. Promote these records in the table with the Promote button. Remember, you can use the <Shift>+click methodology to add or remove individual items from the selected set.

1. In the table, verify that the *Group Number* field is active, and use the Calculate button to activate the Field Calculator dialog box.

2. The Field Calculator is used to set the active field value of the selected records. Like other ArcView query builders, the expression is built in the box in the lower left of the dialog window. ArcView indicates that it will set the value of the *Group Number* field by showing *[Group Number]* = above the expression box. Click in the expression box and enter *1*. Selecting OK calculates the Group Number of the selected South American countries to 1, and closes the dialog box.

Field Calculator dialog box.

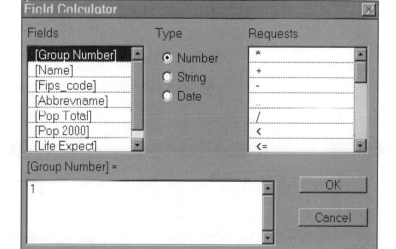

3. In a similar fashion, select two or three countries in Africa, calculate their Group Number to *2,* and select two or three countries in Europe and set their Group Number to *3.* Because the European countries are smaller, you may want to zoom in before you select them.

4. From the Table menu, select Save Edits to commit the changes to the table.

NOTE: *You can also use the Save As function to save the edited version of a table under a new name.*

Queries

1. Add another field to the table with the following parameters: set Name to *pop_dif,* Type to *Number,* Width to *16,* and Decimal Places to *0.*

For a discussion of queries, see Chapter 6, "Selecting Features by Query," page 139.

2. Use the Query Builder button and bring up the dialog box to select records with a logical expression.

3. Under Fields, double-click Group Number and note how it is inserted in the expression box. Because the Update Values box is checked, the values for the *Group Number* field appear in the Values list.

4. Click the Equals (=) button, and double-click the value 1. Continue to build the expression to select all records where *Group Number = 1 or Group Number = 2 or Group Number = 3,* as shown in the next illustration.

Attributes of Countries '92 table query builder dialog box.

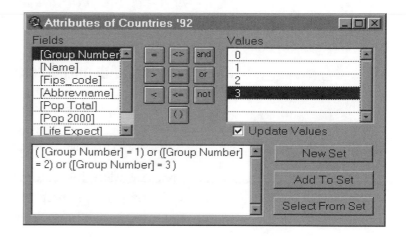

5. Watch the expression as it is built in the box, and be careful to double-click Fields and Values, or they will not be inserted in the expression.

6. Create a new selected set from all records by clicking the New Set button. The other two buttons will add to an existing set or select only from the currently selected set. Close the dialog box.

7. Sort the rows in ascending order, based on the *Group Number* field.

8. Promote the selected records to the top so that you can see them, and make the window larger if necessary.

↝ **NOTE:** *When the Query Builder initially appears, parentheses surround the query. If you make a mistake and choose to delete all text in the text box, you may get a syntax error. In this case, you* *may need to manually add parentheses around the expression.*

Statistics and Advanced Calculations

1. Calculate statistics on the *Group Number* field for the selected records by activating it and selecting Statistics from the Field menu.

2. ArcView also indicates the number of selected and total table records on the tool bar. For instance, if you have selected a total of nine countries, ArcView will show nine records selected from the total of 147.

Statistics on the Group Number field for the selected records.

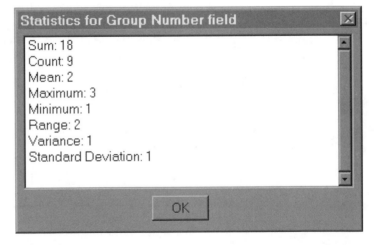

Statistics for Group Number field

Sum: 18
Count: 9
Mean: 2
Maximum: 3
Minimum: 1
Range: 2
Variance: 1
Standard Deviation: 1

OK

3. Switch the selected set with the Switch Selection button. Note the count shown on the tool bar. This changes the selected set by switching to the previously unselected set of records. Use the Switch Selection button again to return to the original set of records.

4. For now, you will leave the selected set intact so that you can work with it. However, you can also select or unselect all records with the Select All and Select None buttons.

5. Activate the *pop_dif* field, and use the Calculate button to bring up the Field Calculator dialog box.

6. Calculate the *pop_dif* field to the difference between the estimated year 2000 population and the population total for 1989 (i.e., *Pop2000* minus *Pop Total*). Be certain to double-click the Fields and Requests items in order to add them to the expression. Select OK to close the dialog box. ArcView calculated the *pop_dif* field for the selected records only.

Field Calculator dialog box set to make a calculation on the pop_dif field.

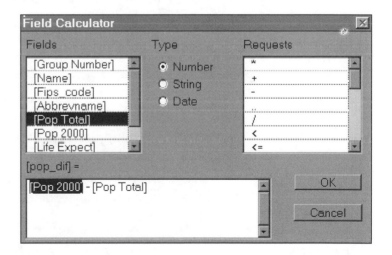

7. Access the Table menu and select Stop Editing. Save the edits.

Index Fields

In ArcView you can index fields in a table. An index creates additional files that store information about the location of records in a table. An index speeds up certain functions, but the trade-off is the disk space used for index storage. Obviously, the larger the data set, the more beneficial the index will be. If you have write access to the data directory, any index you create will be permanent. If you do not have write access, a temporary index will be created for the duration of the ArcView session.

Indexing a Table

An attribute index helps ArcView locate tabular records more quickly, thereby improving the performance of joins and queries. A spatial index helps ArcView spatially locate records and improves the performance of Identify and other spatial operations. A spatial index is automatically created when ArcView performs a spatial join or theme-on-theme selection. A spatial index is simply an index created on the *Shape* field. ArcView's native data format, the shape file, will be explored in subsequent exercises.

You can create an index on a field by activating the field, accessing the Field menu, and selecting Create Index. If an index already exists, the menu will show the Remove Index option, where the Create Index function is normally located.

1. Choose a country from the *Countries '92* theme in the *Countries of the World* view, perform an Identify on the country, and count the seconds the task requires.

2. Make the *Shape* field visible usisng Table Properties and active in the *Attributes of Countries '92* table. Access the Field menu and select Create Index. A spatial index is created.

3. Now try the Identify function again for the same country. Depending on your computer configuration, you should see a performance improvement.

Make a Summary Table

ArcView allows you to summarize the data in a table and store the results in a new table. You can summarize number fields by their average, sum, minimum and maximum values, standard deviation, variance, first and last values, and total count. String fields can be summarized by first and last values, and shape fields can be summarized by merge.

In the case of a merge by shape, features that share the same value of the summary field are *merged* into a single feature. Lines that share an *end point* are merged into one, whereas lines that touch but do not share an end point are all treated as a single entity. Likewise, points that share a common value in the summary field are merged and treated like a single entity. When several lines or points are treated as a single feature, they look like separate graphics but share a single attribute table record, and will all be selected when any one is selected.

Polygons can be merged in several ways. Access the ArcView on-line help system under Merge Operations for a detailed explanation of how the various possibilities are treated. You will now perform a summary on a set of countries categorized by *Group Number*.

1. Make the *Attributes of Countries '92* table active. You will create a new table by summarizing on Group Number. Verify that the Group Number = 1, 2, or 3 records are still selected. Activate the *Group Number* field, and click on the Summarize button to bring up the Summary Table Definition dialog box.

2. Use the Save As button to save the summary table as *$AVEXDS\avexer\dbf\ch3_sum1.dbf.*

3. Select the *Pop Total* field and *Summarize by Average* from the drop-down list boxes, and then click the Add button to add the information to the list on the right.

4. Select each of the following fields and the Summarize-by statistic in parentheses, and then click on the Add button: *Life Expect* (Average), *pop_dif* (Average), *pop_dif* (Minimum), *pop_dif* (Maximum), and *pop_dif* (Standard Deviation). Select OK to close the dialog box.

Summary Table Definition dialog box for a summary on Group Number.

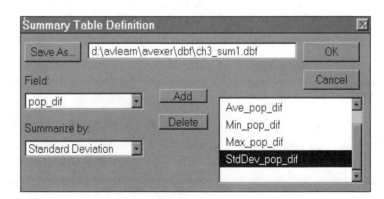

5. Resize the resulting table and fields so that you can see all the fields. This new table contains three

records, that is, one for each distinct value of the summary field Group Number. Each record has a field for the summary items selected above that itemize the average total population, average life expectancy, average population difference, minimum population difference, maximum population difference, and standard deviation for population difference.

Create a Chart from a Table

ArcView provides powerful functions to chart tabular data and make visualizing data easy. A chart is created from the currently selected records. If no records are selected, ArcView will create the chart using all records. Records can be selected in either the table or the view because the table and view are internally linked by ArcView. Finally, you can simultaneously store several different chart documents based on the same data.

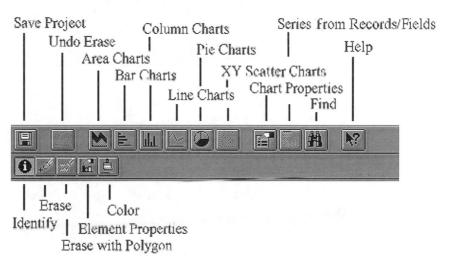

Chart button and tool bars.

For a discussion
of charts, see
Chapter 7,
"Creating a
Chart," page 169.

1. With the *Attributes of Countries '92* table active, verify that the Group Number set is still selected, and then chart life expectancy by clicking the Create Chart button or accessing the Table menu and selecting Chart. This will activate the Chart Properties dialog box. Name the chart *Life Expectancy*.

2. Highlight the *Life Expect* field and click the Add button to add it to the Groups list on the right. In the Label Series Using drop-down list box, select Name. Add a note in the Comments box if you wish, and close the dialog box by selecting OK.

*Chart Properties
dialog box.*

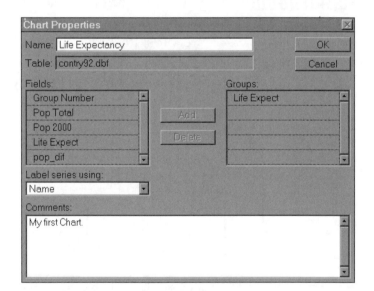

3. ArcView has created a chart of the selected records. Enlarge the resulting chart window to give yourself more room to work. On the Chart menu you can toggle between Hide and Show for the Title, Legend, X Axis, and Y Axis. Access the Chart menu and turn all of these elements off.

Fine Tuning Charts

For a discussion of chart options, see Chapter 7, "Making Changes to a Chart," page 173.

1. Although the chart you have prepared thus far is serviceable, you will add a few enhancements to more clearly present the data. Begin by turning the Title, Legend, X Axis, and Y Axis options back on.

2. Give the chart a meaningful title. Use the Chart Element Properties tool, and click on the title. Enter the text *Average Life Expectancy* in the title field. In the Title Position area, you can click on the center, twelve, three, six or nine o'clock positions for the title. Select the twelve o'clock position and select OK.

3. Depending on the *Life Expect* values for the countries you have chosen, you may note that there is one less chart bar than indicators in the legend. This is because one bar is not clearly visible, given the scale of the Y axis. Click on the Y axis with the Edit Chart Elements tool to bring up the Chart Axis Properties dialog box. If necessary, refer back to the table and observe the smallest and largest Life Expect values in the selected records. You could use the Statistics function to report these values. Set the Scale Min lower than the smallest value and the Scale Max higher than the largest value. Changing these settings will make all of the bars visible.

4. In the Y Chart Axis Properties dialog box, click on the check box for an Axis Label, and change the text for the label from the default Y Axis to Years. The axis position can also be switched between the right and left side of the chart, but leave it in its default position for now. Select OK.

Chart Axis Properties dialog box.

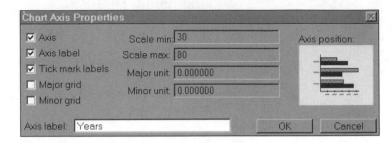

5. Click on the X axis to edit its properties. Turn off Axis, turn off Tick Marks, and turn on Axis Label. Change the Axis Label to Study Area Countries. The Axis position can be switched between top and bottom. Close the dialog box.

6. You can view all table information for any given chart record with the Identify tool. Try identifying several of the bars. When you are finished, close the Identify Results window.

⟿ **NOTE:** *The corresponding chart bar, table record, and view feature all flash when any one of them is identified.*

7. Select the Color tool, which will bring up the Symbol Palette window. Select the Color choice button on the palette. Click on a color in the palette, and apply the color to a chart bar, axis, legend, or title by clicking on the individual chart element. Customize your chart by setting complementary colors for the bars. Use dark contrasting colors for the reference elements, such as the title and legend, so that they are clearly legible. Close the Color palette.

8. If the set of selected records is changed, the chart is updated immediately to reflect the new data set. In the *Countries of the World* view, select a few new countries to chart by using the Select Feature tool. Try several sets and observe the results. Avoid selecting too many countries at once because you may run out of room in the chart.

9. You can remove items from the chart by modifying the selected set in the table or view, or by using the Erase tool. To erase data, click on a chart bar with the Erase tool. Upon observing the view, you will see that the record you erased from the chart is no longer selected in the view.

✓ **TIP:** *If you make a mistake erasing, you can undo the last erase with the Undo Erase button, or by selecting Undo Erase from the Edit menu.*

Completed Life Expectancy chart.

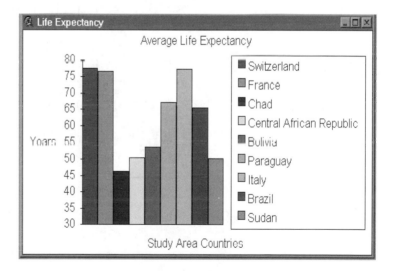

Find Function

The Find button function, which can also be accessed from the Chart menu, is useful for locating specific data records on the chart. Find does not support wild-card characters, but it does perform a substring search on all visible non-numeric fields. Therefore, you can enter part of the string and ArcView will find its first occurrence. Subsequent finds on the same string will find the next occurrence, and so on. Find is not case sensitive. Like Identify, the Find function is found in the view, table, and chart document types.

Try using the Find function to locate a specific bar or data marker on the chart by entering the name of a country you have selected. The data marker will flash. This is particularly useful if you have a large number of data markers on the chart, or if ArcView assigns the same color to more than one marker. The table Find works essentially the same way; however, it changes the selected set to the found record.

Build a New Table

To explore how to create a new table, make a table to store some hypothetical data about selected adminis-trative costs for a small country.

1. From the project window, select tables and click the New button. Name the new table *ch3_tab1.dbf*, and store it in the *$AVEXDS\ avexer\dbf* directory. This action creates an empty table window, and the new table will be listed in the project window under Tables. By default, editing is enabled in the new table.

2. Add a number field named *num_states*, with a width of *2*. Add a second number field named *admin_costs*, with a width of *10*.

3. Add an empty record to the table by accessing the Edit menu and selecting Add Record, or by using the <Ctrl>+<A> shortcut. Repeat this step to add a total of seven records. Note that selected records can also be deleted using the Edit menu.

4. Use the Edit tool to add data to the empty cells. Click in the cell and type in the value. You can use the Copy and Paste selections on the Edit menu to simplify the entry of repetitive values in the *admin_costs* field. Enter the cell values as shown in the following illustration.

Fields and values for the ch3_tab1.dbf table.

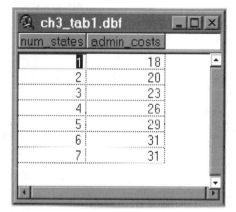

5. After entering the values, access the Table menu and select Save Edits to save your data to the previously specified file name. Finally, select Stop Editing from the Tables menu.

As mentioned previously, charting is performed on selected records; if no records are selected, it is performed on all records. Because the next step will be to chart all records, clear the selected set with the Select None button.

Advanced Charting

1. With the table active, chart administrative costs by clicking the Create Chart button or by accessing the Table menu and selecting Chart. Either action activates the Chart Properties dialog box. Name the chart *Administration Cost*, and note that it references the *ch3_tab1.dbf* table.

2. Click the *admin_costs* field and click the Add button to add it to the Groups list on the right. In the Label Series Using drop-down list box, select *num_states*. Add a note in the Comments box if you wish, and select OK to close the dialog box. Enlarge the resulting chart window to give yourself more room to work. Adjust the Y axis scale to a minimum of *16* and a maximum of *33*, and add a Y axis label called *Million Dollars*.

3. Create a new chart named *Administration Cost by Number of States* from the *ch3_tab1.dbf* table as the active document. Add the *num_states* and then the *admin_costs* field as groups, and label using *num_states*. Enlarge the window. Hide the title and add a Y axis label called *Million Dollars*. The chart shows two sets of vertical bars, or one set for the number of states and another for administrative costs. Use the Series From Records/ Fields button to toggle the way the data bars are grouped. ArcView will toggle between grouping by record and grouping by field, thereby yielding different perspectives on the data.

Administration Cost by Number of States chart grouped by field.

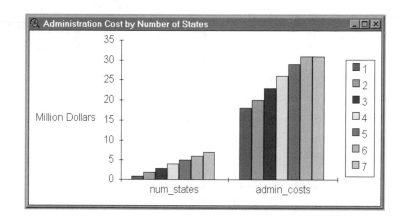

Administration Cost by Number of States chart grouped by record.

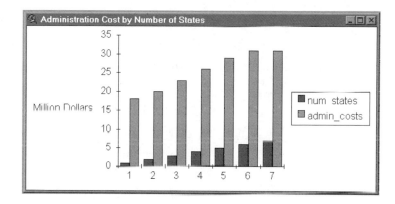

4. The Column chart style graphically displays the data, but a different style would communicate the relationship more clearly. Click the XY Scatter Chart Gallery button and accept the default style from the Scatter Chart Gallery. Hide the legend, because it does not correspond with the information in this chart. Turn on the X and Y axis labels and set the Y axis range to extend from *16* to *34*.

*Administration Cost
by Number of States
scatter style chart.*

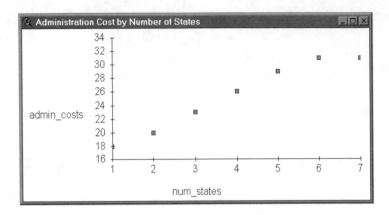

*Chart: Choosing a
Chart Format*

5. Try using the Erase with Polygon tool to remove data from the scatter chart. Click the vertices of the polygon and double-click when you have completed the polygon around the markers to be erased. As with the Erase tool, you can undo one erase if you make a mistake.

6. ArcView supports several chart styles—including Area, Bar, Column Line, Pie, and XY Scatter—to optimize the presentation of various types of data. Chart styles are selected with the gallery buttons of the same names. You will make use of several chart styles in subsequent exercises.

Optional

Practice your table and chart skills by performing the following additional steps.

1. Attribute indexes are stored in files with the extensions *.ain* and *.aih*. All attribute indexes for a given data set are stored in the same two files. Spatial indexes are stored in files with the extensions *.sbn* and *.sbx*. Locate the index files you created during the exercise. Create indexes on other data in the *Countries of the World* view, locate the index files, and compare their size to that of the source data.

2. Explore various chart styles by selecting new styles for existing charts from the Gallery menu or the buttons. Within the gallery for a given style, try several of the options and note the unique characteristics of each.

3. Spruce up the Administration Cost chart with a better title, legend, and axis labels. Use the Print selection of the File menu to print your improved chart.

Summary

In this exercise, you opened table documents and modified their appearance and display. You then edited, summarized, and queried the tabular data, and indexed fields to improve performance. Finally, you used the chart document type to create graphic displays of data stored in tables.

Discussion Topics

❏ When would the ability to set aliases for field names be useful? Why would a table creator use a cryptic field name in the first place?

❏ What is an index and what are the uses of the two types of index? Under what circumstances would you choose to use indexes?

❑ Although the "definition" of the chart is stored in the project, the chart itself changes with the selection set. You may want to retain a very specific chart for future reference or modification. How might you accomplish this?

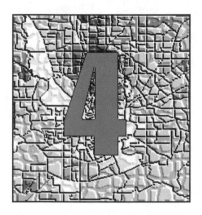

Symbology and Layouts

The purpose of this exercise is to explore the symbolization of features and the layout document type. ArcView provides very flexible tools to symbolize features in ways that help communicate data and relationships. Geographic data and the results of analysis are generally communicated via a hardcopy map. The layout doument represents a map that can contain all other ArcView document types. Each layout is a custom map containing all or a portion of the documents in a project. Multiple layouts can be created, based on the same data, to present the data in various ways.

Topics and Functions

❑ Sett symbology

❑ Alter the Table of Contents legend

❑ Symbolize based on attribute values

❑ Save and restore legends

❑ Modify default symbol palettes

❑ Create a layout

❑ Print and export a layout

Description

In this exercise, you will modify theme symbology for all feature classes. You will investigate layouts, and component graphics and their respective properties. You will create, customize, and print a layout. The steps and topics in the exercise are summarized below:

❑ Open the project

❑ Symbol basics and palettes

❑ Symbol classification

❑ Save and load a legend

❑ Palette Manager

❑ Layout basics

❑ Graphic primitives

❑ Frames

❑ Print and export a layout

Open the Project

If ArcView is not currently running, start the program. Access the File menu and select Open Project. Navigate to the *$AVEXDS\avexer\project* directory and

Symbol Basics and Palettes

select the *chapt4.apr* project. This project is based on the world data project from the exercise in Chapter 3.

You can customize the way ArcView draws theme features. For instance, you can use a single symbol to represent all features in the theme, or you can have ArcView select a symbol based on a value in an attribute field. Symbol classification is a very powerful way to communicate attribute data to the viewer. Arc-View allows you to create a variety of sophisticated thematic maps quite easily.

Symbols are modified using the Legend Editor and Symbol Palette. The Symbol Palette consists of several individual palettes containing all possible choices for symbols and colors. The Fill, Pen, Marker, Font, Color, and Manager palettes are selected with the option buttons across the top of the Symbol Palette window.

INSIDE
ArcView
GIS

For a discussion of symbology, see Chapter 5, "Defining Symbology," page 105.

Marker Symbols

Symbols called "markers" represent point data. You can access the Legend Editor window by double-clicking the theme you want to edit in the view Table of Contents. Alternately, with the theme active, you can select Edit Legend from the Theme menu, or use the Legend Editor button.

1. Activate the Legend Editor for the *Cities* theme in the *Countries of the World* view. Open the Symbol Palette by accessing the Window menu and selecting Show Symbol Window. The <Ctrl>+<P> shortcut noted on the Window menu is not rec-

ommended because it does not work from the Legend Editor. By default, the Symbol Palette will display with the Fill Palette active.

2. When multiple symbols are in use, a given symbol must be highlighted in the Legend Editor before it can be edited. A symbol is highlighted with a click, and you can then open the Palette menu. You can also double-click the symbol to access the Symbol Palette. When you use this shortcut, the Symbol Palette will be activated and preset to the appropriate subpalette instead of the default Fill palette. The latter method is recommended for editing the symbol. Double-click on the only symbol shown for *Cities* in the Legend Editor. Note that this action also synchronizes the Symbol Palette and sets it to the Marker Palette.

3. Position the windows so that you can see the view Table of Contents, the Legend Editor, and the Symbol Palette.

   Note that in the Legend Editor, Theme is set to *Cities* and Legend Type to Single Symbol. This is the simplest type of legend, wherein a single symbol is used for all features of the theme.

4. The current symbol shown in the Legend Editor is identified in the Marker Palette with a box around it. Click on other marker symbols and note how they are updated in the Legend Editor. Select a new marker symbol for the *Cities*, and adjust the symbol size in the Size drop-down list box.

Legend Editor for the Cities theme and the Marker Palette.

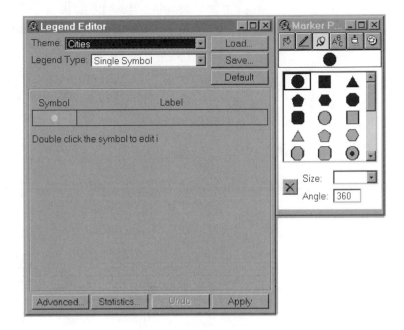

⤳ **NOTE:** *The sample area near the top of the palette window is not a reliable way to keep track of the symbol, because it frequently is not updated as you make changes.*

5. Click the Color Palette button to put the palette into color mode. By default, the Color drop-down list box is set to Foreground, which is the primary color of the symbol. Click on a new foreground color for the *Cities* marker. By selecting Background you can also set the background color for a symbol if it has one. The other two options, Outline and Text, do not affect marker symbols. They will be used later.

6. In the view Table of Contents, show the legend for the *Cities* theme. Click in the Label box next to the symbol and type in *All Cities*. This new label will appear in the View Table of Contents.

7. Click the Apply button to begin using the new symbology in the view. If you make a mistake, use the Undo button to return to the previous settings.

✓ **TIP:** *The Legend Editor Undo can go backward through five symbol settings, but the ability to undo is lost when the Legend Editor is closed.*

8. Turn off the *Cities* theme. Turn on the *Italian Cities* theme and double-click it to set up the Legend Editor to work with it. At this point, both the *Cities* and *Italian Cities* themes can be accessed from the Theme drop-down list box in the Legend Editor.

9. Click the Advanced Button and select *Rotation* as the Rotation Field in the Advanced Options dialog box. This field stores the number of degrees each marker will be rotated counterclockwise. Select OK and apply the change.

10. Note the change in the display of the markers. Take a moment to identify several Italian cities while paying particular attention to the value in the *Rotation* field.

Advanced Options dialog box for marker symbols.

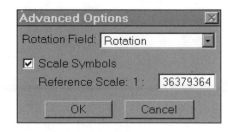

11. Open the Advanced Options dialog box for the *Italian Cities* theme again. This time, click the Scale Symbols check box. This action will cause symbols to get smaller as you zoom out, and larger as you zoom in. They will be displayed at their normal size, as shown in the Legend Editor, at the Reference Scale. By default, Reference Scale is set to the current scale, but you can edit it if you like. Close the dialog box and apply the change. Try zooming in and out, observing the effect on the marker symbols. Resize the view's table of contents if necessary by moving the cursor to the right edge of the table of contents and dragging it to the right.

Pen Symbols

Symbols called "pens" represent linear data.

1. Activate the Legend Editor for the *River* theme.

2. Use the Pen Palette to select a new line symbol for the rivers. The line weight or size is set in *points*. There are 72 points per inch.

3. Use the Color Palette to select a new color. Foreground is the only color setting that affects pens. Apply your new symbol selection.

*Pen Palette
(Dialog Box)*

→ **NOTE:** *On the Pen Palette you can also specify several options for Cap and Join in the drop-down list boxes. The Cap setting specifies the way ArcView draws the end of a line. The Join setting specifies how ArcView will draw a line at each of the vertices.*

*Legend Editor for
River theme and
Pen Palette.*

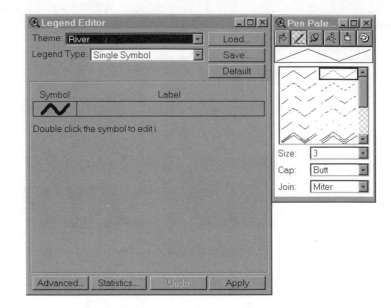

4. From the View Edit menu, copy the *River* theme and paste a duplicate theme into the layout. Rename the new theme *Offset River* and turn it on.

5. Change the color of the *Offset River* theme so that you can distinguish it from the *River* theme. Access the Advanced Options for the Legend of the *Offset River* theme, set the Line Offset to *5*, and apply the change. The line offset is the distance in points a pen symbol is offset from the actual location of the linear feature.

∞ NOTE: *Linear features in ArcView have an internal property of directionality. That is, the* from *end was created first, and the* to *end, last. The right and left sides are denoted as if you were standing at the* from *end looking toward the* to

end. *The offset for linear features moves pen sym-*
bols to the right.

6. Turn off both river themes.

Offset pen symbols
for Rivers.

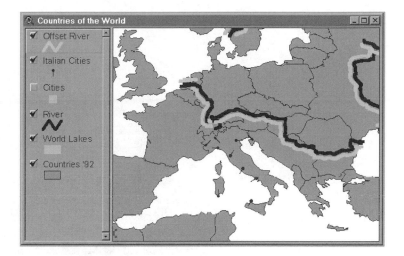

Fill Symbols

Symbols called "fills" symbolize polygon data. Double-click the *World Lakes* theme to set the Legend Editor to modify the symbol for lakes.

1. On the Fill Palette, the Outline drop-down list box
specifics the size of the polygon outline. (Choose
None if you do not want an outline.) Use the Fill
Palette to select a new symbol for the lakes. The
symbol in the upper left corner is a blank fill, and
the one next to it is a solid fill. The others are patterns with which you can use a combination of
background and foreground colors to create
many different fills.

2. Use the Color Palette to select new colors for the background, foreground, and outline as appropriate, depending on the options you have chosen. The line weight for the outline is set in points, just like pen size.

3. Experiment with several more fill symbols, and then turn off the *World Lakes* theme.

Legend Editor for the World Lakes theme and the Fill Palette.

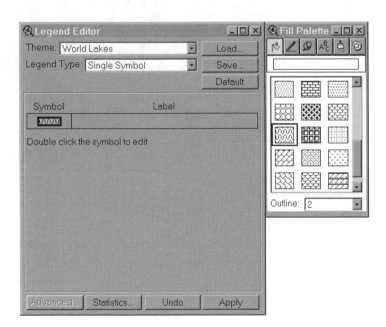

Symbol Classification

One of the most powerful visual presentation tools available in ArcView is the ability to symbolize features based on attribute data. Up to this point, a single symbol has been used to represent all features in a given theme. Now you will see how to use the data values of a specified field to alter symbology. This is often referred to as creating *thematic maps*.

Graduated Color

*For a discussion of
classification, see
Chapter 5,
"Classification,"
page 107.*

1. Open the Legend Editor for the *Countries '92*
theme. In the Legend Type drop-down list box,
select the Graduated Color choice and note how it
changes the Legend Editor dialog box. The graduated color option uses the same symbol for all features, but varies the color to communicate the
selected attribute values.

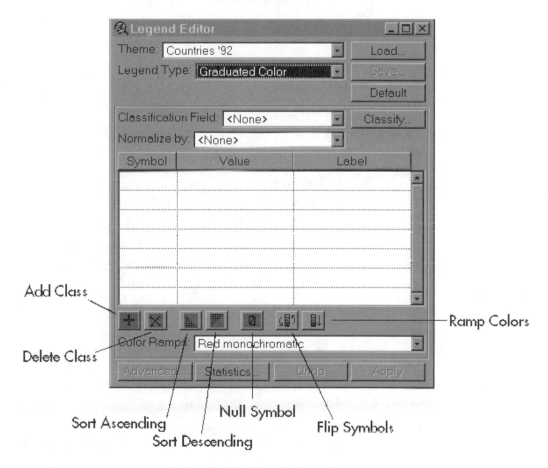

Graduated Color Legend Editor dialog box.

✓ **TIP:** *Even though the Graduated Color option defaults to using the same symbol for all classifications, you can manually override it by highlighting any symbol and selecting a different one from the appropriate palette. If you did this, however, you would not be using a pure, graduated color thematic representation of the data.*

1. Specify the *Tot_pop* field for the *Classification* field. ArcView will create a series of data *classifications* and assign them each a unique color. Apply the change and zoom to the full extent. Turn off the other themes so that you can see the countries clearly.

2. It is often desirable to evaluate the data in a field before using it for a classification. Use the Statistics button to calculate and display the statistics for field of your choice.

3. This thematic map clearly communicates the total population of each country in a general way by putting each into one of five categories indicated by color. However, the "–99" in the table of contents is confusing. In these data, –99 is a special code indicating a no data condition. Certainly, –99 would never be mistaken for the total population.

Click the Null Symbol button to activate the Null Values dialog box. Specify a Null Value of –99 and check the Display No Data Class check box. This will create another symbol classification specifically for the no data condition. Close the dialog box and select a contrasting symbol for the No Data class by double-clicking its symbol box.

Notice that the Value and Label for the top class have been automatically updated from –99 to 57000, which was the next lowest value in the data set. Apply the change and examine the results.

4. The classifications can be sorted in a variety of ways by first clicking one of the headings—Symbol, Value, or Label—and then clicking either the Sort Ascending or Sort Descending button. Try experimenting with a few different sort methods.

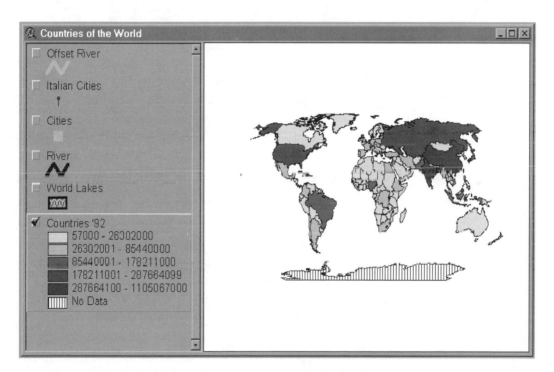

Countries '92 theme displayed as a graduated color thematic map based on total population.

5. To modify the colors, select one of the many predefined Color Ramps at the bottom of the dialog box. Experiment with a few until you find one you like. If you like a color scheme but want to reverse its direction, use the Flip Symbols button. You can always change any symbol manually by double-clicking it and using the corresponding palette.

✓ **TIP:** *If you select one or more colors manually, you can use the Ramp Colors button to calculate and set the intermediate colors. By default, it will calculate the ramp of colors between the first and last colors in the legend. If you select one or more colors in the legend, those colors will not be changed when the ramp is calculated.*

6. ArcView also allows you to normalize the data if desired. Select Percent of Total in the Normalize By drop-down list box and apply the change. This shows each country's total population as a percentage of the total world population. Normalize by Area of the polygons to display the relative population density.

⚬ **NOTE:** *Remember, all Classification and Label values can be edited manually by clicking in the respective box. You can also add or remove classifications manually by using the Add Class or Remove Class buttons.*

Feature Data Clasification Types

The default classification type is Natural Breaks. However, for the population density example, it does not communicate the data in a meaningful way because most of the countries fall into the lowest classification. Fortunately, ArcView provides many ways to classify data, including Equal Area, Equal Interval, Natural Breaks, Quantile, and Standard Deviation.

1. Click the Classify button to access the Classification dialog box. Set the classification Type to Quantile, the Number of classes to *8*, and the Round Values At to *d*. Apply the new classifications and evaluate the resulting data presentation.

Classification Types

❏ *Equl Area* organizes polygon features into groups such that the total area of the polygons in each group is as equal as possible.

❏ *Equal Interval* organizes features so that the range of attribute values in each class is the same.

❏ *Natural Breaks* uses a statistical formula to locate natural divisions in the data.

❏ *Quantile* organizes the features to place an equal number of features in each class.

❏ *Standard Deviations* calculates the mean value and organizes features into classes above and below the mean at standard deviation intervals you specify.

Classification dialog box.

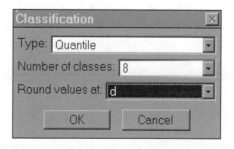

Graduated Symbol

1. Open the Legend Editor for the *Cities* theme. In the Legend Type drop-down list box, select the *Graduated Symbol* choice and notice how it changes the Legend Editor dialog box. The graduated symbol option only works for point and line data, and does not apply to polygons. It uses the same symbol and color for all features but varies the *size* of the symbol to communicate the selected attribute values.

2. Specify the *Population* field for the Classification Field. ArcView will create a series of data classifications and give them each a corresponding size. Apply the change, turn the *Cities* theme On, and, if necessary, zoom in to view the results.

3. Set a No Data value for −99 and a corresponding symbol, as you did previously.

4. Double-click the Symbol box at the bottom of the dialog and set a new symbol, which will be applied to all classifications except the No Data class.

5. Set the Size Range from *2* to *14*. Alternately, you could manually set the size of the top and bottom symbols with the palette and use the new Ramp Symbols button to calculate and set the ramp of intermediate sizes. Apply the changes and examine the results.

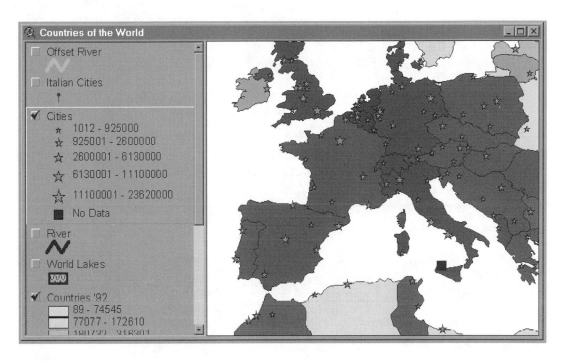

Cities theme with symbols graduated by population.

Unique Value

1. Open the Legend Editor for the *Italian Cities* theme. In the Legend Type drop-down list box, select the *Unique Value* choice and note how it changes the Legend Editor dialog box. The unique value option uses a separate symbol/color combination for each unique data value.

2. Specify the *Name* field for the Values Field. Arc-View will create a classification for each data value in the *Name* field. Apply the change, turn off the *Cities* theme, turn the *Italian Cities* theme On, and zoom to its extent to view the results. Note

that a special category, Count, is available in this Legend Editor. Use it to sort on the quantity of features in each class.

3. Two buttons are available in this legend editor to set unique symbols: Unique Colors and Unique Symbols. Try them or use one of the predefined color schemes to obtain a suitably distinct set of symbols to represent the Italian Cites. In the *Countries of the World* view, show the legend for the *Italian Cities* theme.

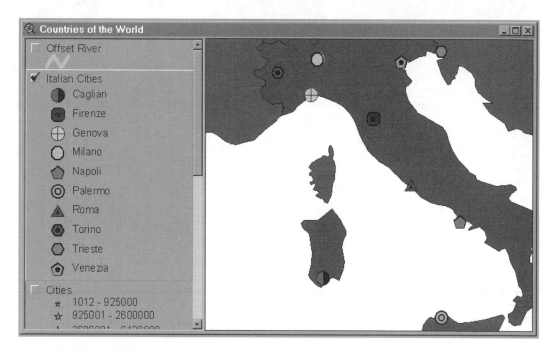

Unique symbols for the Italian Cities theme.

Chart Option

1. Open the Legend Editor for the *World Lakes* theme. The Dot option available for polygon themes will be dealt with in a later exercise. In the Legend Type drop-down list box, select the *Chart* choice and notice how it changes the Legend Editor dialog box. The Chart option uses a custom chart symbol for each feature based on its attribute field values. This is a good option to communicate several attribute values at once, because you can add several values to the chart.

Chart Legend Editor dialog box.

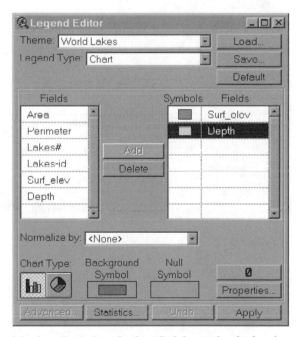

2. Highlight the *Surf_elev* field and click the Add button to add it to the list of fields for the chart. In a similar fashion, add the *Depth* field. Select a Bar Chart Type and apply the settings.

3. Fine tune the charts by selecting attractive symbol colors, and complementary background and null symbols. Access the editor by double-clicking on the current symbol. Adjust the size of the bar chart by using the Properties button.

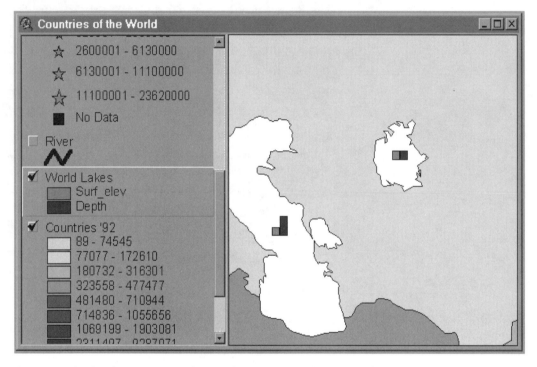

Chart symbols depicting surface elevation and depth of the World Lakes theme.

✓ **TIP:** *You can also change the overall size of a pie chart symbol based on an attribute.*

Save and Load a Legend

Once you have created a legend that classifies and displays the data in a clear and meaningful way, you can save it for future use with other similar themes.

This practice can be a great time saver, and facilitates consistency between themes in one or many different projects.

1. Activate the Legend Editor for the *Cities* theme. To save the legend for the *Cities* theme, click the Save button, navigate to the *$AVEXDS\avexer\project* directory, and save the legend as *chapt4.avl*.

Load Legend (Dialog Box)

2. Access the Legend Editor for the *Italian Cities* theme. Click the Load button, and select the *chapt4.avl* file you created previously. Accept the default settings and click OK in the Load Legend dialog box. The parameters of the saved legend are loaded and applied to the current theme. Apply the changes and close the Legend Editor. Display the *Italian Cities* theme to view the results. Zoom to the extent of *Italian Cities* if necessary.

Palette Manager

Palette Manager, a mode of the Symbol Palette, allows you to customize the symbols available in the Fill, Pen, Marker, Font, and Color Palettes. Palette Manager allows you to load additional symbols, save a set of symbols you have assembled, redefine your default symbols, and reset symbols to the ArcView defaults.

1. Activate the Symbol Palette and select Palette Manager. In theType drop-down list box, specify the palette you wish to action, or select the All of them option. For the moment, select the Marker Type. You can specify which palette to act on, or All of them, in the Type drop-down list box. Select the Marker Type.

2. Temporarily switch to the Marker Palette and scroll through the list of symbols to observe the available symbols. In Palette Manager, click the Load button, navigate to the *$AVHOME\symbols* directory, and select the *municipl.avp* file. Switch back to the Marker Palette, scroll through the list, and note the new symbols appended to the bottom of the list. All marker symbols shown are now available to symbolize features through the Legend Editor.

Palette Manager.

Marker Palette with symbols added.

If you wish to save this configuration for future use, you can do so with the Save button. If you wish to make this your normal default, you can do so with the Make Default button. The Clear button will empty the palette(s) of all symbols.

When Type is set to Marker, an Import button appears. This function allows you to import a GIF, MacPaint, Sun Rasterfile, TIFF, Bitmap or X Bitmap icon file as a new marker. This is a great way to customize your symbol set.

No matter what you change, you can always reset any or all of the palettes to the ArcView defaults. Reset all palettes by selecting All in the *Type* field and clicking the Reset button. Close the Symbol Palette.

✓ **TIP:** *Colored pattern fill symbols from the default ArcView Fill Palette may not reproduce well on a non PostScript printer. Use the fill symbols from the carto.avp file instead.*

Layout Basics

The layout document type represents a piece of paper whereon you arrange graphic objects. When you are satisfied with a layout, you can print or export the results into numerous graphic file formats. Several layouts can be created in a project displaying the same data in different ways.

For a discussion of layouts, see Chapter 8, "Layouts," page 197.

ArcView layouts contain graphic frames and graphic primitives, both of which are referred to as graphics. There are seven types of frames: View, Legend, Scale Bar, North Arrow, Chart, Table, and Picture. Most frames reference other documents in the current project. You can also draw graphic primitives such as points, straight lines, lines, rectangles, circles, polygons, and text. All graphic components have properties that define their look and content.

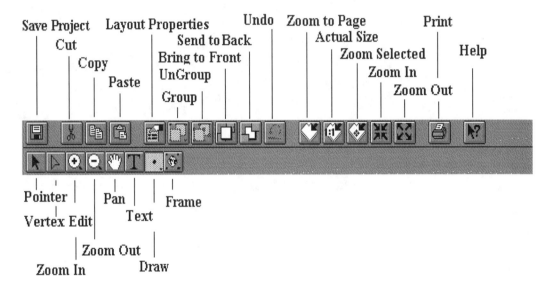

Layout button and tool bars.

1. From the project window, open a new layout. Access the Layout menu and select Properties, or click the Layout Properties button. Name the layout *Population Study*, accept the default Grid Spacings of .25 inch, and leave Snap To Grid checked.

2. The grid is a series of reference dots on the page to which graphics can *snap to* when positioned. The grid aids in organizing and positioning graphics on the layout page. Even if the grid is on, it will not be printed. The grid and the margins can be hidden with the Hide Grid and Hide Margins options in the Layout menu.

Properties of the Population Study layout.

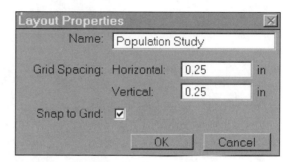

3. Maximize the *Population Study* window and click the Zoom to Page button to fit the page to the window. You can zoom and pan around the page with the zoom buttons or tools to inspect the elements more closely. This feature will become handy after you have placed a few graphics.

4. Access the Layout menu and select Page Setup. ArcView supports a large number of standard paper sizes and units. The units are used for the grid spacing and the positioning of graphics on the page. Accept the default size and click the Landscape Orientation button. Use the printer border as a margin, and set resolution to Normal Output.

✓ **TIP:** *Normal resolution is one-half the device resolution, Low is one-fourth the device resolution,*

*and High is the full device resolution. Use Low or
Normal for draft versions of your map, and High
for the final copy.*

*Page Setup
dialog box.*

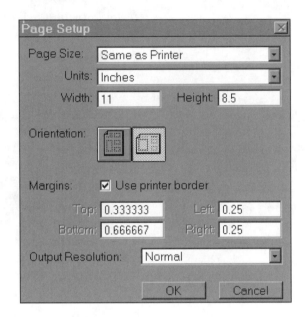

Text

1. Using the Text tool, click near the top center of the
page and enter *Population Study Map*. Click the
Centered Horizontal Alignment button, accept the
default single line Vertical Spacing, and accept
zero degrees for text rotation. Close the Text Properties dialog box.

2. Note that the text graphic remains selected, as evidenced by the *handles*. With the Pointer Tool,
click on the page away from the title and the handles will disappear, indicating that it is no longer
selected. With the Pointer, you can click features

to select them or drag a box to select all features wholly contained within the box. With the title selected, use the Font Palette <Ctrl+P>to change the font to *Times New Roman* and the font size to *24.*

➡ **NOTE:** *The <Shift>+click trick enables you to build a selected set of layout graphics.*

3. When selected, a graphic can be repositioned or resized with the Pointer tool. Grab one of the corner handles and drag it to make the title text larger. If it is no longer centered, put the Pointer tool in the middle of the text and drag it to the center. On the tool bar, ArcView reports the position of the cursor in page unit coordinates. The lower left corner represents 0,0 (zero, zero).

4. Position graphics by dragging them. If snapping is on, they will snap to the grid. The exact size and position of selected graphics can be set explicitly by accessing the Size and Position function from the Graphics menu. With the title selected, access the Graphic Size and Position dialog box. Set From Top at *.5* and From Left at *2.0.* Note how the rest of the values update. Select OK; the title will be moved to the new location.

➡ **NOTE:** *The Size and Position function is not available when two or more graphics are selected.*

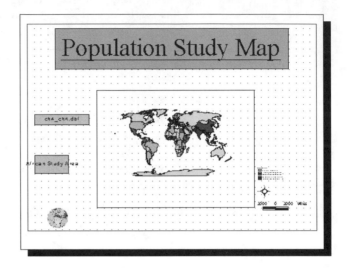

Population Study layout after the various graphics have been added.

Align

The Align function is very useful for spacing graphics on the page, and helps to give your map a professional appearance. Graphics can be aligned relative to each other or to the margins of the page. To illustrate this, the title is placed in the exact horizontal center of the page in the following steps.

1. Select the title text, access the Graphics menu, and select Align to access the Align dialog box. Click the *Align With Margins* box, and click the Center option button across the top of the display box. Close the dialog box. The title text is now centered between the margins of the page. The other option buttons in the Align dialog box across the top and left also allow you to align to the left, right, top, and bottom. See the ArcView help system for a complete explanation.

Align
(Dialog Box)

Align dialog box.

2. Click the *Zoom To Selected* button to set the viewing area to the title; that is, the currently selected graphic. The *Zoom To Selected* function is very useful in helping you navigate around the layout.

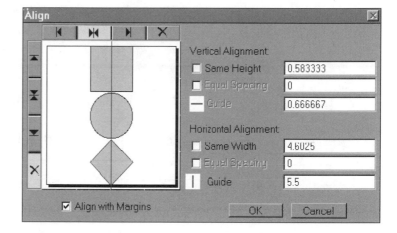

Graphic Primitives

1. Click and hold the Draw tool while you slide down to the Straight Line Draw tool. Release to activate the Line Drawing tool. All Draw tools are accessed in the same manner. The Draw tools include Point, Z Point Line, Straight Line, Multi-vertex Line, Rectangle, Circle, and Polygon. Use the Z Point Line Draw tool to underline the title. Reposition and resize the line to arrange it under the title. If you want to delete the line, select it and use the <Del> key.

✓ **TIP:** *Temporarily turn Snap To Grid in the Layout properties off to allow the line to be placed closer to the title using the pointer.*

2. Try the Zoom Out, Zoom In, and Pan tools, which also allow you to move around the page. Use *Zoom To Actual Size* to see the page in actual or life size.

➤ **NOTE:** *On some systems, the default ArcView settings may be off by a factor of 1.25 when making the screen display the actual size of the page. See the calibration topic in the ArcView help system.*

3. As noted previously, all graphics have properties. The properties for graphic primitives such as lines are limited to their symbol, size, and color. Double-click the line with the Pointer tool (or select it and access Properties from the Graphics menu) to display the Symbol Palette. Use the Pen Palette to make the line size *3*.

4. Use the Draw Rectangle tool to create a box around the title and line to accentuate them. Change the fill symbol to a solid gray pattern. Because this graphic was just added, ArcView placed it "on top" of the text and line. With the rectangle selected, use the *Send To Back* button to "push" it behind the other graphics. The *Bring To Front* button works similarly. In order to see how this works, try bringing the rectangle to the front, and then send it back.

5. The graphic primitives in the layout are essentially identical to the graphics in the view document. The other Draw tools for Point, Line, Circle, and Polygon function similarly to the Straight Line and Rectangle used here. Zoom to the full page once again.

Graphic Frames

Like the Draw tool, the Frame tool is really several tools in one. Each frame is selected by holding the Frame tool down, dragging through the drop-down list to the desired tool, and releasing. There are seven types of frames: View, Legend, Scale Bar, North Arrow, Chart, Table, and Picture. Some of the frames reference other documents in the project as the source of information for the frame. Frame types normally tied to project documents can also be created without this reference. This is known as creating an *empty frame*. Empty frames are frequently used to create layouts for future use as templates. Several standard templates are provided for simple portrait and landscape maps. Templates will be covered in detail in a later exercise.

View Frames

For example, the Live Link check box determines if ArcView will maintain an internal association between the frame with its source, or simply create a "snapshot in time."

The Scale setting has three options: Automatic, Preserve View Scale, and User Specified Scale. If the default Automatic is retained, ArcView will modify the scale as necessary to fit the view into the current size of the frame. When Preserve View Scale is used, the frame will use the scale of the related view. The User Specified Scale option allows you to set the scale that will be used.

For a discussion of frames, see Chapter 8, "Layout Frames in More Detail," page 199.

View Frame Tool

◦ ***NOTE:*** *If Live Link is used, the Display will be adjusted whenever a change is made to the view. This includes Theme Display, Symbology, Graphics and Scale.*

The Extent setting allows you to select either Fill View Frame or *Clip To View*. If you select Fill View Frame, extra data not visible in the view may be used to fill the frame, as determined by its size and shape. Selecting *Clip To View* will restrict the data used by the frame to that currently visible in the view.

The Display property settings include When Active or Always. The When Active option will cause Arc-View to draw and refresh the frame only when the layout is the active document. The Always option will cause ArcView to draw and refresh the frame whenever there is a change in the source. Appearance or quality of frames can also be toggled between Presentation or Draft. When Presentation is set, the frame appears as it will when printed. Note that as your layouts become more complex, the Presentation setting may adversely affect drawing speed. The Draft setting will simplify the frame on the screen by drawing it as a shaded box, and thus increase drawing speed. Draft has no effect on the printed appearance of the frame. It is generally advisable to stick with the ArcView defaults of When Active and Presentation unless performance becomes an issue.

1. Use the View Frame tool and drag a box for the frame. In the View Frame Properties dialog box, select the *Countries of the World* view. Leave the

Live Link box checked so that all changes in the view will be reflected in the frame. Remember, if you remove the check in the Live Link box, the frame will represent a static "snapshot" of the view. Use the defaults for the other settings and select OK.

View Frame Properties dialog box.

2. The view frame now displays a representation of the view. Switch to the view and modify the display. Switch back to the layout and observe the effect of the linkage with the view. With the view frame selected, you can resize and reposition the frame as necessary with the Pointer.

3. Use the Draw Rectangle tool to add a neatline around the view frame. Send the neatline rectangle to the back: otherwise, you will have difficulty selecting the view frame with the rectangle "on top" of it.

Legend Frames

1. Place a legend frame next to the view frame with the Legend tool. A legend references the themes in a view frame.

2. Select ViewFrame1: *Countries of the World* in the Properties dialog box and pick OK. The legend is dynamic because there is a live link to the view. As themes are turned on or off, or as symbology is changed, the legend is updated. Try a few changes in the view to test the link.

Scale Bar Frames

1. Use the Scale Bar Frame Tool to add a scale bar frame next to the view frame and under the legend frame. Reference it to the view frame. The Preserve Interval check box in the Scale Bar Properties dialog box affects how ArcView will adjust the scale bar if it is resized or if the corresponding view frame scale changes. When checked, the specified interval will be retained, but the size of the scale bar may change. When unchecked, the interval will be adjusted and the scale bar size will be retained. Uncheck the Preserve Interval check box.

2. In the Scale Bar Properties dialog box, select the default split filled bar style, miles for units, *2* intervals, and key in *1* in the Left Divisions box. The interval is auatomatically calculated by ArcView. One numeric style and several graphic styles of scale bar are available to choose from. The Units entry sets the display units for the scale bar. The Interval sets the number of units represented by each division. The Intervals entry sets the number of divisions to the right of the zero position, and Left Divisions sets the number of divisions to the left of the zero position. Click OK to close the dialog box.

↠ **NOTE:** *The Interval, Intervals, Left Divisions, and the size of the scale bar are all interrelated. A change in one may result in an automatic change to the others. Sometimes a little experimentation is required to get just what you want.*

Scale Bar Properties dialog box.

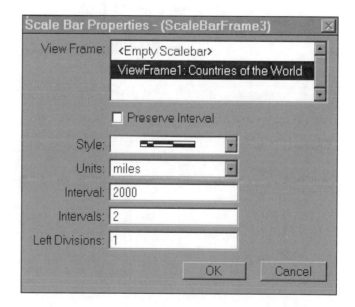

North Arrow Frames

1. Switch to the North Arrow Frame tool and drag a box for a north arrow.

2. Select a style in the North Arrow Manager and select OK.

3. If required, a rotation angle can be specified. Individual styles can be removed from the North Arrow Manager with the Delete button. The Store button will save the modified list of north arrows to a file named *north.def* in the *$HOME* directory. The *north.def* file in your *$HOME* directory can be deleted to restore the north arrow list to the Arc-View default.

☞ ***WARNING:*** *Never delete the* north.def *file in the* $AVHOME\etc *directory, because it is the Arc-View default file.*

North Arrow Manager dialog box.

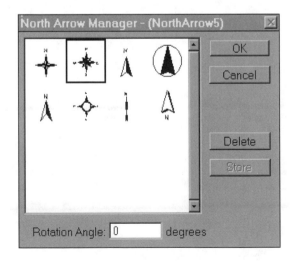

4. Use the Align function to clean up the map. Select the legend, scale bar, and north arrow frames using the <Shift>+click methodology. Select Align from the Graphics menu and click the Left choice button across the top of the display box. This will align all selected graphics on their left edge. Select OK.

5. With all three frames still selected, click the Group button to group them. Now the legend, scale bar, and north arrow can be moved, aligned, and resized as a single unit. Try moving and resizing the new group. Use Ungroup to split up the group.

➥ **NOTE:** *A group must be split to alter the properties of individual members. However, the text font size, foreground, background, outline colors, and so forth can be changed as a unit.*

Chart and Table Frames

1. Open the *African Study Area* chart from the project window.

2. Use the Chart Frame tool to add this chart to the layout as you have done with the previous frames. Chart documents must be open in the project to be visible in the layout frame. All changes made to the chart document will be reflected in the frame.

*Chart Frame
Properties dialog box.*

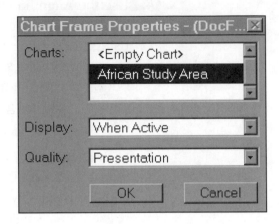

3. The table frame will display a table exactly as it appears in the table window. Like charts, the associated table document must be open in order to see the table in the table frame. Open the *ch4_chrt.dbf* table, and adjust the window to fit the rows and columns with no extra space.

4. Use the Table Frame tool to add this table to the layout. The entire table document will be sized to fit into the table frame, regardless of the frame's size. Therefore, verify that the frame is large enough to allow you to read the rows and columns.

✎ **NOTE:** *The table frame can display a maximum of 80 characters in a table. The table frame will use the leftmost characters and will not display partial columns if it hits the 80-character limit.*

Table Frame
Properties dialog box.

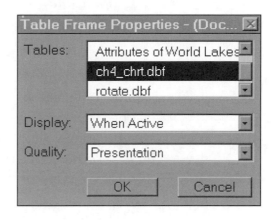

Picture Frames

Picture Frame Tool

The final frame type is the picture frame, which allows you to include a picture or raster graphic image file on a layout. Use the Picture Frame tool to add a frame for the *world.tif* file in the *$AVEXDATA\avdata\misc* directory. ArcView supports a large number of picture formats, listed in the help system.

Picture Frame
Properties dialog box.

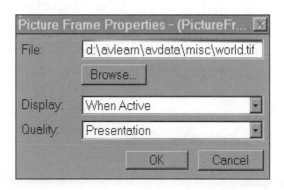

✓ **TIP:** *In addition to dragging, use the arrow keys to move selected graphics. Each key stroke moves the*

graphic one point. When using this method, snapping to the grid is temporarily disabled.

Print and Export a Layout

Select Print Setup from the File menu and confirm that Printer, Orientation, and Paper are correct for your layout. ArcView may not always synchronize with the system printer settings. If necessary, adjust the settings. Use the Print button to print your *Population Study* layout.

You can save the layout to a variety of different file formats using the Export function from the File menu. Use the Options button to set the export resolution in dots per inch (DPI). The export formats vary by platform and are listed in the dialog box.

✓ **TIP:** *You can also use the Cut, Copy, and Paste buttons to copy and paste selected graphics within ArcView or between applications.*

A standard shortcut to several commonly used functions is provided in the form of a pop-up menu on the layout document. This menu is accessed by right clicking the mouse in the layout area. On the Macintosh, hold down the Option key while clicking with the mouse. Access the layout pop-up menu and experiment with its functions.

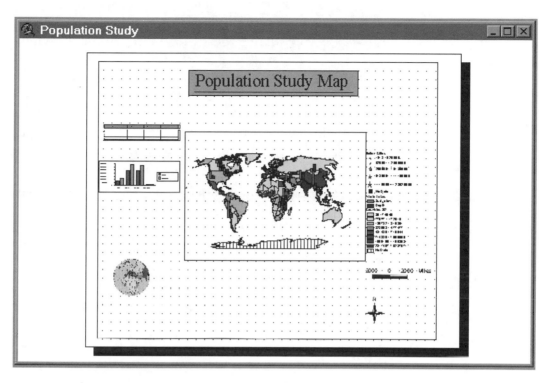

Completed Population Study layout.

Optional

Practice your symbology and layout skills by performing the following additional steps.

1. Try using the other classification types for the *Countries '92* theme. Select the single classification type and corresponding settings that you feel best communicate the data.

2. Load additional symbols from the collection of files in the *$AVHOME\symbols* directory. Next, select a font in the Font Palette and use the Create Markers button to add the font patterns to the set

of available markers. Use these additional symbols to enhance the *Countries of the World* view.

3. Use the graphic primitive tools to draw your own north arrow. Group the pieces. Use the Store North Arrows function from the Layout menu to make your north arrow available as a choice in the north arrow frame. You can also create a north arrow from a frame. Try creating an intricate north arrow by using an image file, or geographic data displayed in a view frame.

Summary

In this exercise, you used the various symbol palettes to change symbols that represent features of all types in the *Countries of the World* view. You also used symbol classification to set symbology based on attribute values, and the layout document type to create a hardcopy map of the project. The population study map included both project documents and graphic primitives.

Discussion Topics

❐ When would the ability to offset pen symbols and rotate markers be beneficial?

❐ When would the ability to classify symbols be beneficial? When would you use each of the classification types?

❐ When would you use a "live-linked" view frame? When would it be advantageous to turn the link off?

❐ Why would you want to export a layout rather than print it?

Theme-on-Theme Selection

The main purpose of this exercise is to explore Arc-View's capability of selecting features in one theme with the features of another. This functionality is fundamental to several forms of spatial analysis. In preparation for the theme-on-theme selection, you will extend theme data by joining additional attributes and select a theme feature with a logical expression of attribute values.

Topics and Functions

❏ Extending theme data by joining additional tabular data

❏ Performing complex Boolean queries to select theme features

❏ Using the Select By Theme capability to select theme features with the features of another theme

Description

In this exercise, you will perform a typical task performed by a city planning department whenever a land parcel is considered for a variance or zoning change. The task consists of generating a mailing list of property owners within a 300-foot notification ring of the subject parcel. A summary of the steps and topics in this exercise follows.

❏ Open the project

❏ Set up the main view

❏ Add spatial data to the view

❏ Add related data to the spatial data

❏ Join the *assessor.dat* table to the *Attributes of Parcels* table

❏ Examine *Parcels* attributes

❏ Select the subject parcel on which to base notification

❏ Select all parcels within 300 feet of the subject parcel

❏ Create a new theme as a shapefile from the selected parcels

❏ Save the mailing list file

❏ Create a map for inclusion in the mailing

Open the Project

If ArcView is not currently running, start the program. Access the File menu and select Open Project. Navigate to the *$AVEXDS\avexer\project* directory and select the *chapt5.apr* project.

Set Up the Main View

You need to create a new view for your data and establish the view properties.

1. Click on the View icon in the *chapt5.apr* project window, and then click on the New button to create a new view. Resize the view window to make it larger.

2. Change the view properties by accessing the View menu and selecting Properties. Change the name to *Redwood Parcels*. Set the map units and distance units to feet. Select OK.

Properties of the Redwood Parcels view.

Add Spatial Data to a View

To add a new theme to the *Redlands Parcels* view, access the View menu and select Add Theme. Navigate to the *$AVEXDATA\ avdata\redwood* directory. Click on the *Parcels* folder and highlight the Polygon feature class. Click OK to close the dialog box and add *Parcels* to the view.

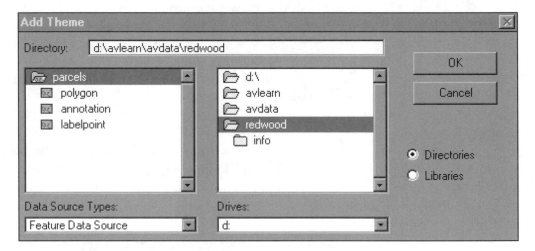

Add Theme dialog box.

→ **NOTE:** *Because* Parcels *is the first theme added to the view, it is active by default.*

Now, change the legend to make it more attractive.

1. Access the Theme menu and select Edit Legend.

2. Double-click the sample symbol shown in the Legend Editor to bring up the Symbol Palette.

3. Reposition the palette menu next to the Legend Editor so that you can see both at once. By default, ArcView selected the solid fill pattern. Select the Color button to place the palette into Color Palette mode.

4. Change the *Parcels* color to gray.

5. Apply the changes, and close the Legend Editor and Palette windows.

6. Verify that the *Parcels* theme check box is on to display the theme in the view.

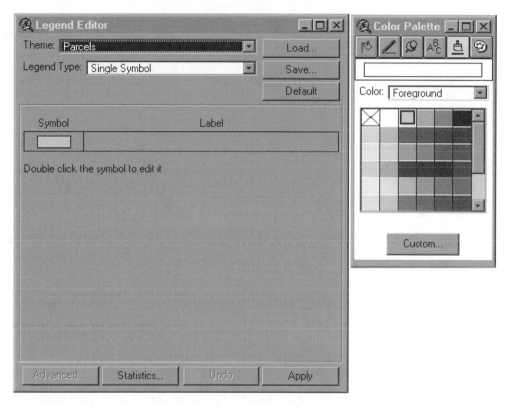

Modifying the Parcels theme symbology.

Add Related Data to Spatial Data

Verify that the *Parcels* theme is still active. Access the Theme menu, and select Table to open the *Attributes of Parcels* table. Note that the *Attributes of Parcels* window becomes active. Access the Table menu and select Properties. In the Table Properties dialog box, remove the visibility checkmarks for the *Area, Perimeter, Parcels#, Parcels-id, Genplan, Landuse,* and *Zoning* fields. Click on the OK button to confirm the changes and to close the dialog box.

Properties of the Attributes of Parcels table.

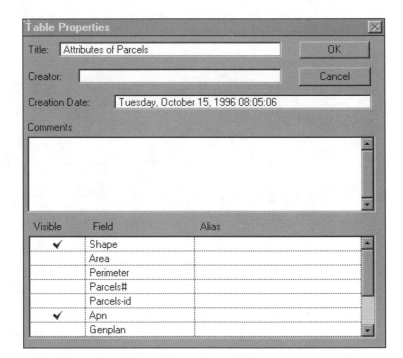

The *Parcels* theme contains the assessor's parcel number designator (*APN*) for each parcel, but lacks address information. To generate a mailing list, you need owner and address data for each parcel. The additional data reside in another table, called *assessor.dat*.

1. Activate the project window.

2. Click on the Tables icon and then click the Add button to add a table to the project.

3. In the Add Table dialog box, navigate to the *$AVEXDATA\avdata\redwood\info* directory, set List Files of Type to INFO, and select the *assessor.dat* table.

4. Make both the *Attributes of Parcels* and *assessor.dat* table windows wider and position them so that you can see both at the same time.

Attributes of Parcels and assessor.dat tables.

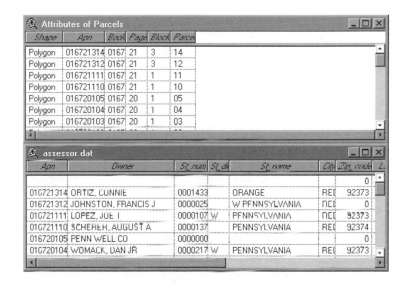

Join assessor.dat to Attributes of Parcels Table

1. Activate the *assessor.dat* table by clicking its title bar.

2. Access the Table menu and select Properties. Remove the visibility check marks for the *Land_val, Imp_val, Prop_val, Exm_val, Book, Page, Block,* and *Parcel* fields. Add your name as Creator and fill in Comments describing the table and its use. Click on the OK button to close the dialog box.

3. Prepare to join the tables by selecting the *APN* field in the *assessor.dat* table.

4. Activate the *Attributes of Parcels* table and click on the *APN* field.

5. Access the Table menu. Select Join to link the two tables based on their relationship through the *APN* field. The result of this action closed the *assessor.dat* table and joined its fields to the *Attributes of Parcels* table.

The selection order of the table makes a difference: the first table is the source, and the second is the destination table. When ArcView joins tables, fields from the source table are added to the destination table.

For a complete explanation of extending tabular data, see Chapter 4, "Joining Tables," page 78.

↦ **NOTE:** *The joined fields can be removed by accessing the Table menu and selecting Remove All Joins.*

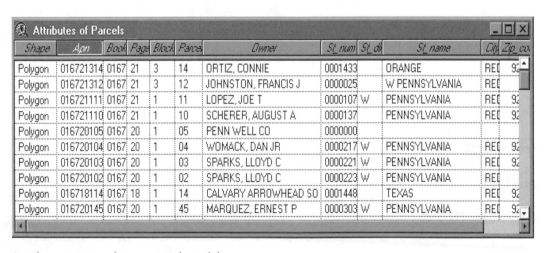

Shape	Apn	Book	Page	Block	Parcel	Owner	St_num	St_di	St_name	City	Zip_co
Polygon	016721314	0167	21	3	14	ORTIZ, CONNIE	0001433		ORANGE	REE	92
Polygon	016721312	0167	21	3	12	JOHNSTON, FRANCIS J	0000025		W PENNSYLVANIA	REE	
Polygon	016721111	0167	21	1	11	LOPEZ, JOE T	0000107	W	PENNSYLVANIA	REE	92
Polygon	016721110	0167	21	1	10	SCHERER, AUGUST A	0000137		PENNSYLVANIA	REE	92
Polygon	016720105	0167	20	1	05	PENN WELL CO	0000000				
Polygon	016720104	0167	20	1	04	WOMACK, DAN JR	0000217	W	PENNSYLVANIA	REE	92
Polygon	016720103	0167	20	1	03	SPARKS, LLOYD C	0000221	W	PENNSYLVANIA	REE	92
Polygon	016720102	0167	20	1	02	SPARKS, LLOYD C	0000223	W	PENNSYLVANIA	REE	
Polygon	016718114	0167	18	1	14	CALVARY ARROWHEAD SO	0001448		TEXAS	REE	92
Polygon	016720145	0167	20	1	45	MARQUEZ, ERNEST P	0000303	W	PENNSYLVANIA	REE	92

Attributes joined to a single table.

Examine Parcel Attributes

Activate the Parcels theme in the view document. Identify several parcels and observe the attributes, and they now include the name and address information you joined to the Attributes of Parcels table. Close the Identify Results window.

Identify results of Parcels with joined attributes.

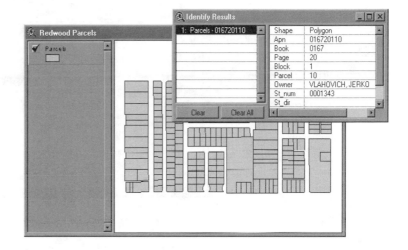

Selecting the Subject Parcel

To simulate a typical query that locates a specific parcel using the query builder, you will use the parcel identified as follows: *Book 167, Page 19, Block 1, Parcel 15.*

For a complete explanation of theme queries, see Chapter 6, "Logical Queries on Themes," page 142.

1. Activate the *Redwood Parcels* view. Access the Theme menu, and select Query.

2. From the Parcels Query Builder dialog window, double-click the *Book* field. Then click the equals button (=), double-click on *0167*, and click on the "and" button.

3. Continue to build the following expression: *Page = 19 and Block = 1 and Parcel = 15.* Note that ArcView displays the expression in the text box as you construct it.

Theme Query Builder dialog window with the constructed query.

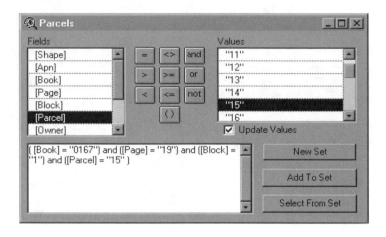

For a complete explanation of selecting theme features with other themes, see Chapter 11, "Theme-on-Theme Selection," page 284.

4. When you have completed construction of the expression, click New Set to establish a new set selected from all features in the theme.

5. Close the Query Builder dialog window. At this point, you have selected a single parcel. ArcView highlights the parcel in both the view and the *Attributes of Parcels* table.

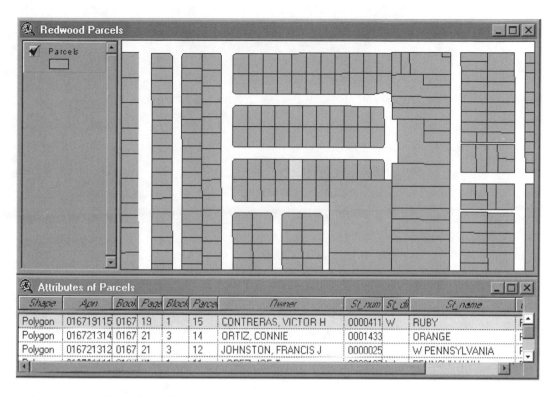

Subject parcel and attributes as selected.

Select All Parcels Within 300 Feet of Subject Parcel

To create a new selected set of parcels within 300 feet of the currently selected parcel, you need to perform a spatial theme-on-theme selection.

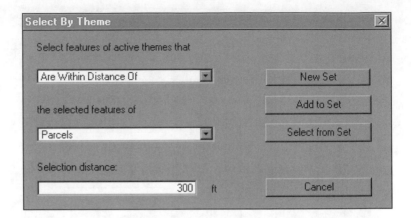

Select By Theme dialog window.

1. Make the *Redwood Parcels* view the active document and make sure the *Parcels* theme is highlighted. Access the Theme menu and click on the Select By Theme function. This will open a dialog box, which you will use to formulate a statement to select parcels within 300 feet of the currently selected parcel.

2. In the Select By Theme dialog box, change the spatial relation to *Are Within Distance Of.* Retain the default of Parcels for the features to be selected.

3. Set the Selection distance to *300.* ArcView has set the units to feet for you from the Distance Units property for the view.

4. Click on the New Set button to build a new selected set of the *Parcels* theme features. The resulting action highlights several parcels within 300 feet of the subject parcel.

5. Access the View menu, and select Zoom To
Selected for a closer look at the selected parcels.

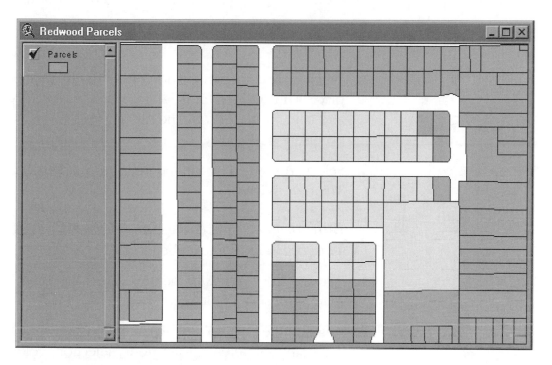

Selected parcels within the 300-foot notification ring.

Create a New Shapefile and Theme

To preserve the selected set, save the selected parcels
as a new *shapefile*. If you only wanted to export a mailing list, you would not have to create a new shapefile.
You will use the new shapefile for your map.

Shapefiles are ArcView's native spatial data format.
Shapefiles store location and attribute data for geographic data. They are not as robust as ARC/INFO
coverages in terms of topology, but they have several
key advantages in ArcView. Shapefiles draw more

rapidly in a view, and ArcView can edit both the graphic and attribute data of a shapefile. In addition, ArcView can create new data in the shapefile format.

For a discussion of shapefiles, see Chapter 10, "Editing Shapefiles," page 255.

1. Access the Theme menu,and select Convert to Shapefile.

2. When asked to name and locate the shapefile, place it in the *$AVEXDS\avexer\shape* directory and name it *notlist.shp*. The file name refers to the notification list. Select OK to close the dialog box.

3. Select Yes when prompted to Add Shapefile As Theme to View.

❧ **NOTE:** *In order to create the shapefile, the* Shape *field must be visible in the* Attributes of Parcels *table.*

1. Activate the *notlist.shp* theme. Access the Theme menu and select Edit Legend.

2. Change the symbology to a contrasting color, preferably different from your selection color, which is a property of the project. Apply the change and close the Legend Editor and the Symbol Palette.

3. Access the Theme menu, and select Properties to change the theme Name to *Parcels Within 300 Feet.*

4. Access the Theme menu and select Table to open the attributes for the new shape theme. Change the table properties to hide everything except the *Apn, Owner, St_num, St_dir, St_name, City,* and *Zip_code* fields.

5. Resize the Table window so that you can see all fields.

Save the Mailing List File

1. After activating the *Attributes of Parcels Within 300 Feet* table, access the File menu and select Export to export the records.

2. In the Export Table dialog box, select the Delimited Text export format. Place the file in the *$AVEXDS\avexer\dbf* directory and name the file *list.txt*. Because this file is suitable for use in a word processor, you can mail a form letter to the affected property owners.

3. If you want a hard copy of the table, access the File menu and select Print.

Create a Map for the Mailing

To create a map for inclusion in the mailing, follow these steps:

1. Make the *Redwood Parcels* view active.

2. Access the View menu, and select Layout to create a new layout depicting the parcels and notification area. Accept the default template Landscape.

3. Enlarge the layout window. The layout page will zoom to fill the window.

4. Reposition the layout parts to your liking. The template uses the view name as the default title for the layout.

5. Remove the scale bar by selecting it and hitting the <Del> key. Access the File menu, and select Print to make a hard copy of the layout.

   ✓ *TIP: Reduce the layout's Grid Spacing property for finer control of the placement of the layout frames. This property can be found in the Layout Properties menu.*

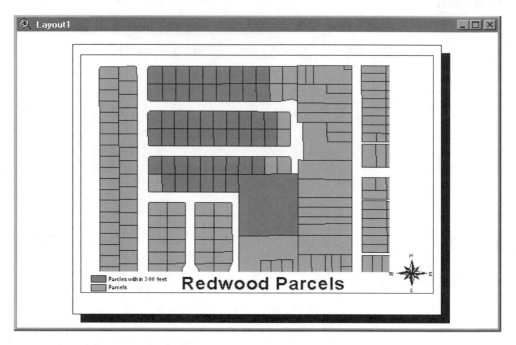

Completed layout of notification parcels.

Optional

You may wish to consider modifying the legend for the *Parcels* theme to classify the shading based on property value, and to further enhance the layout. Take the following steps to accomplish both objectives.

1. Make the *Prop_val* attribute field visible for the *Attributes of Parcels* table. Edit the legend for the *Parcels* theme.

2. Select *Prop_val* as the field on which to base a quantile classification. Select a graduated color ramp for the classification.

3. Return the scale bar to the layout.

4. Use the Zoom In tool to take a close look at the scale bar. You want to change the scale from miles to feet.

5. Double-click the scale bar or click the bar to select it, and then access the Graphics menu and select Properties. Review the scale bar's properties and make any changes you desire.

6. Change the north arrow to a different style.

7. Dress up the layout by adding graphics or text.

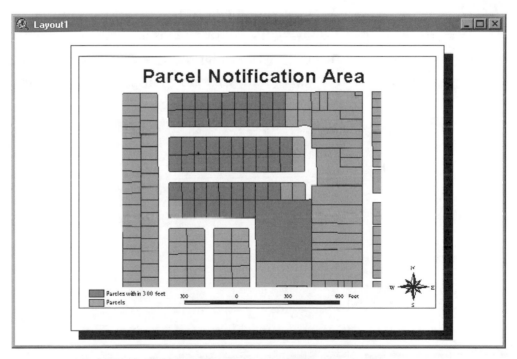

An enhanced layout of the notification parcels.

Summary

In this exercise, you learned how to extend ArcView theme data by joining additional related tabular attributes. You also saw that queries are a powerful means of selecting theme features, and that theme-on-theme selection is useful for choosing features by "buffering" features in another theme. Finally, the exercise included an example of exporting tables for use in other applications, and an example of a simple layout.

Discussion Topics

❐ In what other types of application would the theme-on-theme selection functionality be useful?

❐ What are the advantages and disadvantages of saving the set of parcels as a new shapefile?

❐ When would you use the <Shift>+click method to add or remove features from the selected set?

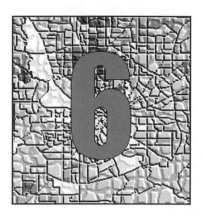

Data Preparation for Trade Area Analysis

The purpose of this exercise is to prepare data for a trade area analysis focused on two stores in two different areas in the United States. Trade area analyses are used to determine the demographics of the population surrounding a business. With this information, you can target marketing to specific groups.

In this chapter, you will apply some of the skills covered earlier to significantly alter the initial view and table properties in preparation for the analysis. In the next chapter, you will perform the analysis.

Topics and Functions

❏   Altering table properties

❏   Joining tabular data to theme attributes

❏   Hiding and changing the names of table columns

❏   Altering theme legends by changing labels

❏   Restoring saved legends

❏   Using Avenue to automatically hide legends

Description

The base data supplied will be altered to suit the analysis. You will change the properties for both tables and views. The steps and topics for this exercise follow.

❏   Open the initial view

❏   Column visibility

❏   Column aliases

❏   Change column order and size

❏   Index the tables

❏   Join the demographic data

❏   Copy the census tracts theme

❏   Change legend symbology

❏   Automatically hide the legends

❏   Save your work

Open
Initial View

Open the *$AVEXDS\avexer\project\chapt6.apr* project. This project contains two views and two tables. The views contain census tracts, zip codes, county boundaries, city streets, major roads, shopping centers, and the two store locations.

The streets and major roads themes are used for reference. The census tracts are the geographic units you will use for the demographic data. You could use the zip codes instead of the census tracts to facilitate the determination of the postal areas in which to target mailing lists. However, for the current analysis, you will use the zip codes for reference.

All data for this exercise were provided by Equifax National Decision Systems as part of their Sparta-Site data product. The legends currently appear to be rather spartan, but you will add several new themes and perform various types of classifications.

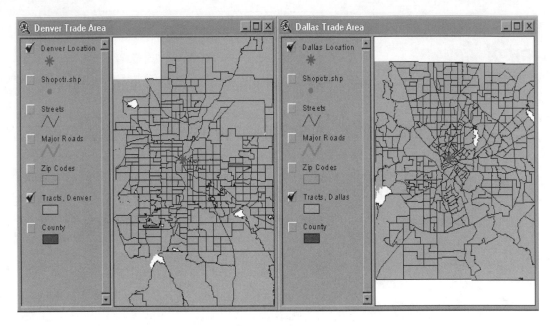

Initial view for the trade area analysis.

Column Visibility, Order, and Size

ArcView allows you to alter the appearance of tables in many ways. In the next few steps you are going to change the default visibility properties for the demographic data. The purpose of these changes is to hide some of the fields not used in this analysis.

1. Open the *Denver Demographics* and *Dallas Demographics* tables. These tables will eventually be joined to the appropriate census tract themes.

2. Change the properties for both tables to hide the *Cy_race_bs*, *Cy_agebase*, *Hh_5y*, *Hh_cy*, *Hh_90*, *Hh_80* and *Hh_grwthc90* fields.

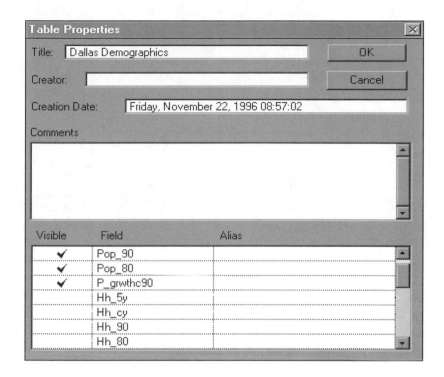

Properties dialog box for the Dallas Demographics table showing some of the columns hidden.

Most of the column names in the demographic data are not very intuitive. In this section, you will change the default column names by creating alias names that make more sense.

1. Access the properties of the demographics tables.

2. Change each of the default columns to its respective alias based on following table.

Field Name	Alias
Pop_5y	5-yr. projected pop.
Pop_cy	Current yr. est. pop.
Pop_90	1990 Census pop.
Pop_80	1980 Census pop.
P_grwthc90	Pop. growth 1990 to current yr.
Abvpvty_65	Age 0–65 above poverty
Blwpvty_65	Age 0–65 below poverty
C90_avginc	1990 Census avg. income
Fy_avginc	5-yr. projected avg. income

✓ **TIP:** *The use of column aliases can be very power-ful. You have just seen how you can change cryptic column names used in the database into more intuitive names. If your data set uses coded values, you could create another table with the code and the English translation and join it to the base table. In this way, you will see the English translation and not be forced to rely on your memory of the coded values.*

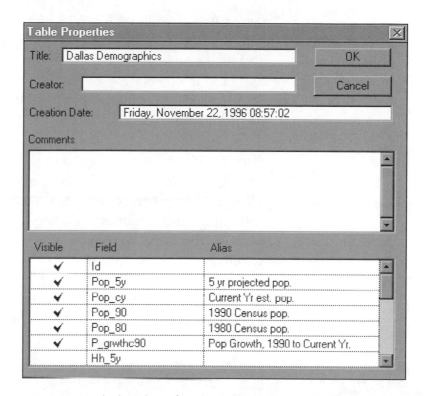

Properties dialog box for the Dallas Demographics table showing some of the aliased columns.

Several columns are aliased, and their headings are too small. In addition, there are columns that appear at the end of the table that should be near the beginning. Recall that you move a column by clicking and dragging the column heading to the position you want. Perform the following steps on the *Denver* and *Dallas Demographics* tables.

1. Resize all column headings for both tables. Remember, you resize a column by moving the cursor to the row that lists the field names. The cursor will change to a two-headed arrow as you pass over borders that separate field names. Click and drag to resize.

2. To reorder the columns, simply click and drag them into the position you desire. Place the columns *Age 0–65 Above Poverty, Age 0–65 Below Poverty, 1990 Census Avg. Income*, and *5-yr. Projected Avg. Income* just after the *Pop. Growth, 1990 to Current Yr.* column. You will have to click and drag the column heading several times because the table window will not automatically scroll.

↝ **NOTE:** *Reordered columns may not be retained after a table join, but resized columns will.*

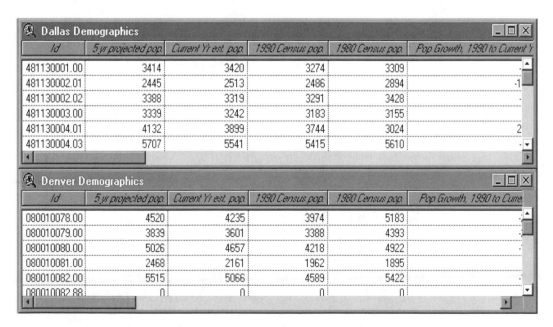

Demographics tables with reordered and resized columns.

Index Tables

Indexes enhance spatial or aspatial access to a table. The amount of data you are reviewing in this exercise warrants creating several indexes to enhance the performance of data access.

1. Open the attribute tables for the *Denver* and *Dallas Census* tract themes.

2. Create spatial indexes for the *Attributes of Tracts, Denver* and *Attributes of Tracts, Dallas* tables. Note that you create a spatial index by indexing the *Shape* field.

3. In a similar fashion, create spatial indexes for the *Id* columns.

4. Create indexes for the *Id, Census 1990 Avg. Income*, and *Age 0–65 Below Poverty* columns for the *Dallas and Denver Demographics* tables.

Join Demographic Tables to Census Tracts

As seen previously, ArcView can attach additional tabular data to a theme in a view. To join tables, you must have a "common" column in each table that "joins" the tables. These columns do not require the same names, but they should contain similar data types.

The order in which you select the columns in the two tables makes a difference in terms of which table is retained as the final table containing both sets of fields. For this exercise, you are going to join the *Dallas Demographics* table to the *Attributes of Tracts, Dallas* table and the *Denver Demographics* table to the *Attributes of Tracts, Denver* table.

1. Make the *Denver Demographics* table the active document. Click on the column *Id* to make it the active column. This column will be the basis of the join for this table.

2. Make the *Attributes of Tracts, Denver* table the active document. Click on the column name *Id.* This is the column that will be joined to the *Id* column in the demographics table.

3. Access the Table menu and select the Join option, or click on the Join button on the button bar. The *Denver Demographics* table should disappear and its attributes should be in the *Attributes of Tracts, Denver* table.

4. Repeat the previous steps for the Dallas demographics and census tracts.

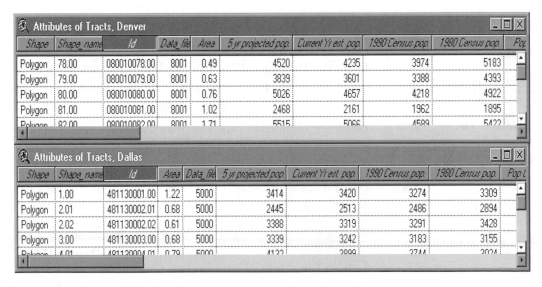

Demographics joined to the census tracts.

Copy Census Tracts Theme

Now that you have prepared the demographic data and joined it to the census tracts, you are ready to copy the theme and create several classified themes.

1. Make the *Dallas Trade Area* view the active document, and make *Tracts, Dallas* the active theme.

2. Select Copy from the Edit menu and Paste the *Tracts, Dallas* theme three times.

3. Open the properties for the three new themes. Change their names to *Below Poverty*, *Average Income*, and *Population*. If you like, you can temporarily turn off the new themes in order to reduce graphic screen refreshing.

4. Move the new themes below the zip codes theme.

5. Repeat for the other trade area.

Change Legend Symbology

Alter Theme Symbology by Using Saved Legends

You are now ready to enhance the symbology of the three tracts-based themes, classifying on several criteria. Because you are performing analysis on two different regions, you need to standardize your classifications so that you can see the same information in each view.

1. Open the Legend Editor for the *Below Poverty* theme and change the contents of the drop-down list from *None* to *Age 0–65 Below Poverty*.

2. Click on the Load button to load a previously saved legend. Navigate to the *$AVEXDS\avexer\project* directory and select *poverty.avl*. Confirm that the field is set correctly in the load legend pop-up dialog box. Change the color sceme to orange monochromatic. Apply the change.

3. Load the legend for the *Average Income* theme using the *1990 Census Avg. Income* field and *income.avl* legend. Change the color scheme to green monochromatic, and apply.

4. Load the legend for the *Population* theme by selecting the *Current Yr. Est. Pop.* field and the *pop.avl* legend. Select a suitable color scheme or default to the red monochromatic.

5. Repeat for the other view.

↝ **NOTE:** *With the Save Legend function, you can create standard legends and reuse them in other projects.*

Displaying Labels Instead of Values in Legends

As seen previously, the legend can be altered to display unique symbology by value. Instead of displaying the values for income, you will display general classes for the income levels.

1. Click on the *Average Income* theme and open the Legend Editor.

2. Click on the topmost label and change its label value to *Poor*. Repeat for the others using the labels *Better, Not Bad, Good, Darn Good,* and *Great*.

3. Repeat for the other view.

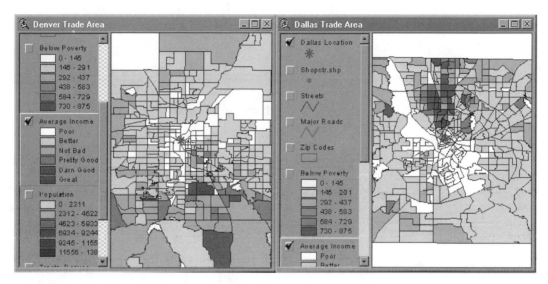

View legends after symbolizing.

Hide Legends

You have probably noted that this view has many themes. Because of the space required by the themes, you now have to scroll through the Table of Contents to access some of the theme legends. Recall that you can hide the legends for themes. However, automatic alteration of legend visibility based on the theme's draw state would be helpful. Through Avenue, Arc-View's programming language, you can create a script to automate or alter the ArcView interface. A sample script provided in the Avenue Help system will serve this purpose.

For further information on how to customize ArcView, see Chapter 11, "Customizing the User Interface," page 349.

Accessing the Script from Avenue Examples

1. Access the project window and create a new script. Once the new script window is active, access the Help menu and select the Help Topics option. Click on the Contents Tab to list the topics. Double-click the Sample Scripts and Extensions topic.

2. Continue navigating through the help topics. Double-click on the *Sample Scripts, Views, Legends* to finally see a list of scripts. Scroll down and double-click on the *Hides the Legend for all non visible themes* script.

3. A help page appears that explains script actions and how the script should be installed. This script hides or shows the legends for the themes through changes in the view document's *update event*. Events are special properties that allow you to associate scripts with an action. An update event occurs when user action alters the state of the active document.

4. To examine the Avenue code, click on the Source Code hot link. Another window will open. Click on the Options button and select the Copy option.

∞ NOTE: *Copying source code from the help system into ArcView is platform specific. The steps presented might not work on your system. If you need further assistance, check ArcView's Help for copying sample scripts into ArcView.*

5. Return to the ArcView window and paste the contents of the clipboard into the script window by accessing the Edit menu and selecting Paste, or by typing <Ctrl>+<V>. Close the Help window.

6. In the Script Properties box, change the script name from *Script1* to *HideLegend.*

7. Click on the Compile button to make the script executable. After it is compiled, close the script window.

```
🔍 HideLegend                                                    _ □ X
'Hides the legend for all non visible themes

theThemes = av.GetActiveDoc.GetThemes

'Get the current state
'
state = av.GetActiveDoc.GetVisibleThemes.Count

'Determine if the state has changed
'
savedState = self.GetObjectTag
if ((savedState <> nil) and (savedState = state)) then
  exit   ' No changes
end

'Save the current state
'
SELF.SetObjectTag( state )

'Update the TOC
'
for each t in theThemes
  t.SetLegendVisible( t.IsVisible )
end
av.GetActiveDoc.InvalidateTOC( NIL )
```

HideLegend script in the script editor.

Install the Script in the View Document

1. As you may have seen on the help page for the script, this script should be installed so that an update event in the view will activate it. The easiest way to attach this script to an update event is to change the update event in one of the view's menu choices.

2. Activate the *Denver Trade Area* view and double-click on the button bar away from any buttons to access the Customize dialog box.

3. Verify that the document Type is *View* and that the category is *Menus*. The File menu option should be highlighted in the list of menu items. At the bottom of the customize dialog box is a list of menu properties. You are interested in the one called Update.

4. Double-click on the Update property to access a list of scripts. Scroll down and select *HideLegend*.

5. Close the Customize dialog box and test the script by turning several themes on and off. Note that the theme legends are hidden when not displayed in the view. Check the *Dallas Trade Area* to verify that it works in that view as well.

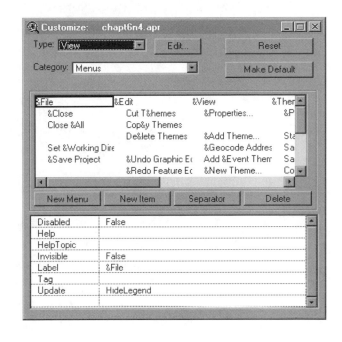

Customize dialog box showing the File menu update event changed to run the HideLegend script.

Save Your Work

To use this project in the next exercise, in which you will continue the trade area analysis, you have to save your project. Switch to the project window, access the File menu, select Save As, and type in a name for the new project file.

Optional

To enhance the view document, you could classify the census tracts on some of the other attributes and label the larger restricted areas for reference.

1. Copy the census tracts theme a few more times and practice classifying on other attributes. Try using some of the other classification techniques you have already learned.

2. For this exercise, you are using a subset of the Sparta-Site demographics provided by Equifax.

   To see all of the variables, look at the *$AVEXDATA\ tracts\dallas\trdaldmg.dbf* or *$AVEXDATA\tracts\ denver\trdendmg.dbf* files. Also included is a customer points file, which could represent the customers for the two stores.

Summary

This exercise built the base data for the trade area analysis. You altered some of the table properties by hiding unwanted columns, and provided aliases for non-intuitive column names. You also resized, reordered, and indexed several other columns. Once the tabular data were in a suitable form, you joined the demographic data to the census tracts.

In the view, you copied some themes and then loaded previously saved legends for these themes. Because you had multiple themes in the view, you installed a script that was provided in the on-line help system to hide the theme legends when they are not being displayed.

Discussion Topics

❑ What types of data could you use if you were trying to identify a consumer base for a drug store?

❑ Take a look at the other sample scripts. Can you identify additional scripts that could be useful in data setup for trade area analyses or other applications?

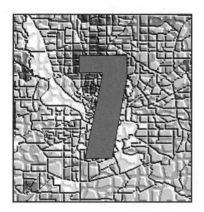

Trade Area Analysis

In this chapter you will perform a trade area analysis on the data prepared in Chapter 6. The analysis will be carried out by creating graphic circles around both stores that will be used to select the demographic data around the two stores. Next, you will create summary statistics, change some of the themes in the view, and create charts depicting the trade area's characteristics.

Topics and Functions

❏ View graphics

❏ Select theme features with graphics

❏ Summarization and spatial aggregation

❏ Outline polygons instead of fill

❏ Charting and advanced chart properties

❏ Advanced layout techniques

Description

The trade area analysis requires that you select the surrounding census tracts for each store, summarize the data, and create charts. The steps and topics in the exercise follow.

❏ Review data

❏ Create trade area circles

❏ Select and summarize census tracts

❏ View aggregated shapefiles

❏ Modify legends for the new themes

❏ Chart the demographics

❏ Create age by range bar charts

❏ Create map layout of findings

Review Data

Open the project file you saved at the end of the previous exercise. Recall that this project contains the data that will be analyzed for the trade areas surrounding the two stores. You also installed a script to automatically hide the legends for themes that are turned off. If you did not complete the previous exercise, open the *$AVEXDS\avexer\project\chapt7.apr* project file and create the indexes from the Chapter 6 section, "Indexing the Tables." To aid in determining which store is which, you need to label the store locations.

1. Verify that the *Stores, Major Roads* and *Census Tracts* themes are on for both views.

2. Open the Symbol Palette by accessing the Window menu and selecting Show Symbol Palette. From the Font Palette, change the text size to *14,* the text font to *Arial,* and the style to *Bold.*

3. Access the Color Palette and change the text color to black. Close the Symbol Palette.

4. Access the Text tool and label both stores with their city name. If you make a mistake, switch to the Pointer tool, select the graphic, access the Edit menu, and select Delete Graphics (or use the <Del> key). Then reenter the correct text.

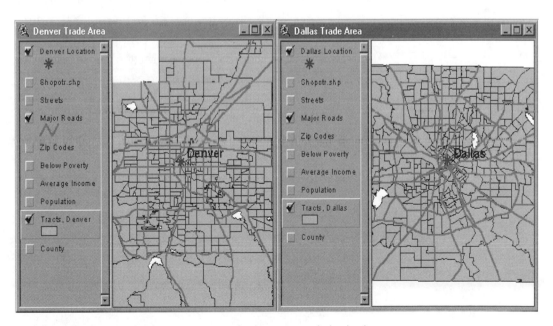

Initial trade area analysis view with the stores labeled.

Create Trade Area Circles

To create the trade areas, you will place two graphic circles around the stores. The circles will be used for selecting the census tracts. They also define the nine-mile radius around the subject stores.

1. Start with the Dallas location. To create the circles, change the Draw tool to Circle. This will allow you to click and drag a circle of any size. As you draw the circle, its radius is displayed in the status line.

2. Create a circle centered over the store location. Try to make the circle 9 miles in diameter. You may have to adjust the map display to place the circle properly.

3. You probably noticed that creating the circle of the proper radius was difficult. To make the circle a specific size, switch to the Pointer tool and select the circle. Access the Graphics menu and select the Size and Position option. In the dialog box, change the radius to 9 miles.

4. Select the circle and access the Symbol Palette. From the Fill Palette, change the outline line weight in the Outline drop-down list box to *2*.

5. Switch to the Color Palette and change the Outline color to red or other color that contrasts well with the other themes in the view.

6. Repeat for the other view.

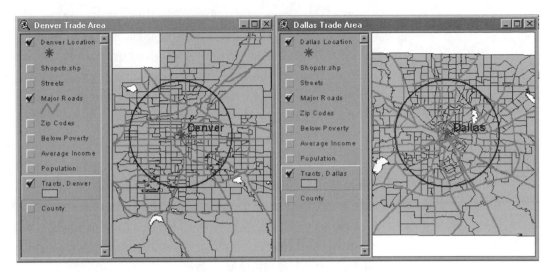

Circles representing the nine-mile radius around each store.

Select and Summarize Census Tracts

There are several ways you could select the census tracts surrounding the two stores. One way would be to use the Select Feature tool and click and drag a box around each store. Another way would be to use the Select By Theme option, whereby you select the store and select the tracts that are within a specific distance of the store. For this exercise, you will use the graphic circles to select the census tracts.

Once you have selected the census tracts, you will need to summarize the selected records in the attribute table. Tables can be summarized in several ways. One way is to convert the selected records into a shapefile, add the shapefile to the view, open the attribute table for the shapefile, and then summarize (which creates yet another table). However, this method is rather circuitous. Instead, you are going to combine these steps by directly summarizing the selected records in the attribute table and performing a *spatial aggregation.* A spatial aggregation is performed when you summarize on the shape field of a table. The merge results depend on the summarize item and feature class you are aggregating.

*Summarizing
a Table,
and Merge
Operations Topics*

For this analysis, you will summarize based on the *Data_file* attribute value. This value is the same for all records; therefore, the resulting summary will create one shape record for each store. The demographic data will also be summarized, and the results will be attached to the shapefile's attribute table.

*For a discussion
of summarizing
tables, see
Chapter 11,
"Merge Themes,"
page 291, and
"Statistics,"
page 309.*

1. Make *Tracts, Dallas* the active theme.

2. Select the circle around the store.

3. Click on the Select Features Using Graphics button. This action selects features intersected by the circle.

4. Open the table for the *Tracts, Dallas* theme.

5. Click on the Promote button to bring the selected records to the top.

6. Click on the column heading *Data_file* so that you can summarize based on a constant value for the entire selected set.

7. Click on the Summarize button to open the Summary Table Definition dialog box. Change the output table to *$AVEXDS\avexer\dbf\dallas.dbf.*

8. Change the Field drop-down list box to *Shape*, and the Summarize By drop-down list box to *Merge*. Click on the Add button to add the current selections to the Summarize statistics box. This action spatially aggregates the tracts on one field, creating one shape record for each unique value in the summarize field.

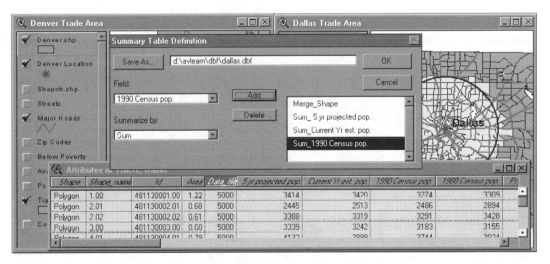

Records from the census tracts theme for Dallas selected in preparation for summarizing and spatial aggregation.

9. Change the Field drop-down list box to *5 yr Projected pop.*, and the Summarize By drop-down list box to *Sum*. This action creates a summary or total of the individual columns. Sum all columns except the *Shape, Shape_name, Id, Area, Pop growth, 1990 to Current, 1990 Census avg. Income, 5 yr. Projected avg. Income, Cyage_avg* and *Cyage_med* fields. These fields are not germane to the analysis.

10. Click on the OK button to create the summary statistics and shapefile. When prompted, add the theme to the *Dallas Trade Area* view.

11. Click on the Unselect button to clear the selected set of records in the *Tracts, Dallas* theme.

12. Repeat using the circle for the Denver store. Name the file *Denver.dbf* and add it to the *Denver Trade Area* view.

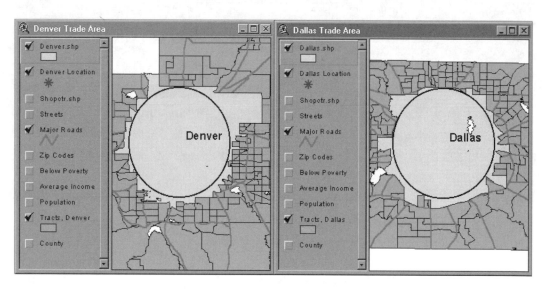

Two new spatially aggregated themes for the stores.

View Aggregated Shapefiles

Now that you have created the summary statistics and shapefiles and placed them in the view, it is time to examine their attribute tables. Because both summary tables are basically the same in terms of data structure, you will examine only the attributes for the Denver store.

1. Make *Denver.shp* the active theme and open its attribute table.

2. Note the single record in the attribute table—an expected outcome because there is only one shape. A single record is the result because you based the summary on the *Data_file* column and the value was constant for all selected tracts. The Count column is the number of records summarized into each row.

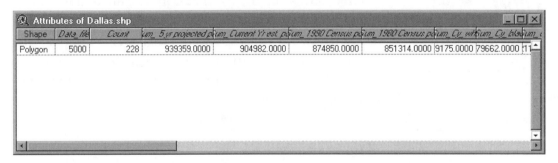

Summarized table record for the Dallas store with aggregated columns.

Modify Legends for New Themes

The shapefiles added to the view display less than desirable colors and shade patterns. However, only the outlines for the shapefiles are important because they denote the census tracts that were aggregated.

1. Select the *Denver.shp* and *Dallas.shp* themes and change their names to *Denver TA* and *Dallas TA*, respectively.

2. Open the Legend Editor for both themes and change the fill patterns to the empty fill pattern located on the upper left in the Fill Palette. Change

the outline line weights to *2*, and change the outline color to contrast with the existing symbology.

3. Move the two themes so that they appear in the Table of Contents above the *Streets* theme. Now you can easily see the boundary of the aggregated census tracts.

4. Turn both themes on.

Chart Demographics

When studying the population within a trade area, marketing professionals usually focus on consumer characteristics and spending patterns related to the products in question. In this section, you are going to chart the ethnic makeup of the population surrounding the two stores.

Create Charts

1. Open the attribute table for *Dallas TA* and click on the Chart button.

2. In the Chart Properties dialog box, change the Name to *Ethnic Origin, Dallas*.

3. Add the following fields to the Groups list: *Sum_Cy_white*, *Sum_Cy_black*, *Sum_Cy_asian*, and *Sum_Cy_rce_otr*.

4. Click on the OK button to create the chart.

5. Click on the Series from Records/Fields button to change the chart from an individual data series to a data group.

6. Repeat for *Denver TA* and name accordingly.

7. Move and resize the two charts so that they are about the same size and are positioned next to each other.

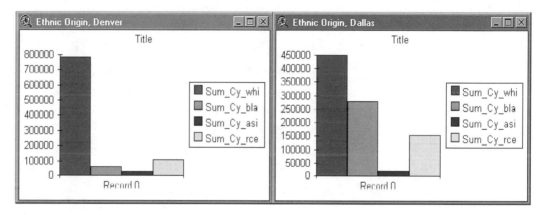

Initial ethnic origin charts for both stores.

Adjust Chart Properties

Standardize the scale for both charts, and clean up the legends.

1. The chart scale for *Ethnic Origin, Dallas* is inadequate because it does not have the same scale as the Denver chart. Switch to the Chart Element Properties tool and click on Y Axis to view the

Chart Axis Properties dialog box. Change the Scale Max value to *800000*. Both charts now have the same scale.

2. The default X Axis label for these charts makes little sense. Remove the labels for both charts with the Chart Element Properties tool.

3. Click on the title for the *Ethnic Origin, Dallas* chart and change it to *Dallas Ethnic Origins*. Repeat for the Denver chart and name accordingly.

4. Finally, remove the *Sum_* prefixes on the legend labels and make the labels meaningful. With the Edit Chart Element Properties tool, click on one legend to bring up the Chart Legend Properties dialog box. Click each box in the scrolling list and edit the label. Remember that you must hit <Enter> after you have edited the label value. Repeat for the other chart.

➥ **NOTE:** *Changing the legend labels also changes the table column aliases.*

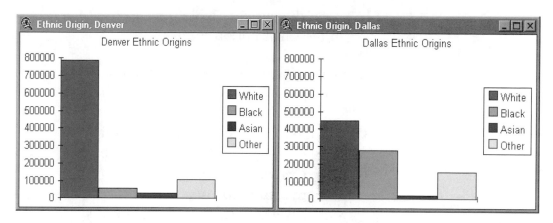

Revised ethnic origin charts for both stores.

Reviewing Ethnic Origin Charts

The two charts clearly show that Denver has a larger population base within the nine-mile radius surrounding the store. In addition, you can see Dallas has a higher ethnic diversity. The total population and ethnic makeup affect the type or quantity of products a store would carry. Furthermore, the information would be used to tailor marketing programs.

Create Age by Range Bar Charts

Create the Charts

To better understand the demographic characteristics of the trade area populations, you will create charts of the age ranges for the population within the two trade areas. Along with other demographic data, age ranges provide valuable information to optimize each store's marketing programs.

1. Open the attribute table for *Denver TA* and click on the Chart button.

2. In the Chart Properties dialog box, change the Name to *Age Range, Denver.*

3. Add the following fields to the Groups list: *Sum_Cyage0_4yr, Sum_Cyage5_9yr, Sum_Cyage10_14, Sum_Cyage15_17, Sum_Cyage18_20, Sum_Cyage21yr, Sum_Cyage22_24, Sum_Cyage25_29, Sum_Cyage30_34, Sum_Cyage35_39, Sum_Cyage40_44, Sum_Cyage45_49, Sum_Cyage50_54, Sum_Cyage55_59, Sum_Cyage60_64, Sum_Cyage65_69, Sum_Cyage70_74, Sum_Cyage75_84,* and *Sum_Cyage85pls.*

4. Click on the OK button to create the chart.

5. Repeat for *Dallas TA* and name accordingly.

6. Move and resize the two charts so that they are about the same size and are positioned above each other.

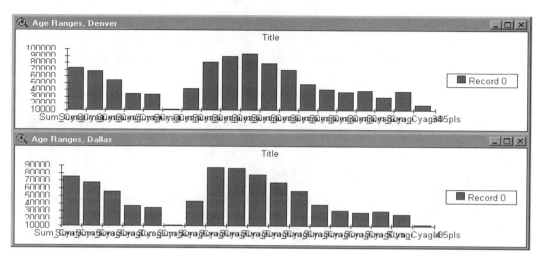

Age by Range charts.

Adjust Chart Properties

The default chart properties chosen by ArcView are not the same for both charts. You will now standardize the age by range charts in the same fashion as the previous charts.

1. Change to the Edit Chart Element Properties tool and click on Y Axis to view the Chart Axis Properties dialog box. Change the Y Axis for both charts so that the maximum scale is *100000*.

2. The chart legends are not necessary. Access the Chart menu and select the Hide Legend option to remove them.

3. Change the chart title for the Dallas site to *Age by Range, Dallas*. Repeat for the other chart.

4. Click on the X Axis and edit the group labels to remove the *Sum_Cyage* prefixes. Review the group label and the available space in the chart, and adjust the group names where necessary.

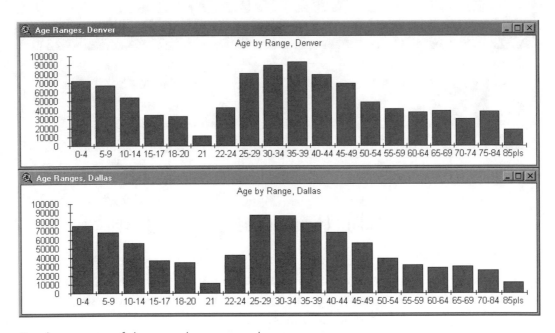

Final versions of the age by range charts.

Review Age by Range Charts

The age by range charts for the two stores show that the trade areas for both stores have a high percentage of the population under 10 and between 25 and 49 years of age. One could guess that both stores should cater to those age groups. However, there are differences between the stores that might indicate target marketing should also occur for other age groups.

Create Map Layout of Findings

In order to easily convey results, you need to create a map. Because the total amount of data you want to convey is beyond the scope of a standard layout, you will have to build the layout from scratch instead of using a standard ArcView template.

Add the Frames and Text

1. Start by verifying that all charts and views are open. In the view documents, verify that only the *Store Locations*, *Trade Areas*, *Major Roads*, and *Below Poverty* themes are on.

➥ **NOTE:** *Layout Frames depict the current state of the document. If the document window is not open, nothing will appear in the Frame. If the document window is resized, its appearance in the layout frame may change.*

2. Open a new layout document and change its Name property to *Trade Area Layout*. Change the grid spacing to *0.05* so that you can move the layout elements with more control. Resize the layout display to make it easier to arrange the elements. Change the page setup to Landscape.

3. Start by building the age by range charts in the lower left corner of the page. Switch to the chart frame tool and add a frame as close to the lower left corner as possible. Do not worry about the exact size: you will set it more precisely later. When prompted, select the *Age Ranges, Denver* chart.

4. Select the Graphics Size and Position menu choice and change the properties so that the chart is *0.38* inches from the left, *3.8* inches wide, and *6.82* inches from the right. In addition, position the chart so that it is *6.4* inches from the top, *1.8* inches high, and *0.3* inches from the bottom.

5. Switch to the Pointer tool and select the chart frame, make a copy of it, and paste it into the layout.

6. Select the newly added chart frame and position it above the original. Change the chart property so that it displays the *Age Ranges, Dallas* chart. For precision, position the chart so that it is *0.38* inches from the left, *3.8* inches wide, *6.82* inches from the right, *4.5* inches from the top, *1.8* inches high, and *2.2* inches from the bottom.

7. Add the other two charts along the left edge of the layout, above the other charts. Position the *Ethnic Origin, Denver* chart first. Position it in the same manner as the previous two charts: *0.38* inches from the left, *2.4* inches wide, *0.1* inches above the *Age Ranges, Dallas* chart, and *1.5* inches high.

8. Place the *Ethnic Origin, Dallas* chart *0.1* inches above the Denver chart.

9. Take a look at the data contained within the chart frames. In some cases, you may need to resize the chart documents to display the data properly in the chart frame.

Chart frames added to the layout.

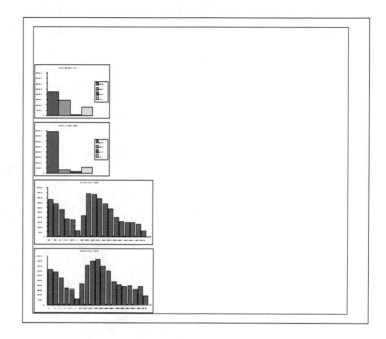

10. Add a view frame in the lower right corner of the page. Make the frame depict the *Denver* trade area. Place the *Dallas* trade area in the upper right corner. Size and position the two frames to fill the right half of the page. If the view data does not fill the frame, resize the associated view window so that ArcView can better fill the frame.

11. Open the Symbol window and access the Font Palette. Change the text font to *Arial*, make the text size *36*, and verify that the text color is black. Add a title to the map. If you wish, add a subtitle in 18-point text and center it with the map title. Unselect all graphics by clicking outside the layout page.

12. In the open space between the chart and the view frames, add a legend and tie it to one of the views.

13. Change the text size to *14* and add the text *Legend* above the legend frame.

The almost complete trade area layout.

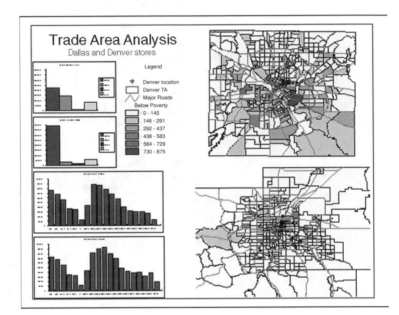

Clean Up Default Legend Frame

1. At this point, you might consider the layout complete. However, you should clean up some of the legend elements to make them more generic to both views. ArcView places in the legend frame exactly what is depicted in the Table of Contents for the associated view. To edit the individual parts of the legend, you need to break the legend frame into its graphic components and edit them individually.

2. Select the legend frame and click on the Simplify option from the Graphics menu. This will explode the legend frame into its individual graphic primitives.

↪ **NOTE:** *When you convert a frame into simple graphics, the link to its associated source document is lost.*

3. The specific text for one store location does not make sense. Double-click on the text and change it to *Store Location.* Similarly, change the specific trade area name to *Trade Area.*

Simplified legend frame with individual, editable parts.

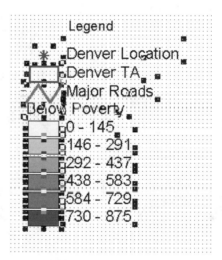

4. The *Below Poverty* caption looks different from the other legend headings. To accentuate this caption, select the caption and all of the elements below it and move them down a bit, leaving a small gap.

5. With all of this legend-element editing, undoubt-edly the *Legend* title needs to be repositioned or resized. After you adjust the title, prevent acciden-tal movement of the individual parts. Select all legend graphic primitives, access the Graphics menu, and click on the Group option. This action groups the graphics so that they are treated as a unit instead of as individual parts. If you need to edit a portion of the group, you can select the Ungroup option.

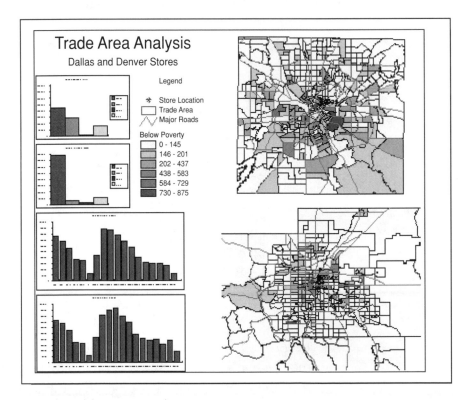

Completed layout ready to print.

Optional

All the steps you previously took to select records in a theme, summarize the theme's attributes, and create a chart can be automated by stringing together two Avenue scripts. Try doing this now with the following steps.

1. The first script can be found in the ArcView script library. This script opens the attribute table for a theme, and then opens the dialog box to create a summary table. Retrieve the script *Summarizes selected fields from active theme*, located under the *Sample Scripts and Extensions, Sample Scripts, Views, Analysis* topic, and paste it into a new script document. Name the script *Theme.Chart*.

2. The windows release of ArcView may be missing two lines at the top of this script. Verify that the following two lines are above the *theTable = theTheme.GetFTab* line. If they are not in the script, add them.

```
theView=av.GetActiveDoc
theTheme=theView.GetActiveThemes.Get(0)
```

The default behavior for the script is not suitable for your use. If you summarize the shape field, the active document is changed back to the view instead of staying with the table. In most situations, this action would be acceptable. However, in the current application you want to immediately create a chart from the table, but the chart script you will use next will not function because the active document is not a table.

1. To remedy this situation, place a single quote at the beginning of the *theView.GetWin.Active* line. The line is located near the end of the script file. The single quote changes the statement to a comment line, making it unexecutable.

2. The second script of interest is *Table.Chart*. This system script takes a table and opens the Chart dialog box to create a chart. To access this system script, move the cursor to the bottom of the *Theme.Chart* script window, select the Script menu, and select Load System Script to open the Script Manager dialog box. Select the *Table.Chart* script.

3. At this point, you have the two scripts linked as a new script. Compile the script and change documents to one of the *Trade Area* views so that you can install it into the View GUI.

4. Install the script by performing the following sequence. Open the Customize dialog box by double-clicking on a blank section of the tool bar. Change the Category drop-down list box to Buttons and verify that the Type drop-down list is set to "view."

5. Move the highlight box to the Table button and click on the New button. This adds a new button to the button bar to the right of the selected button.

6. Double-click on the *Click* field and add the script *Theme.Chart*. Change the default icon by double-clicking on the *Icon* field, and select an appropriate icon.

7. The *Help* field is used to display the tool tip and message in the status bar on the bottom of the Arc-View window. Double-click on the *Help* field and input the text *Summarize and Chart//Summarizes a theme and creates a chart*. (The double slashes separate the help text, which appears on the status bar, from the text, which is displayed for the tool tip.)

8. Finally, you need to change the *Update* field to allow or disallow the use of the button, depending on whether a theme is active or not. Other buttons already have an Update event script developed that you can assign to your new button. Double-click on the *Update* field and select the *View.TabularThemesUpdate* script. This is the same script used on the Open Table button.

9. Close the Customize and Script windows. Test the script and button by selecting a few features in a census tract-based theme, and create a chart.

Summary

In this exercise, you performed a simple trade area analysis for two stores. You created the trade areas by drawing a nine mile radius circle around each store and used the graphics to select the census tracts around the stores. The selected records were spatially aggregated to create totals for the demographic data, and then the data were charted. Finally, you created a map layout of the findings.

Although the process you performed was fairly complicated, real trade area analyses are even more complex. Trade areas are rarely simple circles because the boundaries are typically based on customer locations. To collect customer locations, a business may perform some type of survey that captures customer addresses, or it may ask customers for their zip codes or collect addresses from checks and credit cards. These addresses could then be spatially located to define the trade area.

Other types of analyses could also be performed. You could determine where competitors are located and how customers are distributed. In a true market analysis, you would typically be much more thorough in the demographic analysis and possibly add specialized consumer spending data. All of the foregoing information could be processed to optimize marketing campaigns targeting existing and potential customers.

Discussion Topics

❑ Why might you use an alternate method of creating summary tables without spatial aggregation?

❑ What other types of demographic data would be important for trade area analysis?

❑ Where else might the Layout Simplify function come in handy?

Site Selection

In this chapter, you will perform a site assessment based on the probability of hail and tornado events. You will analyze several potential sites in central Oklahoma for a severe weather monitoring station based on property casualty risk data. Finally, maps to support a final report will be prepared with the use of a template to enhance productivity.

Topics and Functions

☐ Using annotation themes

☐ Spatial joins and point-in-polygon analysis

☐ Dot density mapping

☐ Creating and using layout templates

Description

In this exercise, you will perform a point-in-polygon analysis using spatial joins to determine the probability of hail and tornadoes at candidate sites for a state regional weather station. To support the representation of the geographic data, you will use coverage annotation and dot density mapping. You will also create layouts to convey the results of the analysis. Rather than build two similar maps from scratch, a template will be defined and employed. The steps and topics in the exercise follow.

❏ Open the project

❏ Data overview

❏ Annotation themes

❏ Dot density thematic mapping

❏ Spatial join and point-in-polygon analysis

❏ Analysis of candidate sites

❏ Create the layout template

❏ Create the final maps

Open the Project

If ArcView is not currently running, start the program. Access the File menu and select Open Project. Navigate to the *$AVEXDS\avexer\project* directory and select the *chapt8.apr* project. This project is based on zip code data in the state of Oklahoma.

Data Overview

The meteorological data used in this exercise were processed and provided by Vista Environmental Information, Inc., of San Diego, California. The hail data are organized in four categories indicating the projected number of occurrences according to hail size over a 100-year period. The fifth data category is the sum of all sizes over the century. The hail size categories are .75 in. to 1.5 in., 1.5 in. to 2.25 in., 2.25 in. to 3 in., and over 3 in.

The tornado data are organized into the projected number of tornadoes over a 100-year period in each of the Fujita scale categories. The Fujita scale, the standard method of classifying the intensity of tornadoes, reflects wind speed. The tornado categories are 40 to 73 mph, 73 to 113 mph, 113 to 158 mph, and over 158 mph. The goal of the analysis is to determine the optimum location for a severe weather monitoring station.

1. Open the *Hail Risk* view. The view contains base data and specific hail risk data for 80 zip code polygons in central Oklahoma. The base data consist of several themes, including the zip code polygons for the study area, major roads, and cities. The view also contains specific themes of hail risk by zip code and candidate sites.

2. Open the *Tornado Risk* view. This view is similar to the *Hail Risk* view in construction but features themes for tornado risk data. The *Hail Risk* and *Tornado Risk* views form the foundation of the analysis.

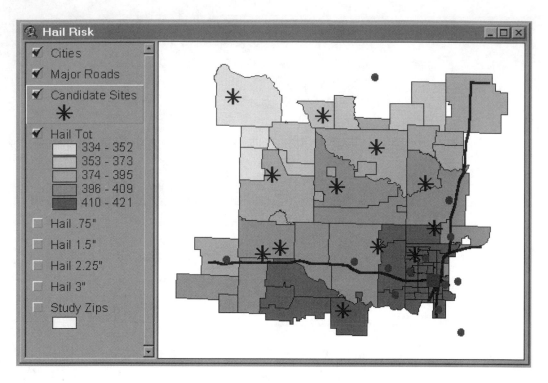

Base data for severe weather probability analysis.

Annotation Themes

The candidate sites are currently shown as point markers in the view. Including descriptive text to identify the sites would be helpful. Although you have previously used labels for this purpose, certain limitations apply. When you are working with several hundred or more labels, labeling can be very compute-intensive and thus time consuming to display. If a coverage has been created with annotation in ARC/INFO, annotation display is frequently faster than labeling. Annotation is usually explicitly positioned for an intended purpose. If annotation matches your needs, it can be a worthwhile alternative to labels.

⊷ **NOTE:** *Unlike labels, annotation cannot be repositioned or resized in ArcView.*

1. In the *Hail Risk* view, turn off the *Cities* and *Major Roads* themes to clean up the display while you work on the candidate sites.

2. Add a new theme to the *Hail Risk* view. Navigate to the *$AVEXDS\avexer\shape\sites* directory, and click once on the yellow *cand_sit* data set folder to open it. Select the *annotation.pt* annotation subclass and close the dialog box.

3. Access the Properties for the new theme and rename it *Site Annotation*. Click the Query Builder button under the Definition option and notice the limited attributes available. Close the dialog box.

4. Set a contrasting color for the text using the *Text* setting in the Color Palette and display the theme. This annotation includes both site numbers and site names. This enhances the presentation significantly. However, it would be beneficial to control the number and name independently.

This annotation was created in ARC/INFO with its own attribute table, known as a *text attribute table* or .TAT. ARC/INFO annotation features may be organized by Subclass, Text Attributes, Level, Size, and Symbol. ArcView has the capability of using any or all of these items (fields) to control the annotation display. The annotation in the *Cand_sit* coverage is organized into two levels: level 1 for numbers, and level 2 for names. ArcView will automatically add the Symbol and Level fields for annotation that does not have an attribute table. However, for annotation data such as with an attribute table, ArcView will not add the level and symbol fields to the annotation theme unless a particular setting is configured through an Avenue request. This will require the use of a simple script.

1. Access the project window and create a new script.

2. In the Script Properties box, change the script name from *Script1* to *SetAnno.*

3. In the script window, enter one line containing the following Avenue statement: *FTab.SetAnnoAddFieldsPreference(TRUE).*

SetAnno script.

4. Click on the Compile button to make the script executable. Click the Run button to execute the *Set-Anno* script.

5. Delete the existing annotation theme and add a new theme for the same annotation, which will take advantage of the new setting set by the script.

6. Access the new theme's properties and set the name to *Site Number.* Click the Query Builder button under the Definition option to access the Query Builder dialog box. New text attributes are now available. Create a query to define all annotations where *LEVEL* = *1* and close the dialog boxes. Turn the new theme on.

Theme Properties dialog box showing level = 1 query.

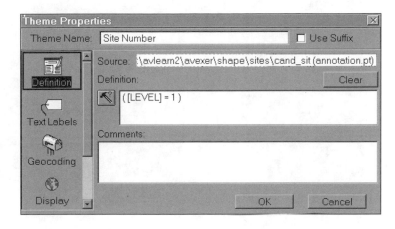

Annotation

7. Copy the *Site Number* theme and use Paste to duplicate it.

8. Change the name of the new theme to *Site Name*. Modify its definition to contain the annotation for *LEVEL* = *2* by replacing *1* with *2* in the text box at the bottom left of the Query Builder dialog box. Close the dialog boxes by clicking on OK.

9. Use the Legend Editor to change the Text color of both annotation themes to black so that they are easily visible on the display.

10. Hide the legends for the new themes and turn them on.

11. Use <Shift>+click to activate the two new themes. Copy the themes and Paste them in the *Tornado Risk* view.

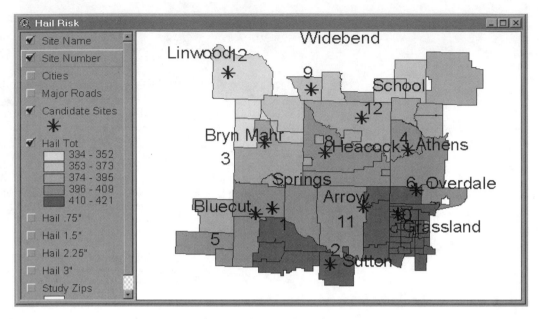

New annotation themes added to the Hail Risk view.

Dot Density Thematic Mapping

Dot density mapping allows you to visually display the incidence of an attribute in a geographical area by placing random dots in proportion to attribute values. The viewer(s) or audience can thus easily perceive trends depicted by the relative concentration of dots on a map.

1. Make the *Hail Risk* view active and maximize it.

2. Duplicate the *Hail Tot* theme. Name the new theme *Hail Dots.*

3. Turn off all themes except *Hail Dots.*

4. Make the *Hail Dots* theme active. Access the Legend Editor. Select a Legend Type of Dot.

5. Select *Hail_Total* for the *Density* field.

6. The *Dot Legend: 1 dot* = setting is used to set the ratio of dots to numeric values in the *Density* field. Use the Calculate button to have ArcView set the value based on the current sizes of the dot symbol and the view window. Apply the results and examine the display. Dot mapping gives a unique visual presentation of the relative weight of the various polygons for the total hail risk. Try entering your own values for *Dot Legend: 1 dot* =. Use the Statistics button to aid you in your decision. What do you think is the optimum setting for these data?

7. Use the Marker Palette to change the size of the dots. Try several settings. What effect does this have on the presentation of the data?

∝ **NOTE:** *Even though you have not used them here, you still have the now familiar options for Normalize By and Null Values with the Dot density thematic map type.*

8. Turn on the *Hail Tot* theme and compare the graduated colors of *Hail Risk* to the new dot theme.

9. In the *Tornado Risk* view, follow the same steps to add a dot density theme named *Tor 73 Dot* based on the *Tornado 73 mph* theme.

10. Compare the graduated colors of the *Tornado 73 mph* theme to the new dot density theme.

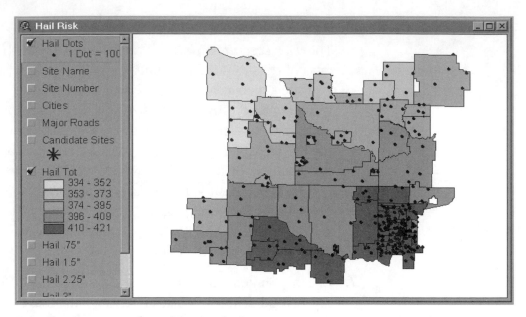

Dot density map of total hail risk data.

Spatial Join and Point-in-Polygon Analysis

In previous exercises you have joined tables based on a common attribute value. To accomplish the point-in-polygon analysis, you will use a spatial join. A spatial join combines two tables in a manner similar to an attribute join, but is based on the spatial relationship between associated graphic features. Each feature in the destination table is analyzed with respect to a feature in the source table that satisfies a spatial condition.

Points can be analyzed for the nearest point, nearest line, or the polygon they are "inside" in the other theme. Lines can be analyzed for the nearest point, nearest intersecting line, or the polygon they are "inside" in the other theme. Polygons can only be analyzed for the corresponding polygon they are "inside" in the second theme. In addition to the transfer of corresponding attributes, when a *nearest* condition is used, a distance field is added to the table. The distance field reports the distance between each feature and its corresponding counterpart feature in the second theme.

For a discussion of spatial joins, see Chapter 11, "Spatial Join," page 286.

You will use a spatial join on two themes to join their attributes based on the respective spatial relationship of individual features. When a polygon theme is spatially joined to a point theme, each point takes on the attributes of the polygon that contains it. This is the source of the common name of point-in-polygon analysis. You will use a point-in-polygon analysis to impart the zip code polygon risk attributes to the candidate sites.

1. Open the attribute table for the *Hail Tot* theme from the *Hail Risk* view. Activate the *Shape* field as the field to be used for the join.

2. Open the attribute table for the *Candidate Sites* theme. Activate the *Shape* field as the field to use in the join.

3. Use the Join Tables button to spatially join the attributes of the *Attributes of Hail Tot* table (source) to the *Attributes of Candidate Sites* table (destination). This action joins both the hail and tornado data to the *Candidate Sites* table in one step.

Shape	Site numbe	Hail_75	Hail_1_5	Hail_2_25	Hail_3	Hail_total	Tor_40	Tor_73	Tor_113	Tor_158
Point	7	224	87	18	5	334	70	48	31	11
Point	9	239	95	18	5	357	76	53	36	12
Point	3	253	100	21	8	382	77	53	34	13
Point	5	261	105	24	8	398	75	52	33	13
Point	2	276	111	21	8	416	78	57	36	15
Point	1	261	105	24	8	398	75	52	33	13
Point	8	263	105	21	8	397	79	56	37	14
Point	12	255	103	21	8	387	78	56	37	13
Point	4	266	108	21	8	403	80	58	38	14
Point	6	276	111	21	8	416	81	60	39	15
Point	10	276	111	21	8	416	81	60	38	15
Point	11	271	108	21	8	408	80	58	37	15

Hail and tornado data joined to the Attributes of Candidates table.

Analysis of Candidate Sites

The optimum site for the severe weathering monitoring station would be where the combined probability of hail and tornadoes is highest. You will examine the tabular results of the spatial join to select the best site or sites.

1. In the *Hail Risk* view, access the table Properties dialog for the *Candidate Sites Attributes.* Hide unnecessary fields and define aliases as desired.

2. Resize the fields as required to properly see the field names and contents.

3. Turn editing on and add a single-string field called *Preferred.*

4. Sort the table in descending order using the *Hail Total* column. Note the high value (416) for sites 6, 10, and 2, indicating a probability of 416 hail events over a 100-year period.

5. Sort the table in descending order using the *Tor_73* column. Note the high value (60) for sites 6 and 10, indicating a probability of 60 tornadoes with wind speeds between 73 and 113 mph over a 100-year period.

6. The conclusion is that sites 6 and 10 are equally good sites for the severe weather monitoring station.

7. Select all records in the table, activate the *Preferred* column, and use the field calculator to set all of the records to "*N*". The double quotes must be used when working directly in the entry box.

8. Set the *Preferred* field to "*Y*" for sites 6 and 10. You will use this field to classify the candidate sites for the final report map. Turn editing off, save the edits, and clear the selected set.

9. In the *Hail Risk* view, classify the *Candidate Site* theme on *Preferred*. Make the symbol for the preferred sites larger and select a color that will be easily visible. Copy the *Candidate Site* theme from the *Hail Risk* theme, and use it to replace the *Candidate Site* theme in the *Tornado Risk* view.

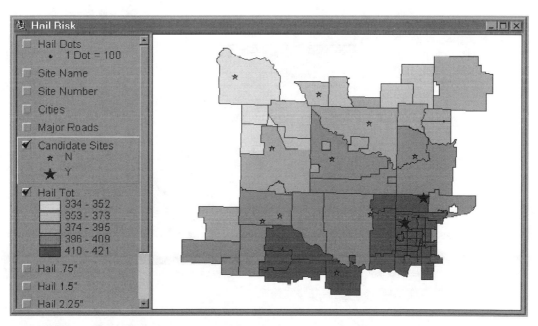

Candidate sites classified on Preferred attribute.

Create Layout Template

You will now create final report maps to depict results of the analysis. You will create two maps, one each for hail and tornado probability. To make the appearance of the maps consistent and avoid duplication of effort, you will use a layout template. Refer to Chapter 4 to review steps required in using the layout document. As you work with the following layouts, remember to use the Pan and Zoom tools as necessary to move around the page.

For a discussion of layouts, see Chapter 8, "Layouts," page 197.

1. Create a new layout from the Project menu. Rename it *Ch8 Template*. Make the page orientation Landscape, and accept the other default properties and page setup.

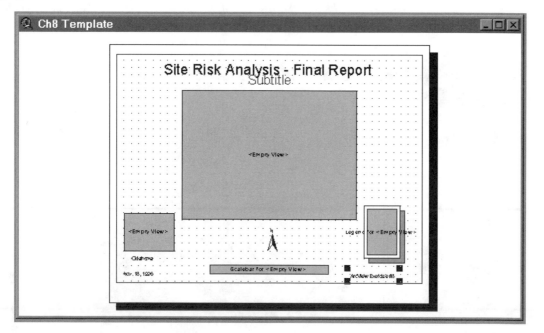

Complete Ch8 Template layout.

Add Frames

1. Add a large empty view frame and align it to the middle of the page.

2. Create a white solid-fill rectangle graphic to be used as a legend background. Copy the white rectangle and paste it. Select the new rectangle, which will be "on top," and change its color to gray. Temporarily turn snapping off, and shift the gray rectangle slightly down and to the left. Send the gray rectangle to the background. The legend will appear to be shadowed.

3. Add an empty legend frame slightly smaller than the white rectangle, and link it to the empty view frame.

4. Add a north arrow frame below the view frame and align it to the middle of the page.

5. Add a scale bar frame below the north arrow, and link it to the empty view frame. Use Align to center it on the page.

6. Add a second small empty view frame in the lower left corner.

Add Text

1. Add the text *subtitle* just above the main view frame. Size the text appropriately and center it. Above the subtitle, add the text *Site Risk Analysis—Final Report*. Resize the title and center it.

2. Add the text *Oklahoma* below the small view frame.

3. Add text for the map date in the lower left corner. Add the text *ArcView Exercise #8* in the lower right corner.

4. Access the Layout menu and select the Store As Template option. Name the template *Risk Report.* Use the Select button to access the Icon Manager. Select an icon for the template and close the Icon Manager.

Risk Report template properties.

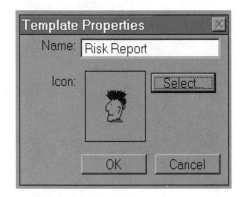

✓ **TIP:** *You can also load your own icon by using the Load button in the Icon Manager. A wide range of graphic file formats are supported. For the best results, make sure that the icon is no larger than 24 x 24 pixels.*

5. Close the Template Properties with the OK button. This action will write your templates to a new file titled *template.def* in your *$HOME* directory. The new *template.def* file supersedes the default ArcView templates.

Create Final Maps

Layout templates can be used in two ways. First, when working with an existing layout document, you can select Use Template from the Layout menu to access the Template Manager. From the Template Manager, you can edit the icons for existing templates, remove templates, and store changes to the *template.def* file. If you select a template and click on OK, it will be applied to the current layout document. View, chart, and table frames will be filled in the order they were created in the template. Project documents will be placed in the empty frames in the same order they appear in the project window list. Additional existing graphics in the layout that are not called for by the template will be automatically deleted.

The second way to use a template is from a view. This is accomplished by accessing Layout from the View menu. When a template is used in this way, the current view is placed in the first empty view frame and the other view frames are "filled" in the project list order. The current view will only be used once. Next, the first text created in the layout template will be replaced by the name of the active view. This is the only piece of text affected in this way. With a little planning, this process can be used to your advantage. North arrow and picture frames are always placed as they were created in the template. With this method, you are presented with the option of using an existing layout document or creating a new one.

1. Make the *Hail Risk* view the active document and turn on the desired themes for the final report map. Access the View menu and select Layout. When prompted, select the new *Risk Report* tem-

plate and click the OK button. Elect to create a New Layout. The *Hail Risk* view was placed in the first view frame because it was the active view. The *Overview* view was placed in the small view frame because the first view in the project window view list had already been used, and *Overview* is the second. The subtitle text was replaced with the name of the active view, *Hail Risk*.

Risk report template in Template Manager.

2. Make the *Tornado Risk* view the active document and turn on the desired themes for the final report map. Follow the same steps to create a new layout using the *Risk Report* template. The *Tornado* Risk view was placed in the first view frame because it was the active view. The *Hail Risk* view was placed in the small view frame because it was the first in the project window view list. The subtitle text was replaced with the name of the active view, *Tornado Risk*.

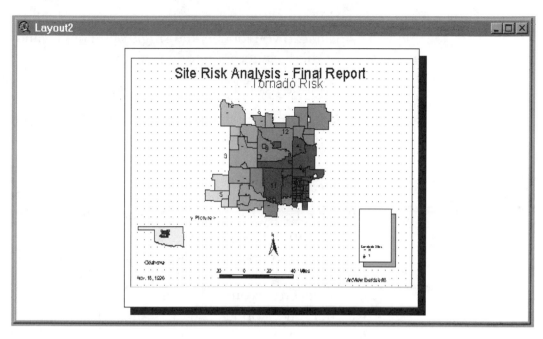

Final tornado risk map.

3. Change the properties of the small view frame to depict the *Overview* view. Reassign frames to the correct view if necessary.

4. Make final adjustments in size or alignment to the layout components. Print both layouts.

Optional

Practice your analysis and layout skills by performing the following additional steps.

1. In the exercise, you examined the *Hail Total* and *Tornado 73* data fields. Evaluate additional hail and tornado data in the tables on hail size and tornado wind speed and compare results to those of the foregoing exercise. By examining additional data, can you identify the *single* optimum location for the weather monitoring station?

2. Chart the risk data for the candidate sites.

3. Further enhance the layout template and final report maps with a frame for the chart.

Summary

In this exercise, you used coverage annotation to enhance the presentation of the candidate sites. You also performed dot density thematic mapping of the zip code based meteorological data. You performed a point-in-polygon analysis to determine the probability of severe weather at the candidate sites for a weather monitoring station. After analyzing the results, you defined a layout template and used it to simplify the creation of multiple maps for a report.

Discussion Topics

❑ Describe other applications for a spatial join that referenced the nearest point in another theme.

❑ The dot density themes in this exercise did not account for the varying size of the base polygons. What are the limitations of this type of cartography? How would you account for this? Describe the effects of changing the number of dots and the size of the dots on the presentation of the data.

❑ Under what circumstances would the use of a layout template be most beneficial?

Proximity Analysis

The purpose of the exercise in this chapter is to analyze a proposed pipeline for proximity to underground storage tanks (UST) and leaking underground storage tanks (L-UST). The exercise represents a portion of the real-life analysis that must be performed to conform with the typical "Phase I Environmental Site Assessment" as defined by the American Society for Test Materials (ASTM). Although private companies are not required by law to perform such site assessments, many companies carry out site analyses under ASTM guidelines for purposes of self-protection in the event of lawsuits.

Topics and Functions

❏ Create a new theme and edit shapefiles

❏ Geolocate tabular data using X-Y event themes

❏ Spatially join linear data to point data

❏ Add graduated point symbols based on attribute values

❏ Importing AutoCAD data

❏ Extensions

❏ Data projections

Description

First, you will create a new theme and draw the proposed pipeline. Next, the L-UST and UST sites are to be located by respective latitude and longitude values. Once the sites are geolocated, you will spatially join them to the pipeline you created to determine pipeline distance from the sites. Steps and topics for the exercise follow.

❏ Open the project and review the data

❏ Create the pipeline

❏ Add AutoCAD data for transmission lines

❏ Geolocate the L-UST and UST sites

❏ Calculate distances to the sites

❏ Symbolize based on distance

❏ Create a buffer around the pipeline

❏ Review the results

Open Project and Review Data

Open the *$AVEXDS\avexer\project\chapt9.apr* project. The view in the project contains data for San Diego, California. Themes in the view represent major roads, streets, military bases, hydrographic features, and landmarks such as hospitals and schools.

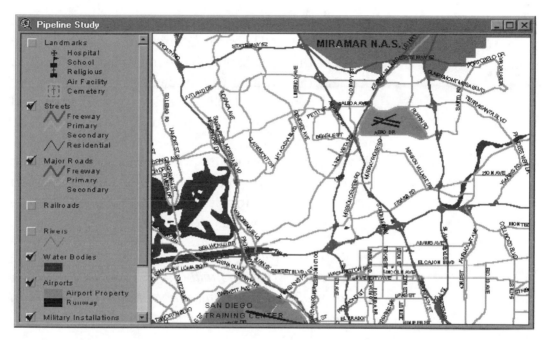

Initial pipeline study view.

Create the Pipeline

Assume that the Miramar Naval Air Station requires a pipeline linking it with the San Diego Marine Corps Recruitment Base. (This is a fictitious condition, used only for purposes of the current exercise.)

To create the pipeline corridor, you will create a new line theme and draw a line between the two bases.

For a discussion
of editing
shapefiles, see
Chapter 10,
"Editing
Shapefiles,"
page 255.

1. Access the View menu and select the New Theme option. When prompted, create a line theme called *pipeline.shp* and save it to the *$AVEXDS\ avexer\ shape* directory. A new theme is added to the view and the check box is highlighted with a dashed line. This notation indicates the theme is being edited.

2. Access the Theme Properties dialog box for the new theme. Change the theme name to *Pipeline*. Select the editing icon and click on the interactive and general snapping check boxes. The general snap rule is used when you add new lines. The interactive snap rule is used when you select a snap option from the pop-up menu. Select OK to close the dialog box. Now that the snap tolerances are set, a new tool is available in the view to interactively set the snap tolerances.

→ **NOTE:** *Changing the values for the snapping tolerances for a theme without features will not have any effect. To change the tolerances, you must have some features in the theme.*

*Editing category of
Theme Properties
dialog box.*

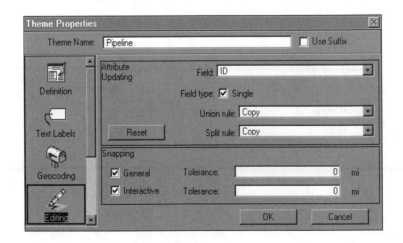

1. Before you begin editing, change the pipeline symbol from its default line to a wider dark gray line.

2. Zoom to the area where Highway 163 crosses into Miramar Naval Air Station. The pipeline will begin here. Switch to the Draw tool. Add the line by clicking along the freeway. Add sufficient vertices to follow the freeway. When you reach the edge of the window, double-click to end line additions.

3. Before you continue the pipeline, set the snap tolerances using the tool on the view interface. Both snap properties are available from the snap tool by clicking on it. Set both snap rules to .20 miles by selecting the tool and clicking and dragging a circle in the view. You can verify the settings by accessing the theme's properties.

4. Pan the display and continue adding the pipeline along the freeway. Switch back to the draw tool. Right click (on Macintosh click <option>+mouse button) near the end point of the previous line. This will open the pop-up menu. Select the Snap to Endpoint option. The next left click will snap the cursor to the end of the previous line.

5. When you reach the edge of the window, pan the display by accessing the pop-up menu and selecting Pan. After the display refreshes, you will still be in line input mode. Continue adding the pipeline between the two military bases. Refer to the pipeline picture for the suggested route. If the line you add seems to collapse or vanish, check the snapping distances and reset them if necessary.

Proposed pipeline.

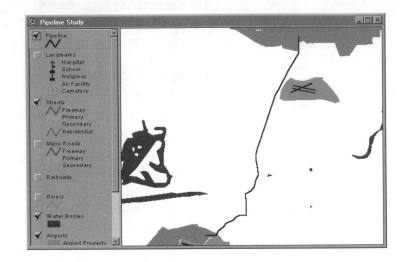

*View pop-up menu.
Note that the menu
is different from
the default menu
because you are
editing a theme.*

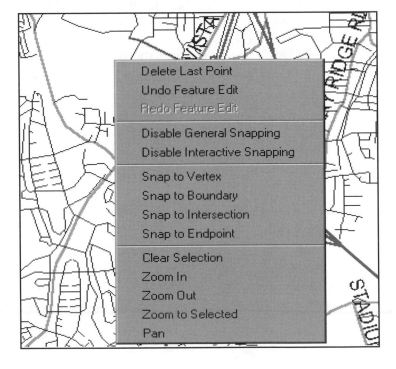

6. When you have completed the pipeline between the two military bases, inspect your work to ensure that it follows the west edge of the freeway. To adjust the line, change to the Vertex Edit tool and click once on the line to show the individual vertices that form the line. The mouse cursor changes depending on the action that can occur to the vertices on the line. If you position the cursor over a vertex, it will change to a cross hair. The <Del> key is used to click and drag the vertex to reposition or remove it. If you position the cursor along the line, the cursor will change to a target, allowing you to click and add new vertices.

A segment of the pipeline depicting vertices.

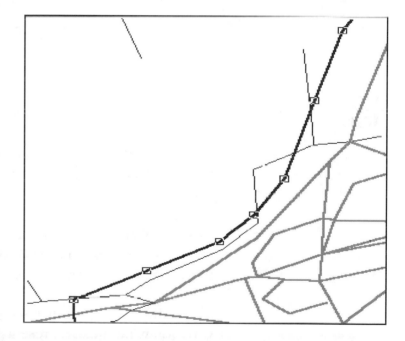

7. When you are satisfied with the pipeline, access the Theme menu and select the Stop Editing option to complete the edit process. When prompted, save the edits.

8. Zoom out to view the entire pipeline.

Add AutoCAD Data for Transmission Lines

ArcView can use computer aided drawings (CAD) as a data source in a view. Depending on your operating system, you can open AutoCAD DWG, AutoCAD DXF, or MicroStation DGN formats. The CAD drawings are treated exactly the same as ARC/INFO coverages or shapefiles for most types of theme manipulation. The only limitation is that you cannot directly edit the theme features or attribute table. To perform edits, you must first convert the CAD drawing into a shapefile.

CAD Drawings, CAD Entity Types, and ArcView Feature Classes

The CAD drawing support in ArcView is implemented as an extension. Extensions bestow additional functionality to ArcView when required. Several extensions come with ArcView, such as the CADReader. There are also several sample extensions included in ArcView that you can add to your projects. You can also purchase extensions from ESRI (such as Network Analyst and Spatial Analyst) and third-party developers, or you can create your own.

For this part of the analysis, you are going to add a CAD drawing that represents overhead electricity transmission lines. This drawing was "supplied" from a fictitious utility company. It depicts the location of the transmission lines between two electricity substations. In that the pipeline follows part of the same corridor, it may be possible to lease part of the utility right-of-way.

1. Load the CADReader extension. Make the project window the active document. Access the File menu and select Extensions. In the Extensions dialog, click the check box next to the CADReader. Press OK to load the extension.

Extensions dialog box.

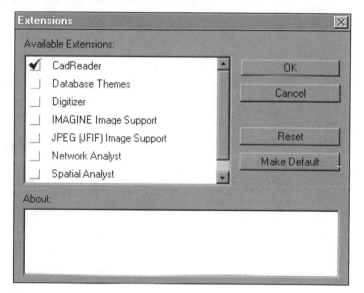

2. Switch back to the Pipeline Study view document and open the Add Theme dialog box. Navigate to *$AVEX-DATA\avdata\pipeline*. Click on the *trnsmssn.dwg* or *trnsmssn.dxf* data folder to open it. Add the line and annotation feature classes to the view. By default, ArcView classifies the themes uniquely by AutoCAD layer. All layers that were on in the source drawing are listed. The legend text represents the symbol number used by AutoCAD.

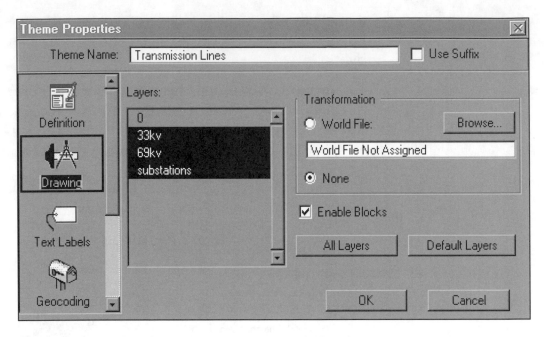

Drawing category of the Theme Properties dialog box.

3. Access the line theme's properties and change the name to *Transmission Lines.* Scroll down the list of properties and select the Drawing properties icon. The All Layers button highlights all drawing layers and the Default Layers button reverts to the default layers that are on in the source drawing. Use <Shift>+click to highlight the *69kv, 33kv,* and *substation* layers. Select OK to close the dialog box.

4. Open the Legend Editor. Change the legend type to Unique Value on the Layer column. Change the line colors and sizes to suit your taste.

5. Open the properties for the annotation CAD theme. Change the name to *Transmission Anno.* Set the active layers to *69kv, 33kv,* and *substation.*

6. Change the legend type to Unique Value, and change the *69kv* and *33kv* text colors to match the line colors. Next, change the *substation* text to black.

7. Zoom in to inspect the AutoCAD theme's features. When you have completed the inspection, zoom out to see both military bases. Reorder the themes to place the linear themes below the annotation and point themes.

Geolocate L-UST and UST Sites

ArcView can add tabular data to a view using positional "event" data contained in the table. Events contain geographic information, such as street addresses or X-Y coordinates, which ArcView uses to place features. There are three types of event themes recognized by ArcView: addresses, X-Y coordinates, and events on ARC/INFO routes. You will use the Add X-Y Events option.

For a discussion of event themes, see Chapter 2, "Why an Event Theme?," page 39, and Chapter 4, "Event Themes," page 81.

1. Change to the Project document and open the *sites.dbf* table. Take a moment to look at the columns. The *Latitude* and *Longitude* columns contain the coordinate information you need.

2. Make the *Pipeline Study* view the active document. Access the View menu and select the Add Event Theme option.

3. In the Add Event Theme dialog box, select the *sites.dbf* table from the Table drop-down list box. Set the *X* field to *Longitude* and the *Y* field to *Latitude*.

*Add Event Theme
dialog box for the
sites.dbf table.*

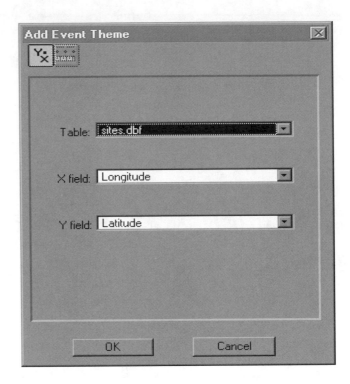

4. Click on the OK button to create a new theme from the table's coordinates.

5. Turn the *Sites.dbf* theme on to view results.

Calculate Distances to the Sites

To determine the distance between the pipeline and the sites, you will spatially join the two themes on their shape fields. The join is thereby grounded on feature geometry and location instead of an attribute. The outcome of the join depends on the feature classes you use. Spatially joining a point theme to a line theme results in a new column in the attribute table containing the distance between the point and the line. The units in the distance column reflect the map units, rather than the distance units of the view.

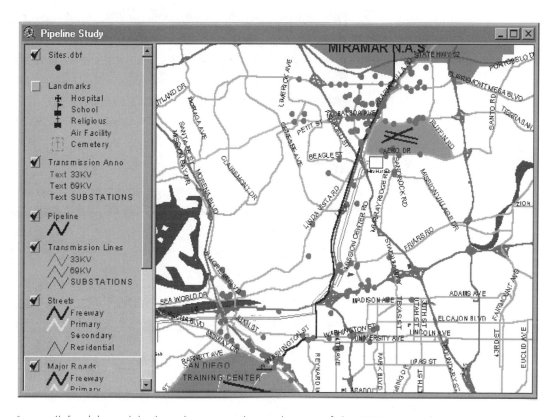

Sites.dbf table added to the view through use of the X-Y event theme.

If the view's map units are in decimal degrees, it is best to project the data before performing the spatial join. This will make the calculated distances meaningful. If the data was projected prior to inputting in ArcView, the map units would be set to the units in which the data was projected. In this case, the data was in decimal degrees but is now projected into UTM, Zone 11. However, the map units are now in projected meters; therefore, you will have to convert meters to miles.

✓ **TIP:** *When spatially joining data, it is considered a good idea to set the map and distance units to the same value. In this fashion, the calculated distance field and measurements made in the view will correspond. If you need to convert the distance field to some other unit, you can use the field calculator.*

Spatial Join

↝ **NOTE:** *Some releases of ArcView GIS may scramble graphic labels attached to a theme if you change the projected map units. To work around this problem, you could delay labeling and attaching the graphics to your themes or delete and redo the graphics after changing the map units.*

1. Open the attribute tables for the *Pipeline* and *Sites.dbf* themes.

2. Click on the *Shape* heading in the *Attributes of Pipeline* table, then click on the *Shape* heading in the *Attributes of Sites.dbf* table.

3. Click on the Join button. The *Sites.dbf* table now has a new column named *Distance*.

4. Convert the distance in meters to miles. Make *Attributes of Sites.dbf* the active document. Access the Table menu and select the Start Editing option. This will make the table editable and will change the column headings from italics to normal fonts. Notice the distance field did not change. This signifies that you cannot perform edits to this field because it is a virtual field that was calculated from the spatial join.

5. Click on the Add Field option in the Edit menu to create a new column. Define the new field, name

it *Distance Miles,* type in *Number,* make the width *10,* and set *4* decimal places.

6. The *Distance Miles* heading should be high-lighted. Open the Field Calculator to calculate the distance in miles from the distance field in meters. Input the expression *[Distance] / 1609.344* and click OK.

7. Stop editing by selecting the Stop Editing option in the Table menu. When prompted, save your edits.

8. Verify the calculations. Change back to the view and identify and measure the distances in miles from the site to the pipeline.

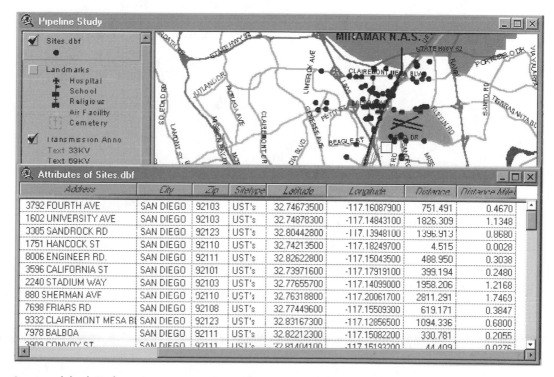

Sites added to the view as an event theme, and the attribute table spatially joined to the Pipeline theme.

Symbolize Based on Distance

ArcView has several ways to symbolize data. To show how close the sites are to the pipeline, you will create graduated symbols, where the larger symbols reflect close proximity and small symbols are farther away from the pipeline. You will select the base sites theme and copy it, creating two additional themes to differentiate between the L-UST and UST sites.

1. Make the *Sites.dbf* theme active. Open the Legend Editor. Change the symbol color to dark red. Create a Graduated Symbol legend with six quantile classes on the *Distance Miles* field. Because you need to identify the sites within specific distances of the pipeline, you will change the default values and labels used in the classification.

2. Change the classification ranges for the Values, and the Labels will change as well. Recall that the values are used to classify the data, and the labels are used in the legend. Use the following ranges for the values.

- ❏   0.0–0.125
- ❏   0.125–0.25
- ❏   0.25–0.50
- ❏   0.50–0.75
- ❏   0.75–1.0
- ❏   1.0–3.0

3. Change the size range to 6 and 13. Click on the Flip Symbols button to make the symbols shrink in size as they get farther from the pipeline.

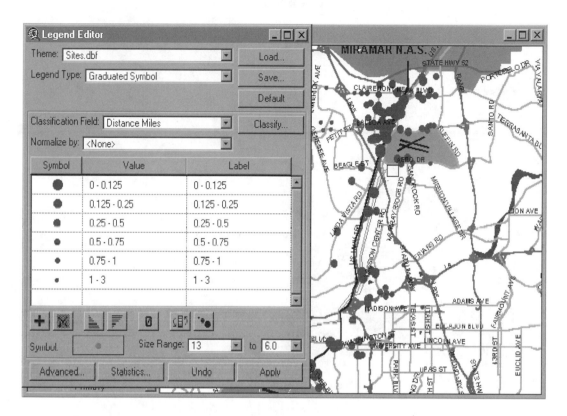

Sites.dbf legend editor with the sites classified by distance from the pipeline.

4. Copy and paste the *Sites.dbf* theme into the view. Select the topmost theme, open Properties, and change the theme name to *UST Sites*. Change the definition to *([Sitetype] = "UST")*, and close the dialog box. Similarly, change the other theme name to *L-UST Sites*, and the definition to *([Site-type] = "L-UST")*.

5. Open the legend editor for the *L-UST Sites* theme and change its symbology to graduated orange squares. Make sure the symbols scale in the proper direction.

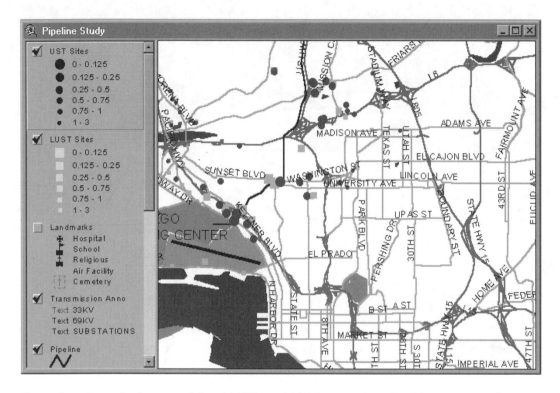

Completed symbolizing of the L-UST and UST sites classified by type and distance.

Create a Buffer Around Pipeline

To enhance the final map, you might like to add a graphic buffer depicting a specific distance from the pipeline. ESRI has provided a sample extension to buffer selected theme features. User-created extensions or ESRI sample extensions can be added to a project by placing them within the extension search path. To add the ESRI sample buffer extension, you will set the environment variable *USEREXT.*

↝ **NOTE:** *In order to perform these steps, you must have the ESRI sample scripts and extensions loaded on your system.*

1. To access the sample extensions, open and run the *SetSampleExtPath* script. This will set a variable to allow you to see more extensions.

2. Change to the project window and open the extension dialog box. Click on the Sample Buffer Extension check box. This will add a new button to the view.

3. Switch back to the view and make *Pipeline* the active theme. If needed, zoom out to the extents of the entire pipeline. Change to the *Select Features* tool and select the entire pipeline.

4. Click on the Buffer button. Make the buffer .5 miles and dissolve the adjoining buffers.

5. If you desire, change the buffer symbology by selecting the buffer graphic and opening the symbol palette.

6. If you plan to close and reopen this project, you will need to install the *SetSampleExtPath* script as the start-up script in the project properties.

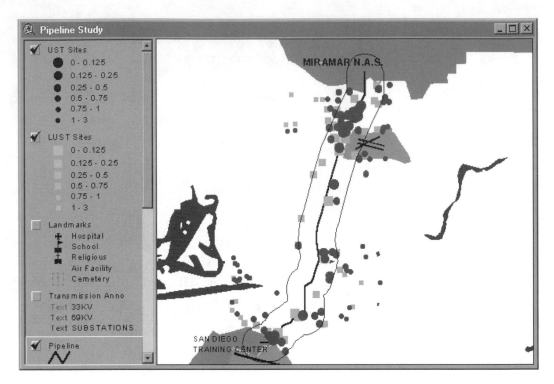

Buffered pipeline.

Review Results

By creating summary tables denoting the number of sites by distance, reports on the site information, and a map of the pipeline, you can fulfill the reporting criteria required for the "ASTM Phase I Environmental Site Assessment." You can identify and recognize the environmental conditions within exact reporting distances for the L-UST and UST sites.

Optional

Apply the techniques you have learned to enhance the analysis by performing the following steps.

1. Spatially join the pipeline data to school locations. Although this analysis is not required as part of ASTM requirements, assume that the project manager is interested in the associated risk of placing a pipeline near a school. To perform this analysis, you will need to create a new theme containing only the schools. Once the new theme is defined, spatially join the schools to the pipeline theme. Add a new field for the distance in miles and calculate. Classify the schools theme based on distance using the graduated point legend symbols.

2. Create tables to summarize the number of sites for each classified distance.

3. Create a layout to accompany the summary tables for a report.

Summary

The previous exercise focused on analyzing the proximity of underground storage tanks to a proposed pipeline. You created a new shapefile and drew the proposed pipeline. Next, you added an event theme to the view containing the storage tank tabular data and tank X-Y locations in decimal degrees

By using a spatial join, you were able to calculate distances between the storage tanks and the pipeline. You were then able to set the legend to graduate the size of the symbols, which clearly showed the sites located in closest proximity to the pipeline.

Discussion Topics

❑ What additional engineering data typically stored in AutoCAD could be used in a pipeline proximity analysis?

❑ In what other types of applications would X-Y event themes be useful?

Geocoding

This chapter contains the first of a series of exercises aimed at tracking the listings of a fictitious real estate office. The first exercise will focus on address geocoding. Properties will be geocoded in order to spatially locate them in the data set prepared for the application you will be developing through the next several chapters. In the final exercise in the series (Chapter 13), you will deploy the real estate application for end users.

Topics and Functions

- ❏ Setting geocode theme properties
- ❏ ArcView address styles
- ❏ Interactive geocoding

❏ Batch geocoding

❏ Using the Locate function

Description

Geocoding is the process of address matching, or spatially locating points based on their tabular address. To carry out the address match, you will prepare the required data, use the Geocoding Editor, review rejects, and examine geocoding settings. You will also perform a rematch and interactively locate individual addresses. The exercise contains the following steps and topics.

❏ Open the project

❏ Data overview and introduction

❏ Convert streets to a matchable theme

❏ Geocoding processes

❏ Locating addresses

❏ Geocode control files

Open the Project

1. Access the File menu and select Open Project. Navigate to the *$AVEXDS\avexer\project* directory, and select the *chapt10.apr* project. This project contains data from Denver County, Colorado.

Data Overview and Introduction

The streets and landmark data used in the exercises appearing in Chapters 10 through 13 are provided by Geographic Data Technology, Inc. (GDT). The business data are provided by Equifax National Decision Systems. Throughout the real estate series of exercises, take time to explore the data in the *Denver*

For a discussion of address events, see Chapter 4, "Address Events," page 83.

County view. The view includes numerous features of interest to both real estate buyers and sellers.

The ArcView geocoding process involves several data sets: the reference theme, the address *event* data, and the geocoded theme. The reference theme contains the base address data for the project area. The event data consist of a table of addresses, which will be *queried* against the reference theme. When matches are found, permanent point features are added to the shapefile of the new geocoded theme. In this exercise, the *Streets* theme serves as the reference theme.

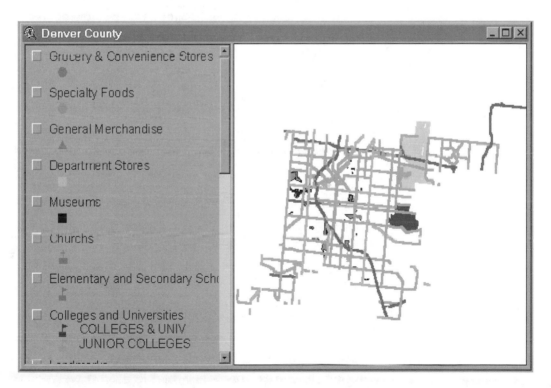

Denver County view.

Convert Streets into a Matchable Theme

Address Styles

In ArcView, an address style must be specified in the properties of the reference theme. As seen in the following table, there are ten defined styles, each uniquely configured to handle matching different forms of event data.

Address Style	Description
US Single Range	Streets with a single address range.
US Single Range with Zone	Streets with a single address range and zone.
US Streets	Streets with left and right address ranges.
US Streets with Zone	Streets with left and right address ranges and zone.
US Single House	Parcel or point addresses.
US Single House with Zone	Parcel or point addresses with zone.
Single Field	Any single field in the reference attribute table.
Zip+4	Zip code and +4 extension.
Zip+4 Range	Zip code and range of +4 extensions
5 Digit Zip	5 Digit Zip code

For this exercise, you will use the *US Streets* address style, which is intended for use without zone information. Because you are dealing with a small geographic area, this is acceptable. If you were carrying out a regional or statewide application where street names may be duplicated, you would use one of the more complex styles that include zone information. For example, the zone could represent city or zip code.

A check box next to a field in the theme geocoding properties indicates that the field is required. All required fields must exist in the data set. The ArcView help system provides details on each style and the preferred field names. The following table lists fields for the *US Streets* style and whether they are required by ArcView.

Setting a Theme's Geocoding Properties

Required	Field	Description
Yes	FromLeft	*From* left house number
Yes	FromRight	*From* right house number
Yes	ToLeft	*To* left house number
Yes	ToRight	*To* right house number
No	Dir	Prefix direction
No	PreType	Prefix type
Yes	StreetName	Street name
No	StreetType	Street type
No	SuffixDir	Suffix direction

Theme Geocoding Properties

1. Access the Theme Properties dialog box for the *Streets* theme. Scroll down to the geocoding settings and select the *US Streets* address style.

✧ **NOTE:** *The reference attributes must be in separate fields.*

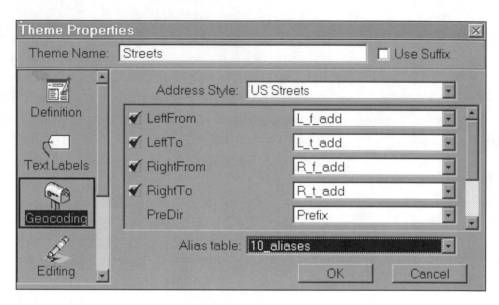

Geocoding category of the Theme Properties dialog box.

2. ArcView has "preferred" names for the various fields. As long as one of the preferred field names is used, it does a very good job of anticipating which fields do what. Because the street data in this example conform to the preferred field names, ArcView sets the fields for you. All required fields have been set correctly. Notice, however, that PreType has no match, as indicated by None in the drop-down list box. Given that PreType has no check box, it is not required. You do not have a field containing such data, so leave the None setting as is. If you needed to set the fields manually, or override ArcView's automatic selection, each field could be set with its respective drop-down list box.

Place Name Aliases

An alias table represents the true address of common place names. Common examples of place names would be City Hall, or County Hospital. The table contains at least two *string* fields. The first string field must contain the alias or place name, and the second must contain the street address.

1. Set the Alias Table in the *Streets* theme geocoding properties to *10_aliases*.

Reference Theme Indexes

1. Click the OK button to close the Theme Properties dialog box and make the *Streets* theme matchable. When prompted, select Yes to build the geocoding indexes.

2. If you have write permission to the data directory, you would write index files there. If you do not have write permission, you can find them in the project working directory. The working directory is a property of the project. Take a moment to examine the project properties for the working directory and the index files. Because the *Streets* theme is a large shapefile with over 23,000 features, it will take a few minutes to create the indexes.

✓ **TIP:** *The paths to the indexes are stored in the project .apr file. If the index files are moved, the .apr file can be edited to point to the new location. Search for the characters .ixs and .mxs to find all references to the indexes.*

Examine the Event Table of Listing Data

1. Open the *10_aliases* table. The table contains a single record for *OLD SCHOOL HSE,* whose address is *3427 PONTIAC ST.*

10_aliases table.

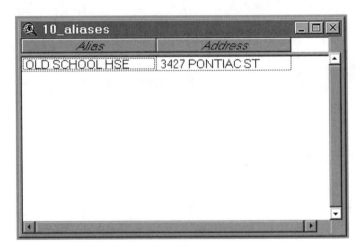

2. Open the *Real Estate Listings* table and examine the *Address* field. All address components, except zone information, must be stored in a single field. In this table, the field is called *Address*.

3. Find the record that contains the place name *OLD SCHOOL HSE.* Compare this to the entry in the *10_aliases* table to see how they work together. Clear the selected set and close both tables.

Price	Address	City	Sqft	Bedrooms	Baths	Style	Name
17900	621 W 4TH AV	Denver	0	0	0.00	Land	Johnson
49500	1353 PERRY	Denver	864	2	1.00	Ranch	Kilgore
55000	1827 E 33RD AV	Denver	936	3	2.00	Ranch	Mcdonald
59900	2655 OLIVE ST	Denver	1038	2	1.00	Ranch	Mickal
68000	4614 LOGAN ST	Denver	1506	3	1.00	Ranch	Estes
69900	356 FOX ST	Denver	1216	3	1.00	2Story	Harvey
89500	309 S XAVIER ST	Denver	1050	3	1.00	Ranch	Pilgrim
89900	2661 S PERRY ST	Denver	850	2	1.00	Ranch	Moore
89900	151 N ONEIDA ST	Denver	764	2	1.00	Ranch	Strout
99950	3060 W CLYDE PL	Denver	1095	4	2.00	Ranch	Timbral
99950	350 S ELLIOTT S	Denver	1000	3	2.00	Ranch	Rutherford
109900	4184 W TENNESSE	Denver	1963	5	3.00	Ranch	Bryant
116900	4893 FLOWER	Denver	1569	3	2.00	BiLevel	Calligon

Real Estate Listings table of address event data.

Geocoding Processes

Initial Geocoding Setup

1. Make the *Denver County* view active. With the *Streets* theme active, access the View menu and select Geocode Addresses. This will bring up the main Geocode Addresses dialog box.

2. You need to define which data sets to use via the corresponding drop-down list boxes. The active *Streets* theme was placed in Reference Theme by default and is correct. The *Using Address Style* field has also been preset to the *US Streets* style, which is currently defined as a property of the reference theme. Although many of these fields are preset in ArcView, you always have the option to override the settings.

3. The *Join* field is a field in the reference theme's attribute table that can be joined to the geocoded

theme. You do not need to use this feature, so leave it blank. Set the Address Table to *Real Estate Listings*. This is the table that contains the addresses to be geocoded. The Address Table drop-down list box contains all tables in the project. Alternatively, you can use the Browse button to use a table that has not been added to the project.

4. Confirm the address field is set to *Address*. This is the field that contains the actual address string to be used.

5. Set the Display field to *Name*. This setting is optional and provides the display field as additional information in the Geocoding Editor to help identify the address on which you are working.

Geocode Addresses dialog box.

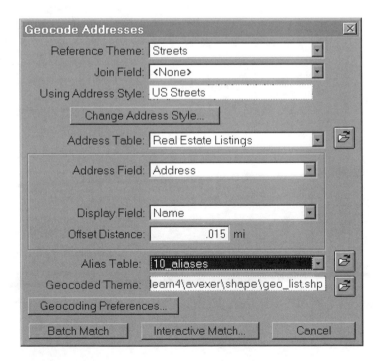

6. With the current address style, you have explicit data about each side of the street. Consequently, ArcView can offset the points on the correct side of the street, and the geocoded points are more visually informative. Set Offset Distance to .015 miles. The view's distance units are miles.

7. Set the Alias Table to *10_aliases*. This is the table that contains the alias information. Again, a browse button is available in order to make use of a table not stored in the project.

8. Set the Geocoded Theme to *$AVEXDS\avexer\ shape\geo_list.shp* with the adjacent browse button. This is the new shapefile to which geocoded point features will be added after they are success fully matched.

9. The Preferences button in this dialog box is one of several ways to access the basic geocoding preferences settings, which control the matching operation. These are discussed under the heading "Geocoding Preferences," to follow. For now, stick with the default values.

For a discussion of geocoding, see Chapter 4, "The Science of Geocoding," page 86.

At this point, you are ready to begin matching addresses. There are two ways to go about this procedure. One is the *batch* mode, and the other is the *interactive* mode. In either case, ArcView will create the output table for the geocoded theme. Records will be added to this table for each address ArcView processes. Points will be added to the theme for each matched address.

Interactive Match and the Geocoding Editor

First, you will examine the interactive mode, which gives you greater control over the matching process and covers all of the fundamentals. Then you will examine the batch method. Click the Interactive Match button to invoke the Geocoding Editor. The Geocoding Editor contains a lot of information. First, it identifies the current address of the set. At this time, you are focused on number 1 of 31. The address counter is displayed in the upper left corner. Note that the Name *display* field is also displayed to help you identify the address.

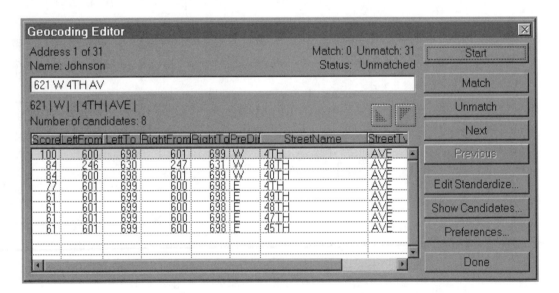

Geocoding Editor.

In the upper right corner, the editor progressively updates the scoreboard for the geocoding process. At this point, you have 0 matched, and 31 unmatched, records.

Directly below the scoreboard is a field that contains the current address record from the *Real Estate Listings* table you are trying to match. Immediately below the field is the address, divided into components by ArcView according to the selected Address Style. ArcView will try to match these address components to a street arc, which is coded to contain the *number* in its range of addresses. If a match is found, ArcView will approximate the location along the arc based on the range data.

ArcView compares the address components for the current address record to the reference theme using the index created previously. Each reference feature is given a *score*. Features that score high enough are considered *candidates* for a possible match. ArcView internally scores each component of the address and presents you with the *total score*, which is the sum of the component scores.

The Geocoding Editor displays the total number of candidates. The score and details for each candidate are listed in the large candidate table.

If an attribute is made active by clicking the column name, the candidates can be sorted using the Sort Ascending and Sort Descending buttons. By default, the candidates are sorted in descending order of their respective scores.

Geocoding Preferences

Several preferences can be set to control the way Arc-View matches addresses.

1. Click the Preferences button to view and set geocoding preferences.

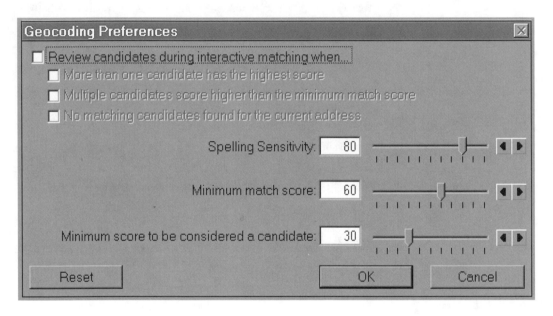

Geocoding Preferences dialog box.

There are three conditions upon which you can be prompted to review the candidates *manually.* Any combination of the three conditions can be selected. The default is to not review candidates.

2. Verify that the "Review candidates…when" box is *not* checked.

3. Do *not* check the "More than one candidate has the highest score" box. If this box is checked, you

would be prompted to make a decision when the scores of two or more candidates are tied.

4. Verify that the "Multiple candidates score higher than the minimum match score" box is *not* checked. You will let ArcView match to the highest scoring candidate, even if several records score above the minimum required for matches.

5. Do *not* check the "No matching candidates found for the current address" box. As another step in the geocoding process, you will clean up records that did not match.

6. Also displayed in the Geocoding Preferences dialog box are three scoring settings: Spelling Sensitivity, Minimum Match Score, and Minimum Score to be Considered a Candidate. The default settings work well most of the time, so you will use the defaults for this portion of the exercise. Depending on the characteristics of your data, these settings can be tuned to optimize the geocoding process. Close the Geocoding Preferences dialog box.

•• **NOTE:** *Settings in the Geocoding Preferences box can be altered at any time during the geocoding process.*

Geocoding Editor Modes

Before beginning to match addresses, it is important to understand the difference between the two modes of the Geocoding Editor. Addresses can be processed sequentially or individually. When working in sequential mode, ArcView will revert to the individual mode if candidates must be reviewed. By not reviewing candidates, you will process the addresses sequentially with minimal user interaction. After reviewing candidates, the sequential mode can be restarted. Several buttons in the Geocoding Editor control this interaction.

The Start button starts the sequential processing. While the geocoding editor is running in sequential mode, this button becomes a Stop button. Sequential mode can be stopped at any time with this button. If ArcView stops to review candidates, this button turns into a Continue button. Use it to continue sequential processing.

The Previous button is used to step backward through the addresses to review them or match them to a different candidate. The Next button skips the current address and proceeds to the next one. Skipped records are recorded as unmatched.

☞ ***WARNING:*** *Quickly clicking the Continue/Stop button in a repetitive fashion may cause a software error.*

The Match button matches the current address to the highlighted candidate. The Unmatch button undoes a previous match and leaves the address record unmatched.

The Show Candidates button brings up the Show Candidates dialog box. This dialog lists the candidates, with their respective scores and all of their attribute fields. The Flash Candidate button will flash the highlighted candidate feature in the view.

The Done button closes the Geocoding Editor.

➻ **NOTE:** *Geocode matching is not case sensitive.*

Match Addresses Sequentially in the Geocoding Editor

1. Click the Start/Continue button to begin sequentially processing the addresses. The Geocoding Editor proceeds through the entire set to address 31 of 31, and the results are 27 matched and 4 unmatched.

2. Click the Previous and Next buttons to cycle through the addresses and observe the various candidates and their scores. Use the address counter at the top left of the dialog box to keep track of where you are in the list of addresses. Click the Show Candidates button, examine several candidates, and try flashing them in the view.

Show Candidates dialog box.

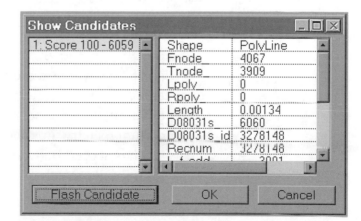

3. Click the Done button to close the Geocoding Editor.

Next, you will be presented with the Rematch Addresses dialog box. The Rematch Addresses dialog gives you the results of the geocode processing by organizing the addresses into three categories. The categories are Good Match, Partial Match, and No Match. If the results are not satisfactory, you can rematch. If you choose to rematch, you can again choose to do so in a batch or interactive process. The batch and interactive processes are essentially the same as those initiated from the Geocode Addresses dialog, except that you select which addresses to act on in the Re-match drop-down list box. For now, you will continue to focus on the interactive method.

Re-match Options

Option	Re-match Function
No Match (default)	All previously unmatched addresses
All Records	All addresses in the geocoded theme table
Partial Match	Only *partial match* addresses
Selected Records	Only selected addresses in the geocoded theme table

Note that of the 27 matches, 25 are considered *good* matches, with a score over 75, and 2 are considered *Partial* matches, with a score of less than 75. Remember that the Geocoding Preferences setting for a minimum match score was 60. Therefore, these partial matches scored between 60 and 75. Select *Partial Match* in the Re-match drop-down list box.

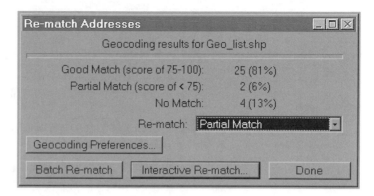

Re-match Addresses dialog box.

1. Click the Interactive Re-match button to examine the *Partial* matches.

2. The first address is *4184 W TENNESSE*, which has been matched to the only candidate with a score of 68. Study the candidate to determine why this match scored low. You can see that *AVE* is missing from the address to be matched. Click in the long thin box below the scoreboard and type in *AVE* after TENNESSE. Hit <Enter> to reevaluate the address after your fix. Note the score improved to 92. Use the Edit Standardize button to view exactly how ArcView handled this address. Close the dialog box by selecting OK.

Edit Standardization dialog box.

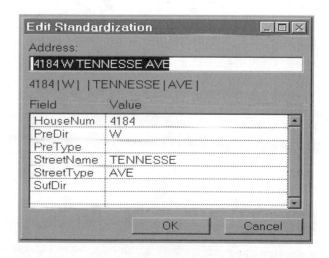

3. Click the Match button to match this address and move to the next one. Fix the *3138 S MILWAUKE* address by correcting the spelling and adding *ST,* as you did previously, then match it. Click the Done button to close the Geocoding Editor.

4. When presented with the Re-Match Addresses dialog box, observe the improved results of your matches and click the Done button. The No-Match records will be covered later, but first take a look at the geocoded theme ArcView is creating as you go.

Examine the Geocoded Theme

1. Return to the *Denver County* view. The new geocoded theme has been added to the top of the Table of Contents. Change its name to *Houses* and turn it on to see the points. These points represent the real estate listings.

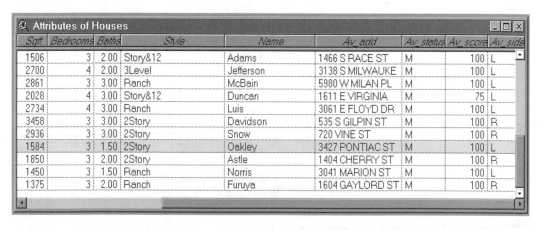

Sqft	Bedrooms	Baths	Style	Name	Av_add	Av_status	Av_score	Av_side
1506	3	2.00	Story&12	Adams	1466 S RACE ST	M	100	L
2700	4	2.00	3Level	Jefferson	3138 S MILWAUKE	M	100	L
2861	3	3.00	Ranch	McBain	5980 W MILAN PL	M	100	L
2028	4	3.00	Story&12	Duncan	1611 E VIRGINIA	M	75	L
2734	4	3.00	Ranch	Luis	3061 E FLOYD DR	M	100	L
3458	3	3.00	2Story	Davidson	535 S GILPIN ST	M	100	R
2936	3	3.00	2Story	Snow	720 VINE ST	M	100	R
1584	3	1.50	2Story	Oakley	3427 PONTIAC ST	M	100	L
1850	3	2.00	2Story	Astle	1404 CHERRY ST	M	100	R
1450	3	1.50	Ranch	Norris	3041 MARION ST	M	100	L
1375	3	2.00	Ranch	Furuya	1604 GAYLORD ST	M	100	R

Attribute table for Houses, the new geocoded theme.

2. All attributes from the *Real Estate Listings* table are present in the new theme, and ArcView has added a few more fields specific to geocoding. Open the attribute table for the *Houses* theme and examine the fields. The following table lists the geocoding fields added to the attributes of the theme.

Field	Values	Description
Name	Name from the *Real Estate Listings* table	The *Display* field
Av_add	string	Actual value that matched
Av_status	U = unmatched M = matched	Indicates matching status
Av_score	0-100	The matching score
Av_side	L R or BLANK	Indicates side of street

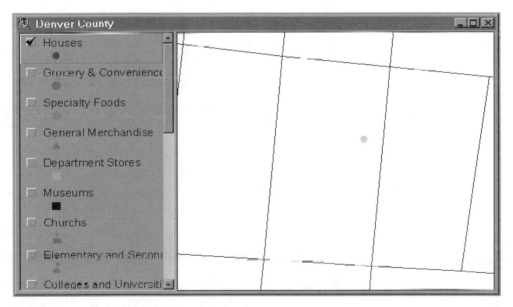

Point for the OLD SCHOOL HSE listing at 3427 PONTIAC ST placed on the correct side of the street.

3. Use the Find function, and zoom in on the point for the *OLD SCHOOL HSE.* Perform an Identify on the house point and the street arc. Note that the point has the original address of *OLD SCHOOL HSE* and that the *Av_add* field contains the address from the alias table. The point is offset from the street center line because you specified an offset distance in the Add Event Theme dialog box.

Identify results for the OLD SCHOOL HSE listing.

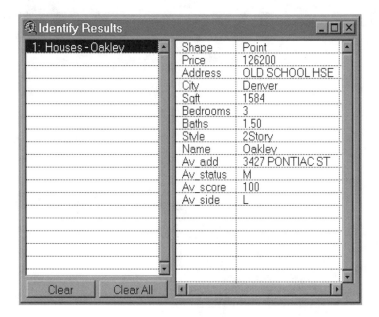

1: Houses - Oakley		
	Shape	Point
	Price	126200
	Address	OLD SCHOOL HSE
	City	Denver
	Sqft	1584
	Bedrooms	3
	Baths	1.50
	Style	2Story
	Name	Oakley
	Av_add	3427 PONTIAC ST
	Av_status	M
	Av_score	100
	Av_side	L

4. Clear the selected set and sort the *Attributes of Houses* table in descending order of the *Av_status* field. The records containing U will appear at the top. There are four records containing U, indicating that they are unmatched, and thus no points are yet associated with them.

5. Return to the *Denver County* view. With the *Houses* theme active, select Rematch Addresses from the

Theme menu to re-geocode the unmatched records.

6. You will once again use the Re-Match Addresses dialog box. In the Re-Match drop-down list box, select No Match to process the four unmatched records. Click the Interactive Re-Match button to invoke the Geocoding Editor.

↝ **NOTE:** *Alternatively you could have selected the* U *records in the table and chosen to rematch* Selected Records.

7. The first address, *350 S ELLIOTT S,* has been mis-spelled. Use the Preferences button and reduce the spelling sensitivity to *70.* Everything seems to line up with the candidate except the spelling of ELIOT. There is only one candidate, and its score is 46. Because this score is below the minimum match score of 60, it was not considered a match. Click the Match button to force a match for this candidate. Keep in mind that the low score will cause this to be classified as a *Partial* match. This action updates the number of matches to 1, updates the number of unmatched to 3, and presents the next address.

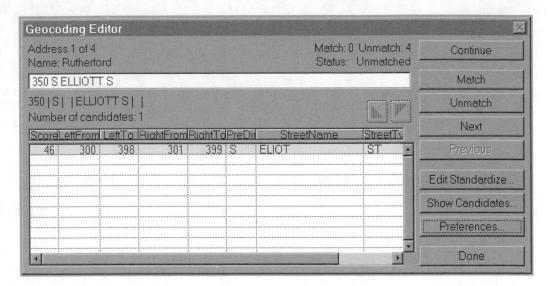

Geocoding Editor during rematching.

8. The second address, *4893 FLOWER*, is missing both a Direction and Street Type. Before matching, you will edit the address to improve its score. Position the cursor in the address box and edit the address to read *4893 S FLOWER WAY*. Use the <Enter> key to re-check candidates for the edited address. The score has improved from 52 to 100. The edited address will be stored in the *Av_add* field column. You could use the Match button, but the score is high enough to match on its own. To demonstrate, click the Continue button. ArcView will match it automatically, match the third record (because of the reduced spelling sensitivity), and take you to the last record. Examine it and determine why it, too, will be noted as a *Partial* match.

9. Now use the techniques you have learned to match the *858 S QUEBEC S* address.

10. Verify that all records in the *Attributes of Houses* table now have an *Av_status* of M. This confirms that all listings have been successfully geocoded.

11. Clear the selected records of the *Attributes of Houses* table, and compute statistics on the *Av_score* field to evaluate the quality of the matches.

Statistics for the Av_score field after all records have been matched.

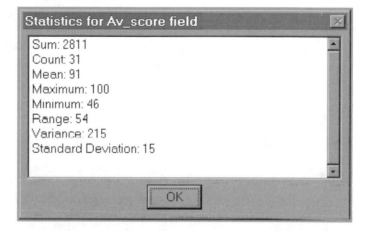

Statistics for Av_score field

Sum: 2811
Count: 31
Mean: 91
Maximum: 100
Minimum: 46
Range: 54
Variance: 215
Standard Deviation: 15

OK

Batch Match

1. Now that you have used interactive matching and rematching, you will look at batch geocoding. In many cases, batch mode can save you several steps. You can run a batch process and view the results in the rematch dialog. Then you can alter the geocoding preferences and rerun the batch process, if necessary.

NOTE: *Several batch iterations may be necessary to yield a complete set of matches. If you need to look* *at or edit individual addresses, you will need to use the interactive geocoding editor.*

2. Add another geocoded theme of the *Real Estate Listings* and save the shapefile as *$AVEXDS\ avexer\shape\geo_bat.shp*. For the Geocode Addresses dialog, use the same settings as those used in the interactive match process.

3. Reset the geocoding preferences and click Batch Mode to begin the processing.

4. The Re-match dialog indicates two partial matches and four unmatched addresses. Adjust the geocoding preferences to a Spelling Sensitivity of *60*, a Minimum Match Score of *40*, and a Minimum Score To Be Considered A Candidate of *30* and Batch Re-Match the unmatched addresses.

5. All addresses matched, but the rematch dialog indicates that six are *Partial* matches. A prudent user would wonder how good these partial matches are, given the lowered spelling sensitivity and minimum match score. Choose to interactively rematch the partials. This time, simply step through the partials with the Next button and look at what the candidates matched with, given the reduced sensitivities. Close the Geocoding Editor and Re-match dialog boxes.

6. Delete the batch geocoded theme.

Locating Addresses

Thus far you have added geocoded *events* to a view and rematched when necessary. The third and final way to use Geocoding is with the Locate Addresses function.

Locate is used to find a single address or street intersection in a view and does not place permanent features into a theme. The Locate result is represented by a simple graphic point marker. These markers can be selected and deleted if desired. If the location is not within the current view extent, ArcView will pan the display and center it on the location.

The Locate function can be performed on any theme whose geocoding properties have previously been set. Aliases are supported if an alias table is specified in the geocoding properties of the theme. The normal geocoding preferences, including the review of candidates, are also supported. The style of address you can enter in the Locate dialog box is dependent on the geocoding properties of the reference theme in use.

✓ **TIP:** *You can locate points or addresses in several themes at once by activating multiple themes in the view. The Locate function will search each theme sequentially until a match is found.*

1. Activate the *Streets* theme in the *Denver County* view.

2. Access the View menu and select Locate Address (or click the Locate Address button). Enter *OLD SCHOOL HSE* in the Locate dialog box and click OK. The Locate function uses the alias table to

find the address and places a point marker there. Because you cannot specify an offset distance for the Locate function, the point marker is placed directly on the Street center line. Select the marker and delete it.

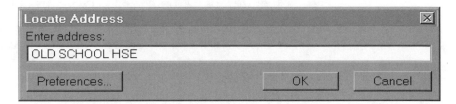

Locate Address dialog box.

3. Use the Locate function again to find a street intersection. Enter *16TH ST & CALIFORNIA ST* in the dialog box. ArcView pans the display to the location and places a marker at the intersection. Street intersection locates are only supported for the US Streets, US Streets with Zone, US Single Range, and US Single Range with Zone address styles. Delete the marker.

4. Save your project under a new name for use in the next exercise.

✓ **TIP:** *Sometimes the Locate dialog box will remain on the screen after locating an address. Resize the view window slightly to refresh the display.*

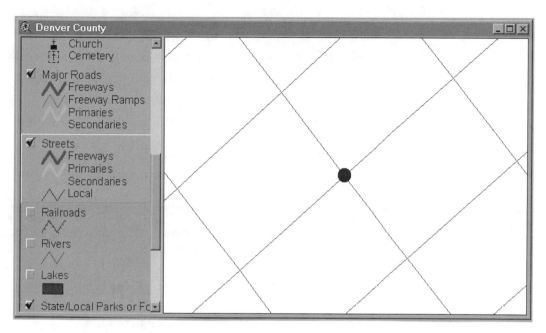

Point marker representing the intersection of 16TH ST & CALIFORNIA ST.

Geocoding Control Files

Several geocoding control files are located in the *$AVHOME/geocode* directory. ArcView geocoding uses sophisticated algorithms to perform address matching. Factors that control the algorithms can be adjusted in the control files. However, this should only be attempted by expert "power users." Information about controlling these factors is available in the *ArcView FAQ* (Frequently Asked Questions), located in the Help system.

➤ **NOTE:** *ESRI does not warranty the performance of geocoding if the *.mat files are modified.*

It is recommended that you initially limit modifications to the *mprefdef.db* file. This file contains the default geocoding preferences used by the Geocoding Editor. Always make a backup copy of configuration files, such as *mprefdef.db*, before making changes. This file can be edited, and the new defaults will be used by subsequent geocoding operations. The following table lists the items in the *mprefdef.db* file, defaults, value ranges, and descriptions.

Item	Default	Value Range	Description
Spell Weight	80	0–100	Spelling sensitivity
MinMatch	60	0–100	Minimum score to be considered a match
MinCand	30	0–100	Minimum score to be considered a candidate
NoReview	1	0 = review, 1 = no review	Review candidates
MultBest	0	0 = no review, 1 = review	Review if several have high scores (if 1, NoReview must = 0)
MultGood	0	0 = no review, 1 = review	Review if several have scores above minimum match (if 1, NoReview must = 0)
NoCand	0	0 = no review, 1 = review	Review if no candidates found (if 1, NoReview must = 0)

*The mprefdef.db
default geocoding
preferences file.*

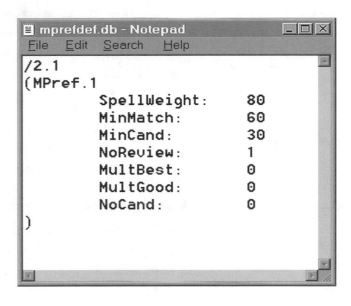

```
mprefdef.db - Notepad          _ □ X
 File   Edit   Search   Help
/2.1
(MPref.1
            SpellWeight:      80
            MinMatch:         60
            MinCand:          30
            NoReview:          1
            MultBest:          0
            MultGood:          0
            NoCand:            0
)
```

Optional

Practice your geocoding skills by performing the following steps:

1. Add another geocoded theme for the real estate listings. Adjust the geocoding preferences to obtain *optimal* matches during the batch process. Set the preferences to review candidates when necessary.

2. If you have adequate file permissions on your system, change the defaults in the *mprefdef.db* file. Try out the new defaults by adding another geocoded theme. Remember to make a backup copy first, and to reset the defaults after the exercise. If you are uneasy, do *not* perform this optional step.

3. Try the Locate function again for *16TH ST & CAL-IFORNIA ST.* Experiment using less and less of the address information with successive locates and

see how ArcView performs locating with incomplete data. If necessary, alter the preferences to lower the score to be considered a candidate, and make the selection to review candidates.

Summary

In this exercise, you defined geocoding properties for the *Streets* theme to make it matchable. You geocoded a set of real estate listings from a table in both interactive and batch modes. You rematched the addresses that did not initially match. This process resulted in a new theme of points for the listings. Finally, you interactively located an address and then a street intersection.

Discussion Topics

❑ If your application requires very precise address matches, what steps would you take to ensure a higher level of confidence in the matching process? What negative impact could these steps have?

❑ You could easily alter the geocoding preferences to make addresses match more readily. What are the risks involved when you alter the geocoding preferences for this purpose? How would you mitigate these risks?

❑ How could you use the *Av_score* field to rematch records that have a low score?

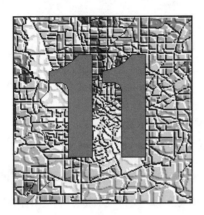

Spatial and Aspatial Queries

In this chapter you will continue the real estate exercise series by performing spatial and aspatial queries to select specific properties that meet a home buyer's criteria. You will perform advanced data editing techniques to split the city and county of Denver into four neighborhoods. Next, to assist clients in locating a house, you will add street names to major roads. Finally, you will add and remove houses as part of everyday activities required to maintain current listings.

Topics and Functions

❏ Create graphic text for street names and attach text to a theme

❏ Split a polygon theme to create neighborhoods

❏ Select listings based on spatial and aspatial criteria

❏ Add and remove real estate listings

Description

This exercise builds on techniques discussed in previous chapters for a real estate company's property review and management. With the use of spatial and aspatial queries, you will select properties, list the properties, and create a map for a prospective home buyer. The steps for the exercise follow.

❏ Open project and review data

❏ Symbolize properties

❏ Add street names to major roads

❏ Create neighborhoods

❏ Chart housing costs

❏ Find a home

❏ Find listings that meet a buyer's criteria

❏ Make a map for the client

❏ Edit the listings

Open Project and Review Data

Open the project you saved at the end of the exercise in Chapter 10. If you did not perform the previous exercise, or experienced problems creating the data, you will need to copy a few data files. If you need to copy the data files, perform the following steps to move the data into the proper directories.

1. Copy the *geo_list.** files from *$AVEXDS\avexer\ results \10* to *$AVEXDS\avexer\shape*. These are the data files for the geocoded event theme representing the real estate listings.

2. Copy the *$AVEXDS\avexer\results\10\ codenvs.ixs* and *$AVEXDS\avexer\results\10\ codenvs.mxs* index files to *$HOME*. These are the geocoding indexes for the *Streets* theme. If you do not perform this step, ArcView will create a new geocoding index file—a time-consuming task.

3. Open the *$AVEXDS\avexer\project\chapt11.apr* project.

Recall that in the last exercise you geocoded the real estate listings for the city of Denver. Now you will analyze and edit the listings.

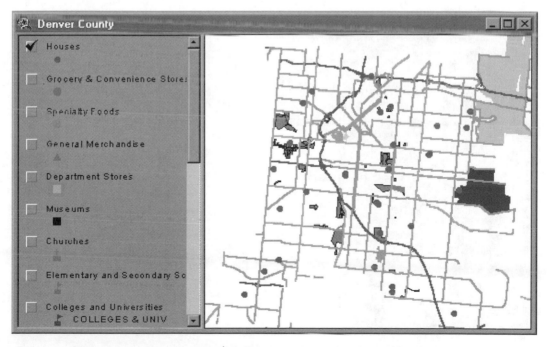

Denver County view in its initial state.

Symbolize Properties

The real estate listings appear as spartan dots on the view. To make them more visually appealing, change the symbols to red houses.

1. Make the *Houses* theme active and open the Legend Editor. Open the Symbol Palette and access the Palette Manager option. Load the *Municipl.avp* palette located in the symbol directory under your ArcView installation directory *$AVHOME*.

2. Access the Marker Palette. Scroll down and select the solid-fill house symbol. Change the default size to *16*, and change the symbol color to red.

   ◆ **NOTE:** *When loading a symbol from another symbol set, only the symbols you use will be stored in the project file.*

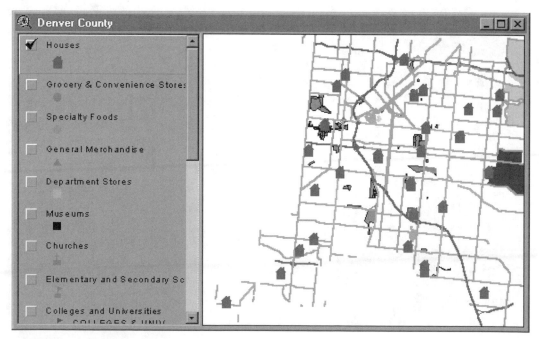

Available residential properties in the city of Denver.

Add Street Names to Major Roads

Navigating around the view is somewhat difficult because of the absence of street names. You could label the streets by setting the theme's Label properties and using the Label tool to create street names for the major roads. If you only have a few features to label, that would work fine. However, you are going to use the auto-label function to quickly label all of the major roads. Another advantage to using auto-label is that the labels are automatically attached to the theme.

For a discussion of auto-labeling features, manually labeling features, and attaching graphics to a theme, see Chapter 5, "Labeling Features," page 118.

1. Set the map scale to 1:100,000. Turn off the *Streets* theme to avoid accidentally editing its text.

2. Open the Symbol Palette and change the Text font to *Arial*, the size to *12*, and the style to *Normal*.

3. Access Auto-label from the Theme menu. Refer to the following illustration for the options. Close the dialog box by clicking on the OK button. The labeled features are specific to the theme, and ArcView automatically attaches the text to the theme so that the text will be displayed when the theme is on. If you needed to, you could select all of the text with the Edit | Detach Graphics menu, and then detach it from the theme with the Graphics | Select All Graphics menu.

Auto-label dialog box.

➥ **NOTE:** *When you have important graphics in your view, be careful to avoid accidentally deleting them. The Select All Graphics option in the Edit menu should be used with caution.*

4. Turn off the *Major Roads* theme to verify that all text turns off. If the text is turned off, you are assured that it is attached to the theme.

5. Turn on the *Streets* and *Major Roads* themes and zoom in and out. Observe the interaction of the associated street names when each theme is displayed.

✓ **TIP:** *Multiple themes with complementary display settings are a good way to add detail as you zoom in. This practice helps maintain a fast drawing speed when zoomed out and does not waste time drawing details you cannot see.*

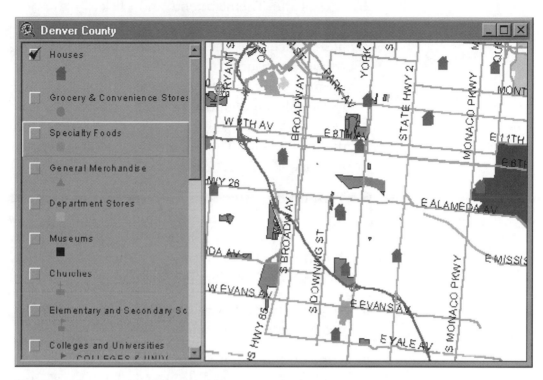

Road names attached to the Major Roads theme.

Create Neighborhoods

You will create four polygons representing four neighborhoods for the city of Denver. The neighborhoods will be used as a spatial criterion for selecting houses.

1. Make the *Denver County* view the active document and add a theme for the *$AVEXDS\ shape\nghbrhd.shp* shapefile. Change the theme's name to *Neighborhoods*. Move the theme to the bottom of the Table of Contents. Turn all of the themes off, then turn the *Neighborhoods* theme on and leave it active.

2. Access the Theme menu and click on the Start Editing option to edit the *Neighborhoods* shapefile. Notice that the theme has island polygons within the county. You can remove these by performing a Union on the selected features. Change to the select tool and drag a box around the entire county. Access the Union Graphics option from the Edit menu. This merges all of the polygons into one shape record.

3. Turn on the *Major Roads* theme. Zoom in to see the street names. Change to the Split Polygon tool located in the rightmost drop-down tool list. Draw a north/south line along Broadway, completely crossing the polygon and splitting it.

4. Draw a line east/west along 6th Avenue, splitting the polygon into quarters.

5. Turn off the major roads theme and inspect your work. If you make a mistake, use the undo options from the edit menu.

6. To code the individual neighborhoods, open the Attribute Table and position it where you can see both the Attribute Table and the graphics in the view.

7. Click on the rows and change the *Neighborhd* field contents to *Northeast, Northwest, Southeast,* or *Southwest,* depending on which area is selected in the view. You will have to switch between the Select and Edit tools to alternate between selecting and editing records. When you finish inputting the neighborhood names, change back to the view document and click on Stop Editing from the Theme menu. When prompted, save your edits.

8. Classify the neighborhoods based on the unique *Neighborhd* values. Select colors that contrast with the existing themes, or load the *$AVEXDS\ avexer\ project\neighbrh.avl* legend.

9. If any of the neighborhoods are selected, click on the Unselect button.

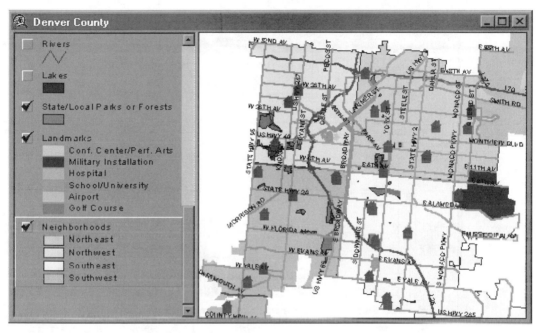

Four neighborhoods for the city of Denver.

Chart Cost for Housing

Prospective buyers always want to know how much they can expect to pay for a house. Although price depends on several factors, you will create a simple chart to show the price range for a three-bedroom house.

1. From the *Houses* attribute table, use the Query tool to select the records that contain three-bedroom houses.

2. Create a bar chart for the listings. Remove the legend and alter other chart properties to create an attractive and informative chart. An example chart appears in the next illustration.

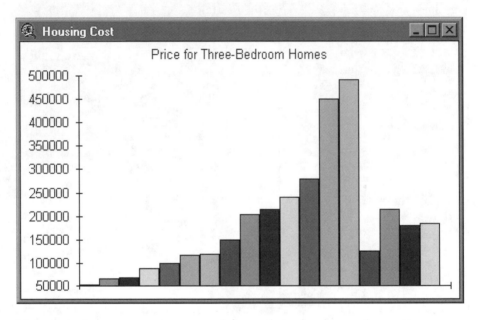

What do buyers want to spend for a three-bedroom home?

Finding a Home

When looking for a home, buyers scour the neighborhoods they find attractive. Sometimes they seek help from a real estate office after identifying a home that interests them. Prospective buyers often have only partial information on the general area. By using the Find tool, you can search for properties using partial addresses supplied by prospective buyers.

1. Make the *Houses* theme active and click on the Find tool. Input the partial address *Perry*, and click on OK. The display will center on the first listing, with *Perry* somewhere in its attribute table.

➝ **NOTE:** *The Find tool locates the desired character string in all of the active themes. If the string is found, the display will be centered on that area. The screen will not zoom in but will retain the same scale. You can repeat the find procedure until all records have been searched. ArcView will notify you when the last record was found or the string was not located.*

2. Assume that the first house located with the Find tool is not the house seen by a prospective buyer. Open the Find tool again. The previous locate text is still on the input line. Click on the OK button to find another house.

3. Assume that the second home located by the Find tool is the house that interests the prospective buyer. Identify the property in order to examine its attributes.

Finding Listings That Meet Buyers' Criteria

As seen previously, you can perform both spatial and aspatial queries to find properties meeting specific criteria. For example, you can locate houses that contain at least three bedrooms, are within a specific price range, are in a specific neighborhood, and are located within 0.25 mile of a grocery store. By organizing your queries, you can be very general or specific in spatial and aspatial criteria for selecting a house.

1. Select the houses that are within 0.25 mile of a grocery or convenience store. Verify that the *Grocery or Convenience Store* theme is displayed. Make the *Houses* theme active and open the Select By Theme dialog box. Create a new selected set of houses within 0.25 mile of a grocery or convenience store. Zoom in to the *Northeast* neighborhood to view the selected properties.

2. Make the *Neighborhoods* theme active and select the *Northeast* neighborhood. Make the *Houses* theme active and open the Select By Theme dialog box. From the existing selected set, select the houses that intersect the *Neighborhoods* theme. To unselect all of the neighborhoods, reactivate the *Neighborhoods* theme and click on the Unselect button. At this point, you should see only houses in the *Northeast* neighborhood that are within 0.25 mile of a grocery or convenience store. To verify this, make sure the *Houses* theme is active and click on the Zoom To Selected button.

3. Now you can perform additional queries based on attributes rather than geographic location. Open the attribute table for the *Houses* theme. Open the Query Builder dialog box and input the expression (*[Bedrooms] = 3*). Click on the Select From Set button. To further reduce the set of houses, specify that square footage must be greater than 1600. The number of properties retained in the selected set is reduced after each expression.

4. Finally, specify a price range of $200,000 to $225,000. Reopen the Query Builder dialog box, and input the following expression: (*[Price]* =

200000) and ([Price] <= 225000). Click on the Select From Set button, and close the dialog box.

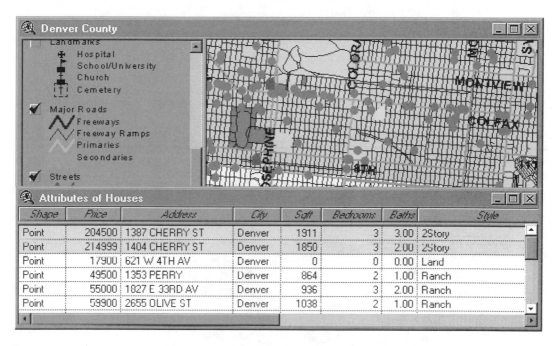

Properties that meet a prospective buyer's criteria.

As seen here, you can quickly select a few houses from a database of hundreds, based on geographic location and attributes. Attribute selection is easily supported because the data are readily available in the real estate industry. You are more limited by geographic data available for queries. Fortunately, several excellent geographic data sets are easily obtained, and others can be easily created. Using geographic data, you can perform spatial queries by neighborhood, or proximity to shopping centers, school districts, special assessment districts, environmental hazards, or other sites.

Make a Map for the Client

Now that you have selected several homes for a prospective buyer, you will create a map to show the client where the homes are located. Use the mapping techniques you learned in previous exercises to create a layout. As a starting point, you can use one of the default layout templates. Refer to the following map.

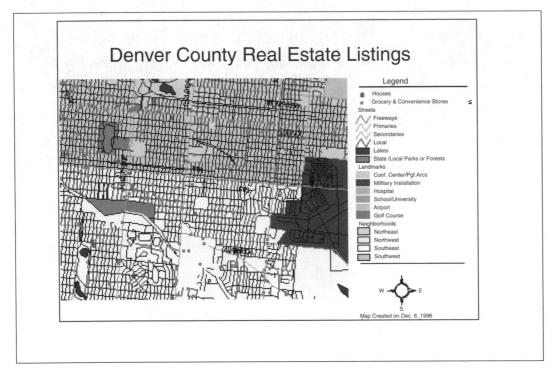

Map of the selected properties.

Edit the Listings

For most maintenance actions, you would rely on periodic updates of homes for sale from the Multiple Listings Service. In order to keep listings up to date between updates, you will manually remove homes that have been sold or are in escrow and add new listings received since the last update from the Multiple Listings Service.

1. To remove a listing, make the *Houses* theme active. Access the Theme menu and click on Start Editing.

2. Click on the Find tool and input a portion of the address *4184 W Tenn*. The display will move to that address and the house will be selected. Access the Edit menu and select Delete Features, or use the <Del> key. Both the shape and attribute records are removed. Select Stop Editing from the Theme menu and save your edits.

3. Add new listings by opening the attribute table for the *Houses* theme. Access the Table menu and select Start Editing. Note that you did not have to select Stop editing in the previous step and then restart here. ArcView will let you edit both the graphic and attributes at the same time.

4. Scroll to the bottom of the table. Access the Edit menu and select Add Record or type <Ctrl>+<A>. Scroll to the bottom of the table. Change to the Edit tool and click on the *Price* field. Use the <Tab> key to move through the fields in the record. After you add the record, type <Ctrl>+<A> to add another empty record, and repeat, adding the data for all other listings in the table. Add the listings appearing in the following table.

Price	Address	City	Square footage	Bedrooms	Baths	Style	Owner
215000	417 S HUMBOLT	Denver	1828	4	2.00	2Story	Beekman
179000	765 IVY ST	Denver	1675	3	2.00	Ranch	Wright
69500	3131 VINE ST	Denver	968	2	1.00	Ranch	Smith
379000	2552 E ALAMEDA	Denver	1835	4	3.00	Ranch	Hall

Shape	Price	Address	City	Sqft	Bedrooms	Baths	Style	Name
Point	339950	3061 E FLOYD DR	Denver	2734	4	3.00	Ranch	Luis
Point	449900	535 S GILPIN ST	Denver	3458	3	3.00	2Story	Davidson
Point	492000	720 VINE ST	Denver	2936	3	3.00	2Story	Snow
Point	126200	OLD SCHOOL HSE	Denver	1584	3	1.50	2Story	Oakley
Point	214999	1404 CHERRY ST	Denver	1850	3	2.00	2Story	Astle
Point	179000	3041 MARION ST	Denver	1450	3	1.50	Ranch	Norris
Point	183500	1604 GAYLORD ST	Denver	1375	3	2.00	Ranch	Furuya
Point	215000	417 S HUMBOLT	Denver	1828	4	2.00	2Story	Beekman
Point	179000	765 IVY ST	Denver	1675	3	2.00	Ranch	Wright
Point	69500	3131 VINE ST	Denver	968	2	1.00	Ranch	Smith
Point	379000	2552 E ALAMEDA	Denver	1835	4	3.00	Ranch	Hall

New listings ready for geocoding.

5. When complete, select all added properties. Click on the column heading *Av_add* and open the Field Calculator. Calculate the *Av_add* field to the contents of the *Address* field. When you have finished, access the Table menu, select Stop Editing, and save your edits. The last step was executed because, when the theme is rematched, ArcView examines the *Av_add* field for the address information.

6. You need to geocode the new records to the map to create points in the correct locations. Verify that the newly added records are selected. Change to the view and ensure that the *Houses* theme is active.

7. Choose Re-match Addresses from the Theme menu to display the Rematch Dialog Box. Select *No Match* in the Re-match drop-down list and click on the Batch Re-match button. The dialog box will return. Verify the results and close the dialog box.

8. Clear the selected set of features.

9. Save your project under a new name for use in the next exercise.

Optional

To further enhance the current project and to hone your skills, take the following additional steps:

1. Create a layout template for future real estate maps.

2. Add graphic text to the *Houses* theme for price, number of bedrooms, or other attributes. Attach the graphics to the theme.

3. Chart the cost versus square footage for three-bedroom houses. Is there a correlation?

Summary

In this chapter you simulated some of the procedures a real estate office would perform to show properties to clients. By using a GIS, you were able to perform queries difficult to execute in a manual system. In performing queries, you demonstrated the power of using geographic and attribute data in concert. In order to support certain queries, you created a new data set for the neighborhoods in the city of Denver.

To assist real estate office employees and clients, you labeled the major roads.

Discussion Topics

❏ If you were in charge of the Multiple Listings Service, how would you collect and organize the listing data to support an ArcView application?

❏ If the previous exercise were a real-life real estate office application, what other functions would you like to include? How might you go about implementing them?

❏ What other types of data would be useful to a real estate agent and clients?

Hot Links

In this chapter you will use hot links to reference additional data for the subject listings. You will use several standard hot link actions and define a custom action with a new script. You will use a sample extension to create an area overview and hot link to other project documents. This is the last real estate exercise before you deploy the end user ArcView application.

Topics and Functions

❏ Hot link theme properties

❏ Text file hot links

❏ Image file hot links

❏ Custom script hot links

❏   Document hot links

❏   Sample Overview Extension

Description

In this exercise you will join additional tabular data to the listings, and use hot linking to reference textual descriptions and photographic images of the listings. You will also load a sample overview extension into the real estate application and use hot links to link from one project document to another. This extension allows you to easily create an additional view that serves as an "overview" of the area of interest. The steps and topics in the exercise follow.

❏   Open project

❏   Hot link basics

❏   Hot link theme properties

❏   Textual hot link

❏   Image hot link

❏   Custom script hot link

❏   Hot link to another project document

Open Project

Open the project you saved at the end of the exercise in Chapter 11. If you did not perform the previous exercise, or had problems creating the data, you need to copy data files. If necessary, perform the following steps to move data into the proper directories.

1. Copy the *geo_list.** files from *$AVEXDS\avexer\ results\11* to the *$AVEXDS\avexer\shape* directory, and replace all existing *geo_list.** files. These are the latest data files for the geocoded event theme representing the real estate listings.

2. Copy the *nghbrhd.** files from *$AVEXDS\avexer\ results\11* to the *$AVEXDS\avexer\shape* directory.

3. Copy the *$AVEXDS\avexer\results\10\code nvs.ixs* and *codenvs.mxs* index files into *$HOME*. These are the geocoding index files for the *Streets* theme. As in previous chapters, if you do not perform this step, ArcView will create a new geocoding index—a time-consuming task.

4. Open the *$AVEXDS\avexer\project\chapt12.apr* project.

Hot Link Basics

The ArcView hot link function allows you to perform preset actions based on feature attributes in the active theme. Hot links let you access other data, such as text and image files, other project documents, or even other projects. By using Avenue, you can perform almost any hot link action by executing a custom script. The hot link action is specified as a hot link property of the theme. You perform the action when you click on features with the Hot link tool. To this point, the Hot link tool has been disabled because you have not defined any hot link properties. The default hot link action is None.

For a discussion of hot links, see Chapter 11, "Hot Links," page 302.

Join Additional Attributes for Houses

The Hot link property requires an attribute field that contains the parameter for the preset action. For example, if you were going to reference a text file, the attribute field would contain the path and name of the text file. A table of related hot link data has been pre-pared for this exercise.

1. Add the *hot_link.dbf* table from the *$AVEXDS\ avexer\dbf* directory to the project. This table contains the hot link data for text and image files for each of the listings. Three text and three image files in the table are used randomly for the listings. (These are fictitious descriptions and pictures for demonstration purposes only.)

2. Join the *hot_link.dbf* table to the *Attributes of Houses* table through the common *Address* field.

3. Examine the new fields in the *Attributes of Houses* table. Resize the columns if necessary.

✓ **TIP:** *Some operating systems use a forward slash path delimiter and some use a backslash. The* hot_link.dbf *table was created with a forward slash because ArcView supports it on* all *platforms. Use this feature along with an environment variable to make your projects platform independent. Examine the files in* $AVEXDS\avexer\project *and search for* Path: *to see how this is done.*

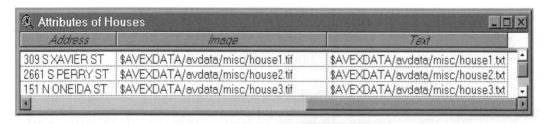

Joined attributes to support text and image file hot links.

Hot Link Theme Properties

At this point, you have the data necessary to support text and image file hot linkshot links. Before you can use the links, you must define the theme hot link properties. In the Theme Properties for Hot Links dialog box, *Field* is the field containing the data the hot link will use to perform the defined action. This action can be one of the actions listed in the Predefined Action drop-down list box, or it can be a custom script you specify. In the Predefined Action drop-down list box, you can choose between four common actions: Link to Text File, Link to Image File, Link to Document, and Link to Project.

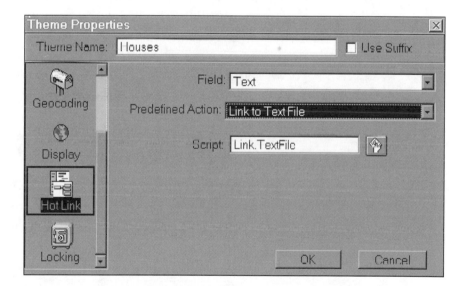

Hot Link category of the Theme Properties dialog box.

The script setting is loaded automatically if you select one of the predefined actions. Optionally, you can set your own script with the button that accesses the Script Manager, and thus ignore the Predefined Action setting.

> **↝ NOTE:** *The predefined actions are simply standard scripts. You can just as easily use your own scripts.*

Textual Hot Link

The first predefined action you will examine is the Link to Text file. This feature links features to ASCII text files.

1. Access the theme properties for the *Houses* theme, and scroll down and select the Hot link category.

2. Set the Field drop-down list box to Text, and set the Predefined Action drop-down list box to Link to Text File. The script will be automatically set to *Link.TextFile*. Select OK to close the dialog box.

> **☛ WARNING:** *When the hot link properties are accessed, the Predefined Action setting may reset itself to Link to Text File without warning. Verify that all settings are correct before you click on OK in the Hot Link Theme Properties dialog box.*

3. With the *Houses* theme active, use the Hot link tool and click on several houses to test the hot link to text files. When the Hot link tool is used on a feature, the script seeks the specified attribute value for the name of the text file to display. Zoom in if necessary.

4. When you click on another feature with the Hot link tool, the previous window seems to disappear. However, a new window is added every time, and the previous ones remain, even though they may be hidden behind other windows. When you have finished with a hot link-generated window, it is recommended you close it.

Image Hot Link

*Defining a Hot Link
for a Theme*

At this juncture, you will examine another of the pre-defined hot link actions: the Link to Image File. Several image formats are supported by ArcView. Check the ArcView Help system for a complete listing.

1. Change the theme properties for *Houses* to hot link to an image file by using the *Image* Field.

2. Try the new hot link action on several listings. Close each window when you are finished.

3. On some systems, the default *Link.ImageFile* script for image viewing may provide inadequate image quality. To solve the image quality problem, you can employ a custom script to display the images differently.

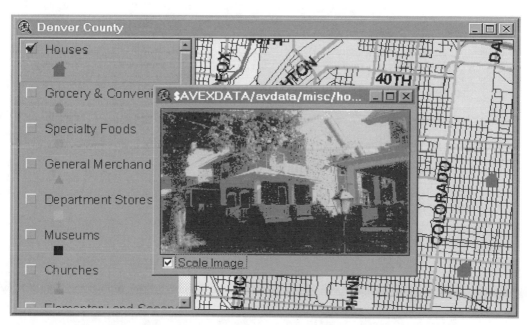

Photographic image file displayed with the standard image hot link.

Custom Script Hot Link

For a discussion of Avenue programming, see Chapter 11, "Avenue," page 354.

The image display capabilities of the view document are better and faster than those of the default *Link.ImageFile* script. You will use a sample script from the ArcView Help system to add the image file as a theme in a new view—to take advantage of improved image display capabilities.

1. From the project window, open a new script and call it *View.HotLinkImage*.

2. Access the ArcView Help system, find "View.Hot-LinkImage (Sample Script)," and copy the script.

3. Paste the source code into the *View.HotLinkImage* script and compile it.

4. Set the hot link properties for the *Houses* theme directly to the *View.HotLinkImage* script. Click on the button to access the Script Manager. When you set the hot link script explicitly in this way, you can ignore the Predefined Action setting. Verify that the hot link Field is set to Image.

5. Try the new hot link action on several listings. A new view will be created for each image displayed. These new views will automatically be added to the project. If you close the view windows, they will be deleted from the project.

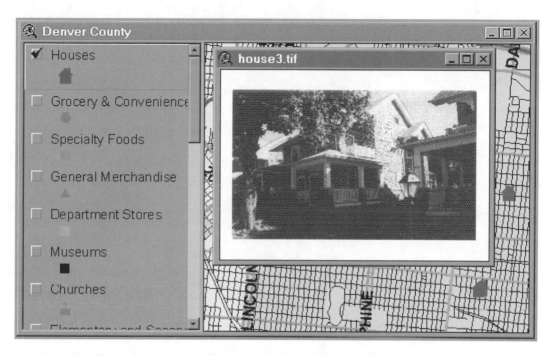

A photographic image file displayed using a custom hot link script.

Hot Link to Another Project Document

Document Preparation

Finally, you will examine the Link to Document predefined hot link action. With this action, the Field stores the name of another document in the current project. The hot link action will open the other document if necessary, and then make it active. The linked document can be a view, table, chart, layout, or script. For this exercise, you will prepare four special neighborhood views to serve as hot link documents.

1. From the project window, create four new view documents and name them *Northeast, Northwest, Southeast,* and *Southwest.*

2. For each of the four new views, set the view properties to those of the *Denver County* view. This will make the views and themes compatible.

3. Copy the *Neighborhoods* and *Houses* themes from the *Denver County* view and paste them in each of the four new views. The neighborhood views will provide a high aerial view of the houses available in each area.

4. For each of the new views, set the display extent to the respective neighborhood. Close the four views.

Southeast neighborhood view.

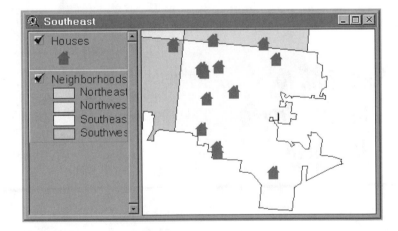

The Overview Extension

As the next step in developing the real estate application, you will load an overview extension. This action adds new functionality to the project, allowing you to easily create an *overview* for an area of interest. The *Overview* view is designed to work with a regular view document to provide the user with an overview and a detail view. After the two views are set up, the user will be able to select an area in the *Overview for Denver County* view, and the *Denver County* view will automatically set to the same area. Changes in either view extent will be reflected in the other. The *Overview for Denver County* view will also serve as a platform to use the Link to Document hot link.

1. ArcView always checks the *$HOME* directory for extensions. Copy the *$AVEXDS\avexer\scripts\ overview.avx* and *overview.apr* files to the *$HOME* directory.

➤ **NOTE:** *The $HOME environment variable should have been set according to the instructions in the introduction to this book. If you have difficulty, verify that it has been set correctly.*

2. With the project window active, select Extensions from the File menu. Scroll down and click on the *Overview Utility* and close the dialog box. In the Overview Install dialog box, select the *View* GUI and close the dialog box. This makes changes to the graphical user interface (GUI) named View. GUIs will be covered in more detail in Chapter 13.

*Extensions
dialog box.*

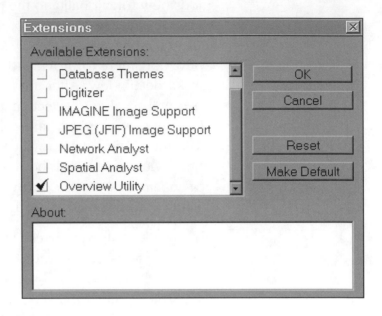

3. Make the *Denver County* view active and examine the View menu options. There are two new choices, Create Overview and Display Overview. When you create the overview view, it will mimic the current view. Therefore, you must set up the *Denver County* view with the desired settings before the *Overview* is created.

For a discussion of the user interface, see Chapter 14, "Customizing the User Interface," page 349.

4. Set the hot link properties for the *Neighborhoods* theme. Set Field to *neighborhd*, and set Predefined Action to *Link to Document*. The *Neighborhd* field contains the names of the neighborhoods that coincide with the names of the four new views. Turn off all themes except *Neighborhoods*. Make the *Neighborhoods* theme active and leave it active.

Hot link properties for the Neighborhoods theme.

5. Access the View menu and select Create Overview. This action will create a new view document named *Overview for Denver County*. The *Overview for Denver County* view contains a rectangular graphic that represents the current view extent of the *Denver County* view. Scripts keep the two synchronized with each other.

6. Resize and position the *Denver County* and *Overview for Denver County* views next to each other so that you can see both.

7. In the *Denver County* view, use the Zoom In tool to move into a small area in one of the neighborhoods. Observe the accompanying update in the *Overview for Denver County* view.

8. Change the size of the rectangle in the *Overview for Denver County* view by moving its handles with the Pointer tool. This will change the extent in the *Denver County* view. Experiment with the

interaction between the views until you are comfortable with them.

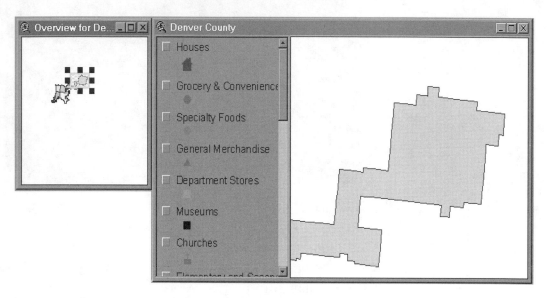

Overview *for Denver County and Denver County views.*

Test the Document Hot Link

Use the Hot link tool to click on the neighborhoods in the *Overview of Denver County* view. The hot link action will open and activate the corresponding neighborhood view.

1. Reestablish a display in the *Denver County* view that shows the houses, streets, and other important themes. Save your project under a new name for use in the exercise in Chapter 13.

Optional

For a discussion of interapplication communication, see Chapter 14, "Communicating with Other Applications," page 365.

Practice your hot linking skills by performing the following additional steps:

1. Examine the system scripts for the predefined hot link actions to determine how they work.

2. Write a new script using a *System.Execute* statement to execute an operating system command with a hot link. Consider launching a text editor application, which could be used to update a text file for the listing. To study the details of *System.Execute*, access ArcView Class Hierarchy in the Avenue Help system. Create a new table with the required field for your script and join it to the *Attributes of Neighborhoods* table. Set the Hot link Properties to use your new script.

Summary

In this exercise you set hot link theme properties and hot linked the real estate listings to text files and photographic images. To overcome limitations in viewing hot linked images, you linked to a script that displayed your images in view documents. Finally, you added an extension and used hot link functionality to link from the overview directly to the corresponding neighborhood view.

Discussion Topics

❏ The only predefined action you did not use was Link to Project, which imports another project *.apr* file. How would this capability be useful in your intended applications for ArcView?

❏ What other uses can you think of for the predefined hot link actions?

❏   What potential custom script hot link capabilities can you envision?

❏   With a little Avenue programming, issuing commands to the operating system using hot links is fairly straightforward. What types of processes could you automate in this way? How might you tie ArcView to other applications?

Application Deployment

This is the final chapter in the real estate series of exercises. In this chapter you will take the project from Chapter 12 and turn it into a deployable application. To create an end user application, you will add a script to simplify queries, remove unnecessary functionality, and render the project so that it cannot be changed.

Topics and Functions

❒ Lock themes

❒ Load script from text file

❒ Altering the ArcView user interface

❒ Creating start-up and shutdown scripts

❒ Embedding and encrypting scripts

❒ Deploying an end user application

Description

This exercise uses advanced techniques to lock themes, remove user controls, and alter default scripts to create a project that cannot be altered. To make finding homes easier, you will add a script that prompts the user for information and selects houses meeting user criteria. The steps and topics for the exercise follow.

❒ Open project and review data

❒ Simplify queries

❒ Lock themes

❒ Lock legend access

❒ Prevent reordering of Table of Contents

❒ Alter application start-up

❒ User interfaces

❒ Remove unnecessary controls

❒ Remove unnecessary documents

❒ Prevent new documents from opening

❒ Prevent users from saving changes

❒ Prevent further customization

❒ Embed and encrypt scripts

❑ Save locked project file

❑ Deploy the application

Open Project and Review Data

If you are using the project file you saved at the end of Chapter 12, you should make a copy of it before starting. This exercise will make extensive and permanent changes to the project, and you may need to revert to a previous version to undo or redo steps that did not work as expected.

Open the project you saved at the end of Chapter 12. If you did not perform the previous exercise, or had problems creating the data, you will need to copy data files. If necessary, perform the following steps to move the data into the proper directories.

1. Copy the *geo_list.** files from *$AVEXDS\avexer\ results\11* to the *$AVEXDS\avexer\shape* directory, and replace all existing *geo_list.** files. These are the latest data files for the geocoded event theme representing the real estate listings.

2. Copy the *nghbrhd.** files from *$AVEXDS\avexer\ results\11* to the *$AVEXDS\avexer\shape* directory

3. Copy the *$AVEXDS\avexer\results\10\code- nvs.ixs* and *codenvs.mxs* index files into *$AVEX- DATA\avdata\denver*. These are the geocoding index files for the *Streets* theme. If you do not perform this step, ArcView will create a new geocoding index—a time-consuming task.

4. Copy the *$AVEXDS\avexer\scripts\overview.avx* file to the *$HOME* directory.

5. Open the *$AVEXDS\avexer\project\chapt13.apr* project.

Previous exercises geocoded the real estate listings for the city of Denver, demonstrated editing and analysis of the listings, added an extension to the main and overview views for navigation, and created hot links showing text and images for the homes. Now you can begin the process of turning your project into a deployable application.

Real estate application.

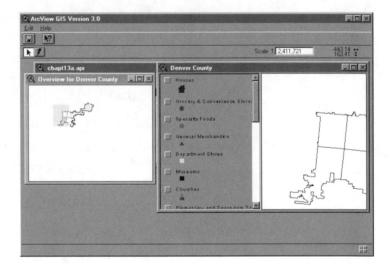

Simplifying Queries

The process of creating spatial and aspatial queries is too complex for the novice user of your real estate application. You will create an Avenue script to request input from the user and automatically select the homes that meet user requirements. Query simplification is an example of customizations that can be used to deploy specific end user applications.

1. Open a new script and change the script name to *House.Query.*

2. Access the Script menu and choose the Load Text File option. Load the script *$AVEXDS\avexer\scripts\houseqry.ave.* Compile the script.

✓ **TIP:** *Loading a script from a text file and saving a script as a text file is a good way to transport scripts and to create a library of reusable scripts. Saving scripts as standard ASCII text files also allows you to edit them outside ArcView.*

3. This script performs a single spatial query to select houses that are not near a railroad. It then performs aspatial queries to select homes with a minimum number of bedrooms and within a specific price range. See the comment lines to understand what each section of the script does. Take a look at the Avenue code to see how the user is prompted for information and how the input is translated into queries.

4. Double-click on the tool bar away from any controls to open the Customize dialog box. Change the Type drop-down list box to *View.*

5. Change the Category to Button, and select the Query Builder button. Add a new button for the script by clicking on the New button. Install the script into the Click field and change the Help field to *House Query//Performs a custom query on houses.* Change the Icon field to the hut icon. Close the Customize dialog box.

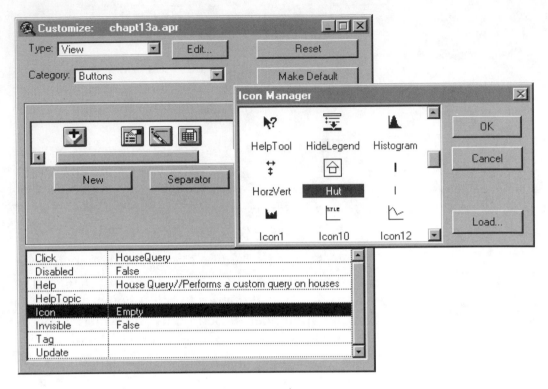

Hut icon used for the Custom Query tool.

6. Change to the *Denver* view and make sure at least the *Houses, Major Roads,* and *Railroads* themes are on.

7. Test the script by clicking on the new hut button. The first dialog box asks for a minimum distance from a railroad track: input *0.5.* If you click on the Cancel button, the script will select all houses regardless of distance from a railroad. Next, fill in the form for maximum price, minimum price, square footage, minimum number of bedrooms, and minimum number of bathrooms. All input lines must be filled in before the OK button will activate. If you hit Cancel on the form, you will not perform any attribute-based queries.

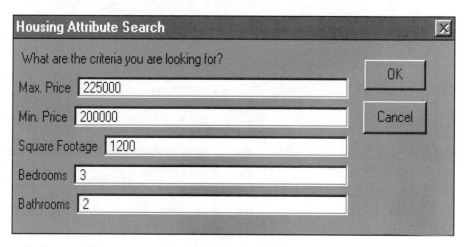

Multi-input box requesting housing details.

You could further enhance the script by adding spatial queries to select homes relative to any point or line themes in the view. You could also query the user to input one or more neighborhoods.

Lock the Themes

The easiest way to secure thematic data in a view is to lock individual theme properties. Locking prevents unauthorized users from making changes to properties.

For a discussion of locking themes, see Chapter 13, "Theme and Project locking," page 346.

1. To lock the theme properties, select all themes in the *Denver County* view. Access the Theme Properties dialog box and click on the locking icon for each theme.

2. The dialog box changes to display a check box titled Locked and a Set Password button. To lock the theme, click on the check box and on OK. If

the theme does not have a password, the Password dialog box will appear to request a password. Be careful: you will type in the password only once, and you will need it to reopen the theme properties. For this exercise, use the password *test.*

3. To remove the password from a protected theme, access the Theme Properties dialog box and uncheck the Locked check box. The theme password is retained until you change it with the Set Password button.

✓ **TIP:** *The theme password is stored in the project file. The password is not encrypted. If you forget the theme password, you can open the project file in a text editor and search for the keyword* Password.

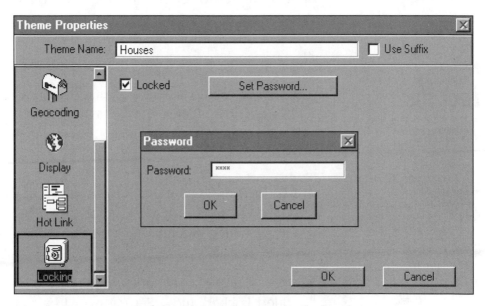

Locking category of the Theme Properties dialog box.

Another simple way of locking theme properties is to remove the theme properties functionality from the user interface. Later in this exercise, you will remove the functionality to open the Theme Properties dialog box. If you remove access to theme properties, locking themes is unnecessary.

Locking all themes in the project file will prevent accidental or unauthorized changes. However, locking a theme will not prevent a user from altering the legend, deleting the theme, or reordering themes in the Table of Contents.

Lock Legend Access

In the previous step, you manually locked theme properties. To further prevent changes, you need to lock theme legends. To prevent users from changing the theme legend, you need to alter the default script that is run. The *SetLegendEditorScript* property usually points to a script run when a user double-clicks on the theme, clicks the *Edit Legend Button* or accesses the Theme | Edit Legend menu.

1. Open a new script and change its name to *NoLegend*. Type the single line *exit* in the script editor. Compile the script.

2. Open a new script and name it *AlterThemeProperties*. Input the following lines to change the legend script to your script. This script also shows the Avenue method of theme locking, yet another way to lock theme properties.

```
' Set theView to the current document.
theView = av.GetActiveDoc
' Loop through all of the themes and prevent
' the user from altering theme properties and
' opening the legend editor.
for each t in theView.GetThemes
    t.SetPassword("test")
    t.SetLocked(true)
    t.SetLegendEditorScript("NoLegend")
end
```

3. Compile the *AlterThemeProperties* script. Click on the *Denver County* view to activate it and then reactivate the script and run it. This action tells ArcView you want the active document to be the view, but to run the script from the script editor. This is one way to test and debug your Avenue code.

4. Test the script by attempting to open a theme legend.

✎ **NOTE:** *If you set the* SetLegendEditorScript *property to nil (" ") and attempt to access the theme legend, ArcView will present you with an error message when you attempt to access the legend. Creating a simple script that does nothing is preferable.*

Prevent Reordering the Table of Contents

To prevent users from altering the theme order, you will issue the *SetOrderLocked* request to the view Table of Contents.

1. Open a new script and name it *LockViewTOC.* Input the following lines to lock the view's Table of Contents.

```
' Set the view to the current document.
theView = av.GetActiveDoc
' Get the Table of Contents for the view.
aTOC = theView.GetTOC
' Lock the theme order on the Table of Contents.
aTOC.SetOrderLocked(true)
```

2. Compile the script. To run the script on the view, click on the *Denver County* view to activate it, and then reactivate the script and run it.

3. Test the results. Select a theme and attempt to reorder it.

To allow the Table of Contents to be reordered, simply change the word "true" to "false," and recompile and rerun the script.

Alter Application Start-up

The initialization process is a good place to customize ArcView. From the initialization process, you can perform numerous tasks, such as opening a customized start-up bitmap image or changing the application window title. You can also open other applications; create data before a project opens; or ensure that specific hardware, such as a global positioning system (GPS) receiver, is set up and running.

The ArcView start-up process can be controlled with a number of scripts that provide you with several opportunities to customize an application. Some of the scripts affect how ArcView starts, and others affect what happens when a user starts ArcView or opens a specific project.

First, ArcView executes the start-up script. This script, called *startup,* resides in the ArcView installation's *etc* directory. By default, this script sets the *$HOME* environment variable if it is not already set, displays the ArcView banner, and, in Windows, starts the DDEserver. This script can be altered to set environment variables and other setup conditions outside ArcView. You can also use the *startup* script to change the default image displayed when ArcView starts.

Next, the system default project is loaded. This project resides in the ArcView installation's *etc* directory and is named *default.apr.* This project stores all standard ArcView user interfaces and scripts. Making changes here affects the interfaces for all new ArcView projects.

Third, the user default project is read if it exists. Residing in *$HOME* and called *default.apr,* this project can contain scripts and changes to user interfaces that differ from the system default project. On networked systems, this is probably the first place you will have sufficient privileges to make changes. Because the project is tied to *$HOME,* you can control which user *default.apr* is employed for specific users or applications. You can create a user *default.apr* by opening the Customize dialog box and clicking the Make Default button. This will create a *default.apr* in

$HOME containing all user interface changes and scripts in the current project. To reset to the original system settings, use the Reset button.

Fourth, ArcView executes the *appl.initialize* script. This script resides in either the system or user *default.apr*. The user *default.apr* takes precedence. The command line is passed to this script, and by default it opens the named project or creates a new one. If you need to customize the command line, this is the place to perform that task.

The final script ArcView checks and runs is the project start-up script, set as a project property. This script is executed at project start-up just before control is passed to the user. In this exercise, you are going to create a start-up script and reference it in the project start-up property.

INSIDE
ArcView
G I S

For a discussion of startup and shutdown scripts, see Chapter 14, "Start-up and Shutdown Scripts," page 366.

1. Open a new script and change its name to *Project.Start*.

2. Input the following two lines. The first line changes the application name from ArcView to Real Estate Sample Application. The second line opens a custom banner for your application. The forward slash for path names is a platform-independent designator. ArcView automatically converts the forward slash to the proper designator.

```
av.SetName("Real Estate Sample Application")
MsgBox.Banner("$AVEXDATA/avdata/misc/banner.bmp".AsFileName, 2, "" )
```

3. Compile the script and click on the Run button to make sure it works. Access the Project Properties dialog box and add the *Project.Start* script to the Startup option.

4. Save the project and reopen it to see the results.

✓ **TIP:** *The start-up and shutdown scripts are good places to control opening and closing procedures in your project. The start-up script could be used to create or update tables that might change outside the project. The shutdown script might be used to delete temporary files or close other applications.*

User Interfaces

You can use ArcView and Avenue to modify the default graphical user interface (GUI) for each document type. As you recall, a GUI consists of the menu, buttons, and tools for the document. If you make a change to the view document interface, all view documents incorporate the same change. Through Avenue, you can make a copy of a document's GUI, make changes to it, and assign the new GUI to any other document. In addition, you can make changes, install new interfaces on the fly, or change functionality with extensions.

The *Overview for Denver County* and *Denver County* view documents illustrate two different user interfaces. The Overview interface is added on the fly from the Overview extension. Adding or removing controls on the *Denver County* view will not affect the *Overview of Denver County* view document because the controls are parts of different GUIs. This is a very effective way to dictate how a user works with each document.

For a discussion of GUIs, see Chapter 14, "Customizing the User Interface," page 349.

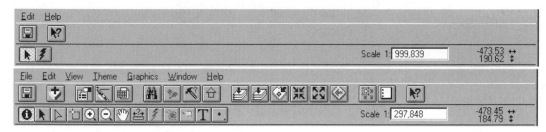

Overview and View GUIs.

Remove Unnecessary Controls

End users of the real estate application need to perform very specific tasks. Thus, they do not require all ArcView functionality. You also do not want end users to be able to make changes to the project. To simplify the user interface for the application, you need to remove unnecessary user controls. The controls you do not need fall into three categories: unused, dangerous, and too complex for the anticipated users. You will use the Customize dialog box to make changes to the user interfaces.

The Customize dialog box allows you to change the user interface for specific classes of user interfaces. For example, you can add or remove controls to the Table GUI or the View GUI. The Type drop down list box shows the GUI types available for editing. The Category drop-down list box shows the four types of controls you can customize. The editor control property sheet and the editor control panel change according to which control category is active. The control properties are listed below the editor control panel. The control properties manage such things as the name of the control, whether or not it should be enabled, and what script to execute when it is used.

For the real estate application, you are primarily interested in removing unnecessary controls. However, controls can also be added or modified.

1. Before you start removing controls, you should save a backup of the project file. Save the current version of the project. To save a backup version of the project, access the project window and select Save As from the File menu. Give the project a new name and save it to the *$AVEXDS\avexer\ project* directory. This new version is now the current project.

2. You will begin by removing controls for the *View* view document GUI. For this application, you need only a select set of controls. Access the Customize dialog box and change the Type dropdown list box to *View*.

3. From the Menus category, delete all items from the File menu except the Print, Print Setup, and Exit options by highlighting them and clicking on the Delete button. You do not need any of the functions in the Edit or Graphics menus. Highlight the menu names and click on the Delete button to remove the entire menus rather than the menu options.

4. Review all remaining menu picks under the View, Theme, Window, and Help menus. Delete anything that might edit data, create new data, or perform actions not suitable for this application.

5. Continue removing functionality from the button and tool bars. Delete any tools or buttons that might edit or alter data or the way it is displayed.

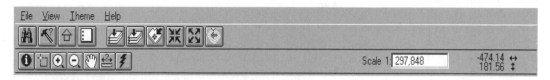

View GUI after removing unnecessary controls.

The Overview GUI is installed from its extension. Making changes to the Overview GUI from within this project will not affect the GUI permanently. In fact, the next time the project is loaded, the original GUI would be installed when the extension is loaded. To change the Overview GUI, you would need to open the project that created the extension, make the changes, and rebuild the extension. The exact procedure is covered in the optional exercise at the end of this chapter.

In the deployed real estate application, you would remove the unnecessary controls on the table, chart, and layout documents as well. You will not remove all controls for all documents in this exercise. In addition to the document interfaces, you will need to alter the interface for the project window. In subsequent sections of this exercise, you will alter and remove controls for the project window.

Remove Unnecessary Documents

Create a backup of the project. Remove the *Alter-ThemeProperties* and *LockViewTOC* scripts, and the *Housing Cost* chart.

Prevent New Documents from Opening

There are several ways to create new documents in a project. The obvious way is to access the project window and click on the New or the Add button. However, you can open a new table by accessing the attributes for a theme, and you can import all documents from another project by using the Import option from the Project menu.

To prevent a user from opening or adding a new document from the project window, you will alter the first and third buttons on the project window for the view and layout document. Depending on the document, different scripts may be run. The actual script run is a property of the document. These properties can be edited from the *Customize Types* dialog box, which is accessed using the *Edit* button on the *Customize* dialog box. Other properties can be adjusted from the Customize Types dialog box, including whether or not the document is listed in the project window.

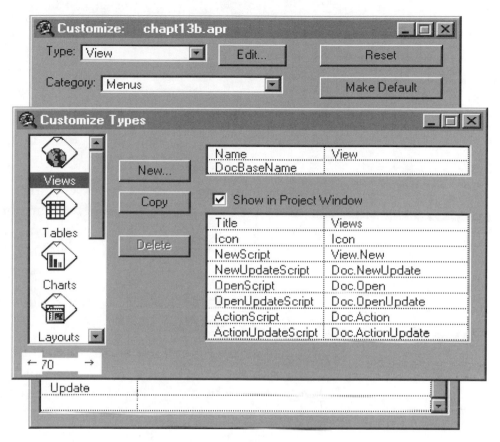

Customize Types dialog box.

◆ NOTE: *Double-clicking on a document listed in the project window runs the script associated with the New or leftmost button.*

If you create a new version of a system script with the same name, you can take advantage of the script execution search order to ensure that your scripts are run instead of the default scripts. ArcView seeks scripts by searching embedded scripts, script documents, user default project scripts, and system default scripts. The first script found with the correct name is run.

1. Begin by backing up the project as in previous steps.

2. From the project window create five new script documents. These scripts will be used in later steps.

3. To prevent a user from adding or creating new view or layout documents, you need to create three scripts. Open three more script documents and change their names to *View.New*, *Layout.New*, and *Doc.Action*.

4. For the three scripts, type in the single statement *exit* and compile them.

5. Test the scripts by clicking on the first and third buttons in the project window for the view and layout document types. Note that no new documents are opened or any actions performed.

6. Open the Customize Dialog box and click on the Edit button. This opens the Customize Types dialog, where the document properties can be altered. Take a moment to look at the properties for each of the icons. You might think you could simply change the properties for the default document types and everything would work. However, ArcView does not save the default document properties to the project file but does save any changes to document types you create.

↝ **NOTE:** *You can delete or rename the standard document types, but the next time you load Arc-View, they will appear in the project because Arc-View resets the types at start-up.*

7. For this project, you do not need tables or charts. To remove them from the project window, you must delete them from the project window after ArcView starts. You will do this by adding several lines to the *Project.Start* script. Open the *Project.Start* script and add the following two lines.

```
av.FindGUI("Table").SetVisible(false)
av.FindGUI("Chart").SetVisible(false)
```

8. Compile the *Project.Start* script and click on the Run button. The table and chart documents should be hidden in the project window.

*Project window
with the table and
chart document
types hidden.*

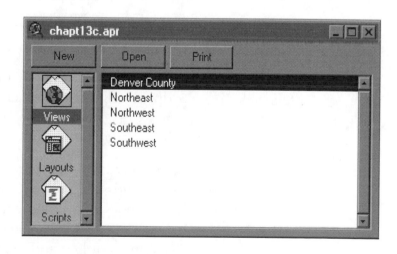

Prevent Users from Saving Changes

Because the real estate application will be used by several people, you should prevent them from saving changes to the original project.

Remove the Save Changes Dialog Box

Removing save options from all menus and buttons for all documents in your application is the first step toward making the application *read only*. However, ArcView will still prompt users to save any changes before exiting the program with the Save Changes dialog box.

To remove the Save Changes dialog box, you will alter two system scripts, *Project.Exit* and *Project.Close*. Two other scripts, *Project.New* and *Project.Close*, also check to determine whether the project should be saved. These scripts will not be edited, but rather removed from the project entirely.

1. Open the *Script1* document.

2. Access the Script menu and select Load System Script. Scroll down and select the *Project.Exit* system script. This is the script run when ArcView exits. Change the script's name to *Project.Exit*.

3. Select all lines between "if (nil <> theProject) then" and "theProject.Close." Access the Edit menu and select Comment. This will place a single quote at the beginning of each line, denoting it as a comment line and thus nonexecutable. Compile the script.

```
Project.Exit                                        _ □ ×
theProject = av.GetProject

if (nil <> theProject) then
'   if (theProject.IsModified) then
'     if (av.Run("Project.CheckForEdits",nil).Not) then
'       return nil
'     end
'     res = MsgBox.SaveChanges("Do you want to save changes to "
'                          + theProject.GetName + "?", "ArcView
'     if (nil = res) then return nil end
'     if (res) then
'       av.Run("Project.Save", nil)
'       if (theProject.IsModified) then return nil end
'     end
'   end
theProject.Close
end

av.Quit
```

Project.Exit with the save prompt commented out.

4. Open the *Script2* document and repeat the previous process for the *Project.Close* script. Add comment quotes to the lines between "if (nil <> theProject) then" and "theProject.Close." Compile the script.

```
theProject = av.GetProject

if (nil <> theProject) then
'   if (theProject.IsModified) then
'     if (av.Run("Project.CheckForEdits",nil).Not) then
'       return nil
'     end
'     res = MsgBox.SaveChanges("Do you want to save chan
'     if (nil = res) then return nil end
'     if (res) then
'       av.Run("Project.Save", nil)
'       if (theProject.IsModified) then return nil end
'     end
'   end
    theProject.Close
    theProject = nil
end
```

Project.Close with the save prompt commented out.

5. Switch to the project window and save the project. Once the project is saved, you can test the scripts. Open the *Northeast* view document and make a simple change in the project. Exit ArcView without saving. If the *Project.Exit* script is correct, ArcView will quit without prompting you to save the changes.

6. Restart ArcView with the latest project. Remember, this is the latest version, not the original version.

7. You should also test the *Project.Close* script. Open the *Northeast* view document to make a change to the project. Access the project window and select Project Close from the File menu. If the script is correct, ArcView will close the project without prompting you to save.

8. Reopen the latest project.

Remove the Save Buttons and Menu Picks

You are now ready to remove all controls that save changes to the project. The task of removing the save buttons and menu picks sounds easy. However, if you remove all controls that save, how do you save the project in its final form? Fortunately, you can create a script that will delete itself, and save the project. You need to create this script now, while the functionality still exists in the project. You will run this script after you complete *all* modifications.

1. Back up the project file in the same way as executed previously.

2. Open *Script3* and name it *LockUp*. Input the following lines to delete this script, save the project, and move the project window to a place where it cannot be found.

```
av.GetProject.GetWin.Move(-1000, 1000)  'Move the project window off the display
theDoc = av.GetProject.FindDoc("LockUp")  'Get this script
av.GetProject.RemoveDoc(theDoc)          'Remove this script
av.GetProject.Save     'Save the project, making it read only
```

3. Compile the script but do not run it.

4. Finally, to remove the remaining save functionality, open the Customize dialog box, visit each type of document GUI except the project GUI, and delete the save buttons and save menu picks.

Prevent Further Customizing

You have prevented users from opening new documents and removed the controls that allow them to save changes to the project. You still need to prevent the ability to open the Customize dialog box by double-clicking on the tool or button bars. You will do this by adding a line to the project start-up script that will disable customization capabilities.

1. Before you start, save a backup of the project file. Save the current version of the project before using the Save As option from the project window. Save the new version to the *$AVEXDS\ avexer\project* directory. This new version is now the current project. This is the last version you will be able to return to if you need to alter other scripts—a result of removing the ability to customize the interface.

2. Open the *Project.Start* script created earlier. This script is used to set the application name and open a custom banner.

3. Add the following line to the script:

```
av.SetCustomizable(FALSE)
```

4. Compile the script but do not run it. This will prevent a user from double-clicking on the GUI and accessing the Customize dialog box.

↦ **NOTE:** *If Customizable is set to false, you cannot invoke the Customize dialog box or open a new Script Document. If customization is off when the project opens and before the* Project.Open *script executes, the Script Editor icon does not appear in the project window.*

Embed and Encrypt Scripts

You now have several scripts in the project. To prevent users from seeing or modifying the scripts, you can embed them into the project file or encrypt them to protect your programming investment. Embedding scripts offers several advantages over keeping them in the script editor document. For instance, you reduce the number of documents in your project by eliminating a script editor document for every script in your project. More importantly, embedded scripts are located more quickly than scripts in script editors. If you need to make a change to an embedded script, all you have to do is create a new script with the same name, load the system script, make your changes, compile, and embed. The previous version will be overwritten.

When you encrypt a script, it is automatically embedded into your project. You can also encrypt scripts already embedded. Once a script is encrypted, it cannot be unencrypted, nor can it be viewed. You can encrypt scripts individually or you can encrypt all scripts in a project at once. If you intend to encrypt scripts, make a backup copy of your project in case you need to make changes or want to reuse your scripts in other projects.

☛ *WARNING: Use caution when encrypting scripts. Once the script is encrypted, it cannot be unencrypted. Make a copy of your project file before performing encryption and embedding so that you can undo your actions if necessary.*

The *Encrypt Project* script encrypts all scripts in the project, whether or not they are embedded. This script appears to encrypt the project file, but in fact it only encrypts scripts. There is no way to encrypt the project file. To encrypt a single embedded script, you will need to write a short Avenue program. The following code will encrypt and embed the script named *House.Query*, the script you loaded to perform the advanced queries on the houses theme.

INSIDE
ArcView
GIS

For a discussion of encrypting and embedding, see Chapter 14, "The Finished Application," page 368.

```
' EncryptEmbedded
' This script will encrypt an embedded script.
EncryptThis = "House.Query"
aScript = av.GetProject.FindScript(EncryptThis)
if (aScript = nil ) then
  msgbox.warning("Cannot find Script " ++ EncryptThis,"")
else
   aScript = EncryptedScript.MakeFromScript(aScript)
   aScript.SetName(EncryptThis)
   av.GetProject.AddScript( aScript )
end
```

1. Embedding a script is easy. Make the script document active and select the Embed Script option from the Script menu. Make the *House.Query* script the active document. Click on the Embed Script option from the Script menu.

2. To examine the results, look for the script in the project window. To verify that it is still usable, open the *Script4* document. Access the Load System Script menu option from the Script menu. Scroll down to *House.Query* and click on it to load the embedded script.

3. You will use the *EncryptEmbedded* script to make the embedded script unreadable. Open the *Script5* document and input the *EncryptEmbedded* script found above.

4. When you have input the script, compile and test it by clicking on the Run button.

5. Open *Script4*, scroll to the bottom, and try to load the *House.Query* script. Because this script is encrypted, ArcView reports in the Script Editor that "This script is encrypted."

6. Delete the *Script4* and *Script5* documents.

7. Open and Embed all remaining scripts, except the *LockUp* script.

Save the Locked Project File

You are ready to save the final project.

1. Before you start, save a backup of the project file. Save the current version of the project before using Save As from the project window. Save the new version to the *$AVEXDS\avexer\project* directory. This new version is now the current project.

2. Open the Customize dialog box and access the project GUI. Remove all controls in the File menu except Exit. Remove the Project menu, the Window menu, and all controls in the Help menu except *About ArcView GIS*. Remove all buttons. Close the Customize dialog box.

3. Verify that the project window, *LockUp* script, and both views are open.

4. Arrange the *Overview for Denver County* and *Denver County* views and place the project window behind the *Denver County* view so that you can set the initial displays.

5. Zoom out on the *Denver County* view to see most of the county.

6. Make the *LockUp* script active. Click on the Compile button and run the script. This action will delete the *LockUp* script, move the project window from the view, and save the project using the latest name.

7. Close ArcView and test the final project.

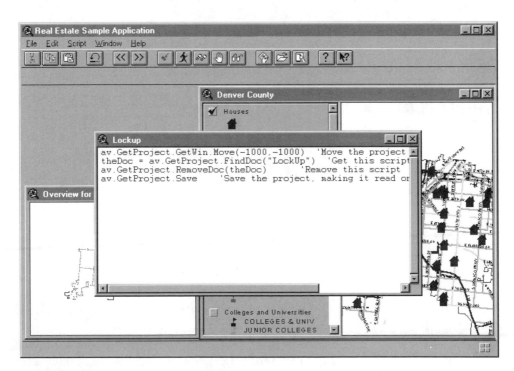

Real estate application ready to be locked.

Deploying the Application

Through the *Appl.Initialize* system script, ArcView can process the command line passed to it. Depending on your system, you can create an icon or script that starts ArcView and passes the project name at the end of the command line.

Optional

To further enhance and complete the application, perform the following on an early version of the project. The final version will not allow you to make the necessary changes.

1. Create a new chart and layout for the application. The goal is to prepare a dynamic chart that shows the prices for the selected homes. The goal for the layout is a simple layout that will be available as a one-button map of the view.

2. Remove unnecessary controls from the table, chart, and layout documents.

3. Alter the Overview GUI found in the Overview extension. Open the overview project located in *$HOME*. Access the script menu and inspect some of the scripts. The *Install* script is used to install the extension when you add it to a project. This script controls what and how ArcView is changed through the use of the extension. *Uninstall* removes the extension and any changes it made to ArcView.

4. Open the Customize dialog box. Change the Type drop-down list to *Overview*. Delete the edit menu and everything under help except the About ArcView GIS option. Delete all of the buttons.

5. Open the *Make.Extension* script. This script converts the project file to a deployable extension. Click on Run to create the new extension, *overview.avx*.

6. Open the final version of the Real Estate application to see the changes to the overview extension.

Summary

In this chapter you transformed the project from Chapter 12 into a deployable application. The end user application was tailored to simplify queries and to view available houses. You used advanced techniques to lock themes, remove user controls, create a custom start-up script, make the project read only, and embed and encrypt the scripts.

Discussion Topics

❏ What else might you change for the ultimate real estate application?

❏ Consider additional customization objectives that could be executed by modifying the shutdown script.

❏ When would you choose to alter the *system default.apr*? What sacrifices would you make by altering this file?

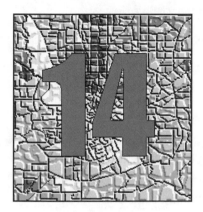

Network Analyst Extension

For a discussion of Network Analyst, see Chapter 12, "Network Analyst," page 328.

In this chapter you will explore the functionality provided by the Network Analyst extension. This extension is an optional module that may be purchased separately from ArcView. Network Analyst provides new tools and Avenue requests to solve routing, service area, and closest facility problems. Network Analyst only runs on Windows 95, Windows NT, and UNIX operating systems.

Topics and Functions

❏ Solve network problems

❏ Find optimum routing for deliveries

❏ Find the closest facility

❏ Determine service areas

Description

This exercise uses the advanced Network Analyst extension. You will focus on the three types of network problems it solves and explore the various options that can affect the manner in which the problem is solved. The steps and topics for the exercise follow.

❏ Open project and review data

❏ Install the Network Analyst extension

❏ Set up the network data

❏ Find the best route

❏ Create directions for the driver

❏ Find the closest facility

❏ Compute service areas

Open Project and Review Data

Open the *$AVEXDS\avexer\project\chapt14.apr* project. The view in the project contains data for Dallas, Texas. Themes in the view represent streets, the distribution center, customers, shopping centers, warehouses, and landmarks such as hospitals and schools.

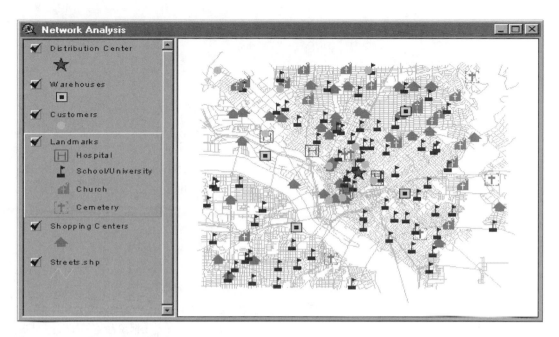

Base data for the distribution center.

Install the Network Analyst Extension

When the Network Analyst extension was installed, Arc View placed it so that you can access it from the extensions dialog box located in the project menu. Load the Network Analyst extension. Change back to the view document and note the GUI modifications. The view now has a new menu, two new buttons, and one new tool, described below.

The menu accesses the dialog boxes, which perform the analysis based on user criteria. The button depicting a push-pin and a flag is a special address locator. The located address is added as a point that then becomes part of the analysis. The second button solves for the current problem definition. A problem definition states what should happen in the analysis.

The tool button is used to interactively add a location to the network.

What Is a Network?

A network is a connected set of lines. Typically the lines represent streets, but the lines could represent any linear feature. The line theme can be an ARC/INFO coverage, a CAD drawing, or an ArcView shapefile. Special fields in the theme can affect how ArcView determines the paths through the network. The fields may include drive time (based on speed limit and length) or one-way streets. In addition, you can create a table that ArcView will use to calculate the costs associated with making turns, or to allow and disallow turns. ArcView can also use a turntable associated with a coverage.

The street data used in the exercise do not include speed limits or one-way streets. Assume that there are no one-way streets and that the speed limits are accurate. You can purchase data sets with a higher level of accuracy, and which contain attributes for direction and speed.

Set Up Network Data

For this exercise, you will create a new field in the streets theme that reflects the time it takes to traverse the line segment. Because you have the length and speed limit, the task is easy.

1. Open the attribute table for the streets theme. Make the table editable.

7. Add a new number field called *Minutes*, with a width of 5 and with 2 decimal places.

8. Convert the speed limit to drive time in minutes. Click on the minutes column and open the field calculator. Input the following expression without hard returns.

```
NetUnits.VelocityToTime([Shape].ReturnLength, #NETUNITS_LINEAR_DEGREES,
[Speedlmt],#NETUNITS_ LINEAR_MILES,#NETUNITS_TIME_HOURS)/ 60
```

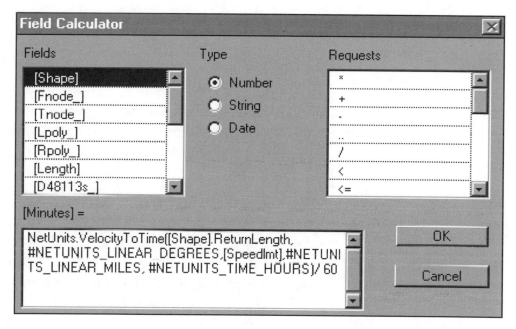

Calculation to create travel times based on speed limit and length fields.

9. Save the changes and stop editing the table.

Network Analyst requires additional changes to the data to better label attributes. The point data used in the analysis require the *Label* field to make site names meaningful. Otherwise, ArcView defaults to using labels such as Stop #1.

5. Alias the *Store_Name* field to *Label* for the *Distribution Center* theme.

6. Similarly, alias the Customers attribute table *Bus_Name* to *Label*. For the *Warehouses* theme, alias the *Warehse* field to *Label*.

Find the Best Route

In this exercise, a delivery truck delivers products to customer sites. You will explore several ways to find the best route. Let's begin with the default, and then optimize it for both time and distance.

1. Make *Streets* the active theme. Access the Network menu and select the Find Best Route option to open the Find Best Route dialog box.

2. The list with the headings *Label* and *miles* is the list of stops. The first stop in the list is the starting point. If the return-to-origin check box is set, the route will return to the first stop. The label field will list the stops in order (in the form "Stop #1") unless the stops are loaded from a table and there is a field named *Label*, which would then be used. The other field represents the linear measure used. This may be a distance or time value.

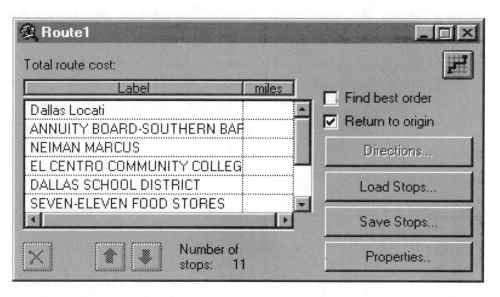

Find Best Route dialog box.

3. Click on the Load Stops button and select the *Distribution Center* theme. This will serve as the starting point.

4. Load the customers as the rest of the stops. Click on the return-to-origin check box.

5. Click on the Solve button located in the upper right corner of the dialog box. Review the new theme, which represents the resulting route. The route follows the order set in the stops list.

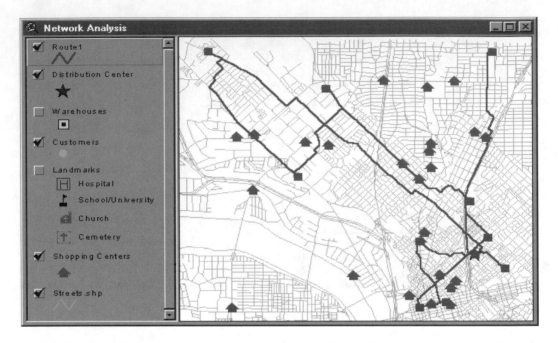

Under the default route, customers are visited in the order they appear on the stop list.

6. To find a better path visiting all of the customers, make the route theme active. Access the Network menu and select the Show Problem Definition option to redisplay the Find Best Route dialog box. Click on the Find Best Order check box and re-solve. This action will find the best order based on the number of miles traveled, and change the data in the route theme.

7. Rename the theme *Best Route by Mileage.*

8. Create a new route connecting the distribution center and customers that is optimized on time rather than distance. Open the Find Best Route dialog box, load the same stops, and click on the two check boxes.

9. Click on the Properties button and change the cost drop-down list to *Minutes.* Round the values to *d.d.*

10. Click on the Solve button and compare the results to the previous route.

11. Rename the theme *Best Route by Time.* Move both routes below the street theme.

Note the differences between the two routes. The route based on time selected streets with high speed limits, whereas the other selected the shortest path based on distance alone.

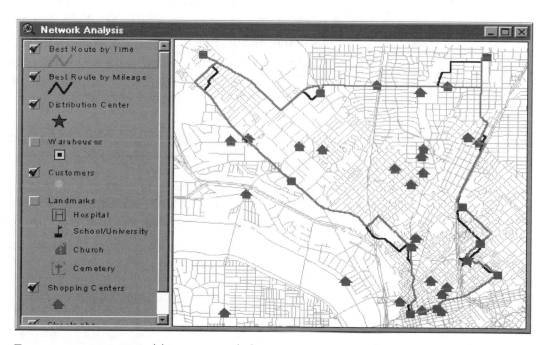

Two routes optimized by time and distance, respectively.

Create Directions for the Driver

Another task you can perform that will make deliveries more efficient is to print directions for drivers. Additional options allow you to reference landmarks, which are added to the directions.

1. Open the Find Best Route dialog box for the *Best Route by Time* theme. Click on the Directions button. The default directions are typically a little weak. You will alter the data presentation to better suit the driver.

2. Click on the Properties button to alter the directions. Because the theme is based on time, the directions are also relayed by time. The first drop-down list, the Directions cost field, displays *Minutes*. Change the field to *Line length* to calculate directions by distance. The way in which the directions are displayed will be alerted, not the route.

3. Change the Landmarks drop-down list to *Shopping Centers* and the Landmarks label field to *Ctr_Name*.

4. In the bottom right list, delete the *Name* field. Add the *Prefix*, *Name*, *Type*, and *Suffix* fields, in that order. The four fields are required to fully articulate the street address.

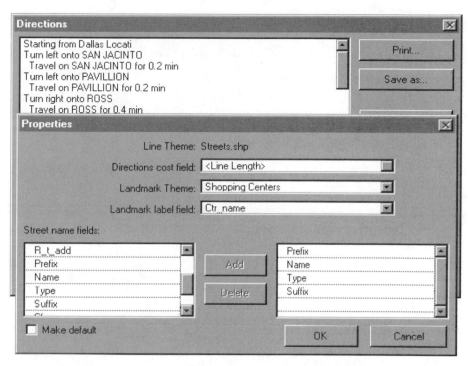

Directions properties dialog box.

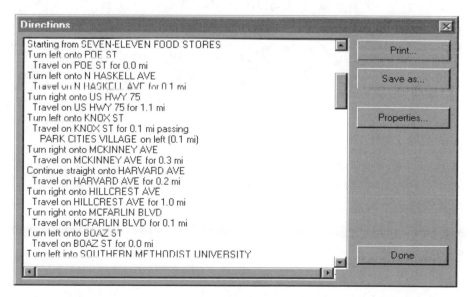

Complete directions to visit all customers optimized by time.

Find the Closest Facility

Finding the closest facility is a variation of the previous exercise, except that each facility is evaluated to determine which point is the closest based on the criteria set. In some cases, a given point might be the closest in time but not distance. In this exercise, you will choose the two warehouses closest to the distribution center. You will optimize for time and distance.

1. Verify that the street, distribution center, and warehouse themes are displayed. Make the *Streets* theme the active theme.

2. To open the Find Closest Facility dialog box, select Network | Find Closest Facility.

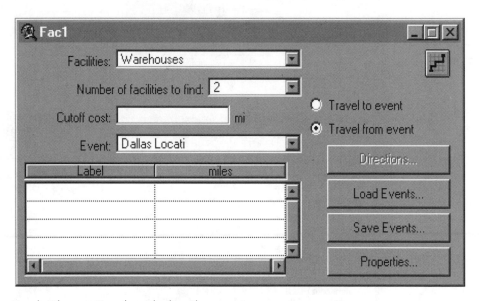

Find Closest Facility dialog box.

3. Select *Warehouses* from the facilities drop-down list box. This is the theme used to determine which facility is closest to the event. Change the number to be found to *2*.

4. Click on the Load Events button and select the *Distribution Centers* theme.

5. Click on the Travel from event radio button to set the direction of travel from the event to the facilities. In the current example, this is the appropriate action. In contrast, the Travel to event option could be useful in identifying the fire truck closest to a fire.

6. Click on the Solve button (upper right corner) and dismiss the dialog box. Rename the theme *Closest facilities by distance.*

7. To run the analysis solving for time, click on the Properties button in the Find Closest Facility dialog box. Change the Directions cost field to *Minutes.*

8. Rename the resulting theme *Closest facilities by time.*

9. Move the two themes below the streets theme.

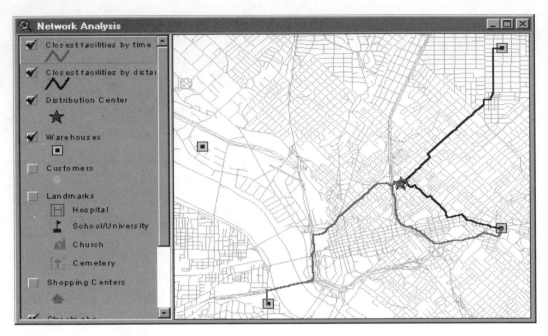

Resulting themes depicting the closest facilities based on time and distance.

The routing results were different because varying speed limits affected total driving time. Consequently, different warehouses were selected.

Compute Service Areas

A service area shows accessibility from or to a site. Service areas can be calculated according to distance or driving time from a site. For example, a pizza shop owner may not want delivery drivers to travel beyond a certain distance from the store. Driving time for potential customers/clients is important to most retail business and service providers. Directionality of streets and other barriers might greatly affect traveling from or to the site. Never assume that the to and from routes are equal.

For this service area calculation, you will compute the area within one, two, and three miles of a distribution center. You will then compute another area within one, two, and four minutes.

1. Turn on the *Streets, Distribution Center, Customers*, and *Shopping Centers* themes. Make the *Streets* theme active.

2. Access the Network menu and click on the Find Service Area option to open the Find Service Area dialog box.

3. Click on the Load Sites button and choose the theme *Distribution Center.* Double-click on the miles field, input *1, 2, 3*, and hit <Enter>. Hit <Esc> to finish editing the values. Verify that the Travel from site radio button is selected and that the Compact Area check box is not checked.

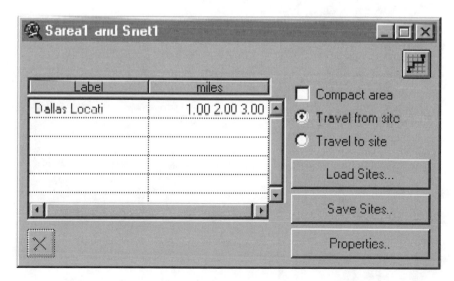

Find Service Area dialog box.

4. Click on the Solve button (upper right corner) to execute the computations for the two new themes. A polygon and a line theme are created representing distance in miles from the site. Close the dialog box.

5. Name the themes *Service Area, Miles.* Move the new themes just below the *Streets* theme, with the line theme above the polygon theme. Turn both themes on. As you can see, the polygon theme is very smooth. This is because ArcView creates a general service area by default.

✓ **TIP:** *If you do not need the* snet *or* sarea *theme, you can delete them before solving to increase performance. By default, ArcView solves for both.*

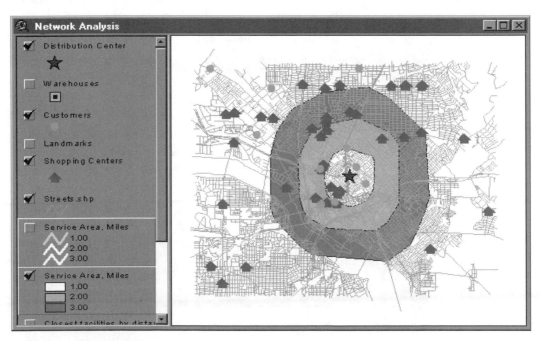

Service areas within one, two, and three miles of the distribution center.

6. Now that the service area has been calculated by distance, a service area will be created by travel time. You will also compact the service area to more accurately depict the territory. Create a new service area from the *Streets* theme. In the dialog box, load the distribution center as the site. Verify that the Travel from site radio button is selected and the Compact Area box is checked.

7. Click on the Properties button. Change the Directions cost field to *Minutes* and click on the OK button.

8. Change the minutes column to *1, 2, 4*. Click on the Solve button to create the new service area.

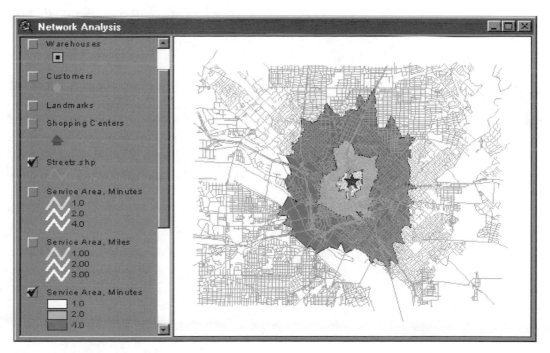

Service area based on travel time. The theme perimeter is jagged because the service area was compacted.

9. Name the new themes *Service Area, Minutes.* Move the new themes just below the *Streets* theme, with the line theme above the polygon theme. Turn both themes on and turn the other service area themes off. The polygon theme is more jagged, and better represents the area by travel time from the site.

➤ **NOTE:** *Network Analyst cannot generate a compact area in certain situations. Examples are instances where the area of the line theme you are working with contains line features that cross over other line features, such as in the case of an overpass. In these instances, Network Analyst generates a message indicating that it cannot create a compact area and creates a general one instead.*

Optional

Practice with the Network Analyst functionality by executing the following steps.

1. Use the Add Location tool to interactively add more customer stops. Use the add location button to add more customers. Re-solve the delivery routes.

2. Use spatial selections or joins to determine the number of shopping centers within each of the service areas.

Summary

This exercise was an overview of the major functionality in the Network Analyst extension. Through the user interface, you can determine the best route to visit sites, find the closest facility, and create service areas. All of these computations can be solved based on specific criteria, such as distance or travel time. In addition, directions can be created, further aiding navigation to locations.

The base linear data can be created so that rules can affect network solutions. Rules are in the form of legal turns or directionality. Impedances can be added to the data such as in raising the cost of making turns or traveling on certain line segments.

Discussion Topics

❏ How could the Network Analyst extension be used to aid in police dispatching? What additional information would you need to make the analysis accurate?

❏ Based on what was covered in this chapter, could you plan a route by which you could tell each of 15 customers when a delivery truck would arrive? Why or why not?

Spatial Analyst

The main purpose of the exercise in this chapter is to explore the Spatial analyst extension to ArcView GIS. Spatial Analyst provides many tools to perform raster GIS functions such as display and analysis. Raster-based GIS is similar to that of vector-based GIS, yet there are important differences and additional capabilities. The San Francisco elevation data used in this exercise is a digital terrain model derived from USGS sources, and was provided by SPOT Image Corporation.

For a discussion of Spatial Analyst, see Chapter 12, "Spatial Analyst," page 331.

Topics and Functions

❏   Types of grids

❏   Managing grids

❏   Histograms

❏   Displaying grids

❏   Grid analysis

❏   Derive slope

❏   Find distance

❏   Assign proximity

❏   Interpolate surface

❏   Grid queries

Description

In this exercise you will use the Spatial Analyst extension to view and analyze raster data. You will explore the content and display of raster GIS data. A variety of analysis techniques will be employed to identify patterns in the data and derive new data. Finally, you will locate geographic areas in which specific conditions exist. This exercise provides a solid foundation of skills required to use Spatial Analyst. Additional functions exist, some of which are accessible only through the Avenue programming language. The steps for the exercise follow.

❏   Loading Spatial Analyst

❏   Grid theme basics

❏   Exploring grid data

❏   Displaying grid themes

❏   Spatial analysis

❏   Map query

Loading Spatial Analyst

If ArcView is not currently running, start the program and begin a new project. From the File menu, select Extensions and load the Spatial Analyst extension. The Spatial extension is a separate product from the base ArcView product. If you have not purchased the Spatial extension, it will not be available to load. Loading the Spatial Analyst extension will add menu options, tools, buttons, and Avenue requests.

ArcView ordinarily deals with vector data, including points, lines, and polygons. These data sets are best used when modeling distinct objects. In contrast, raster data sets model the real world by dividing the area of interest into squares and storing information about each square. The Spatial Analyst extension adds GIS raster functionality to ArcView.

The primary data sets for Spatial Analyst are ARC/INFO grid themes. Grids are raster data sets with individual squares, or *cells*, covering the geographic area. Each cell stores a value that can be used in display, selection, and analysis. The values of these cells can be either integers or floating point numbers (numbers with decimal points). If integers are used, an attribute table may exist and additional fields can be added to it, just like shapefiles. Normally, discrete values such as zip codes or land use types are represented with integers, and continuous values such as elevation or pollutant levels are represented with floating point numbers.

*Extensions
dialog box.*

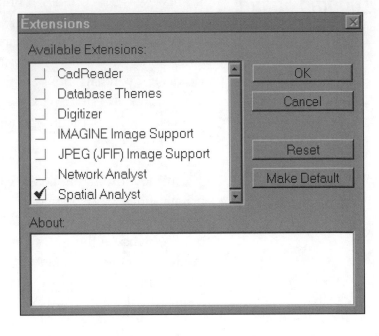

*How Projections
Affect Analysis*

Map projections can become a bit tricky when mixing grids and vector data in the same view. There are four cases to be considered, which are presented in the following table. See the ArcView help system for additional information.

Vector and grid data, both in projected coordinates	Do not use a projection in the view.
Vector and grid data, both in decimal degrees	Do not use a projection in the view.
Vector data are in decimal degrees and grid data are projected	Set the view projection to that of the grid data.
Vector data are in projected coordinates and grid data are in decimal degrees	The data must be altered to one of the above three cases.

Grid Theme Basics

Grids are a special type of data set that requires its own subdirectory and stores files in an INFO database. If you examine a directory containing grids, you will see these subdirectories and an INFO directory. Due to these complications, grids cannot be simply moved, copied, deleted, or renamed using the native file system. A Grid Manager is provided to help you manage these data sets.

Managing Grid Data Sets

Many permanent and temporary grids will be created when using Spatial Analyst. Unless you select Save Data Set from the Theme menu, or save the project, the temporary grids will be deleted automatically when the corresponding theme is deleted. They will also be deleted if you exit ArcView without saving the project.

1. Create a new view and name it *Elevation*. With the view active, access the File menu and select Manage Grids. This dialog box allows you to copy, rename, and delete grids. Practice using the Manager to copy the grid *$AVEXDATA\avdata\grids\elev* to a new grid named *newelev*. Then use the Grid Manager to delete the *newelev* grid. Close the Grid Manager.

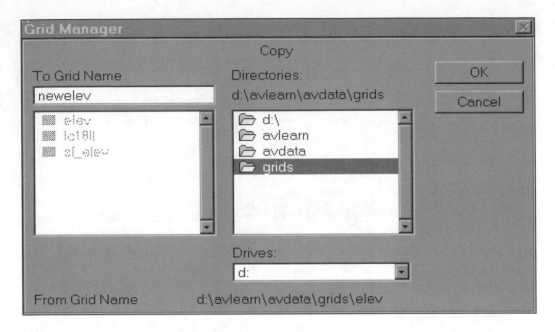

Grid Manager dialog box.

2. During spatial analysis, many temporary grids will be created. These will be written to the project's working directory. Set the project property for Working Directory to *$AVEXDS\avexer\tempgrid* so that you can easily keep track of the grids.

✓ **TIP:** *Many temporary grids will be created, and corresponding themes added to your view. Check the theme properties to determine the data sets that are being used by particular themes.*

You can also import and export grids to other formats using the File Menu's Import Grids and Export Grids options.

➥ **NOTE:** *Grid Manager, Import Grid, and Export Grid are only available when the current document is a view and the Spatial Analyst extension is loaded.*

Exploring Grid Data

1. Add a theme to the *Elevation* view. In the Add Theme dialog box, set the Data Source Type to Grid Data Source. Navigate to the *$AVEXDATA\avdata\grids* directory and select the *elev* grid.

2. Access the Legend Editor and select Graduated Color on *Value* using the red monochromatic color scheme with nine equal interval classes.

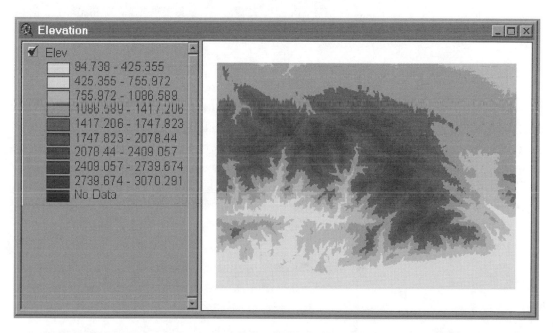

New Elev grid theme in the Elevation view.

✓ **TIP:** *Image themes can be transformed into grids with the Convert to Grid function in the Theme menu.*

3. Click on several cells of the *Elev* grid theme with the Identify tool to determine their values.

Results of Identify on the Elev grid theme from the Elevation view.

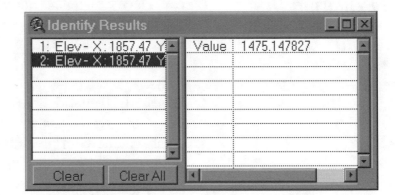

4. It is frequently desirable to get an overview of cell values in a given grid theme. *Histograms* allow you to view the distribution of cell values as a chart. With the *Elev* theme active, click the Histogram button. A chart will be created using the current classification and symbology settings of the theme's legend. Each bar on the chart depicts the quantity of cells in the class. The resulting chart will be added to the project as a chart document.

↦ **NOTE:** *As a general rule, functions that access grid attributes will access the values as they are specified in the Legend Editor.*

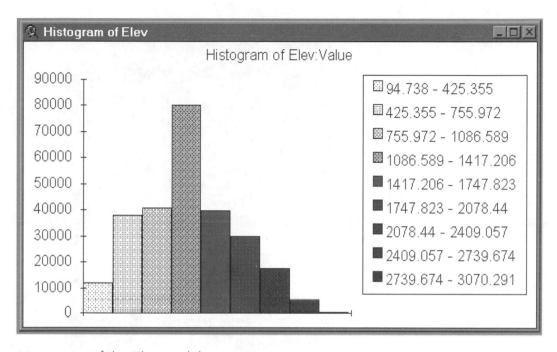

Histogram of Elev:Value

Histogram of Elev

Legend:
- 94.738 - 425.355
- 425.355 - 755.972
- 755.972 - 1086.589
- 1086.589 - 1417.206
- 1417.206 - 1747.823
- 1747.823 - 2078.44
- 2078.44 - 2409.057
- 2409.057 - 2739.674
- 2739.674 - 3070.291

Histogram of the Elev grid theme.

*Reclassify Values
(Dialog Box)*

5. The *Elev* theme of elevation data is of the *continous* floating point type and therefore has no accessible attribute table. If it is desirable to have access to an attribute table, floating point grids can be reclassified. With the *Elev* theme active, select Reclassify from the Analysis menu. Many available classification options are very similar to those of the Legend Editor. Accept the defaults and close the dialog box. A new theme called *Reclass of Elev* will be added to the view.

*Reclassify Values
dialog box.*

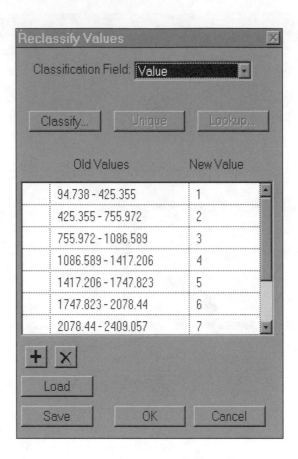

6. By default, ArcView has assigned a Unique Values classification to the legend of the new theme because the reclassification generated a discrete value *integer* grid theme. Change the Legend Editor for the new theme to mimic the settings of the *Elev* theme. Compare the displays of the two themes; they should be identical.

7. Access the table for the new theme. It contains two fields: *Value*—the reclassified value from the parent grid—and *Count*, the number of cells with each of the given values.

*Attributes of the
Reclass of Elev table.*

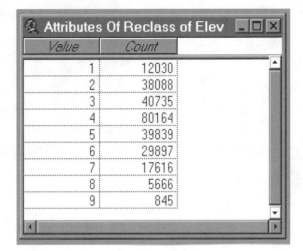

Value	Count
1	12030
2	38088
3	40735
4	80164
5	39839
6	29897
7	17616
8	5666
9	845

8. Verify that the *Reclass of Elev* theme is the only theme turned on. Use the Select tool to select the row from the *Attributes of Reclass of Elev* table where *Value* is equal to 6. All cells of the same value will be highlighted in the view.

9. Clear the selected set from the *Attributes of Reclass of Elev* table.

➻ **NOTE:** *Because there is no one-to-one relationship between cells and records in the attribute table, you cannot, as you can with vector data, select grid cells directly in the view with the Select Feature tool.*

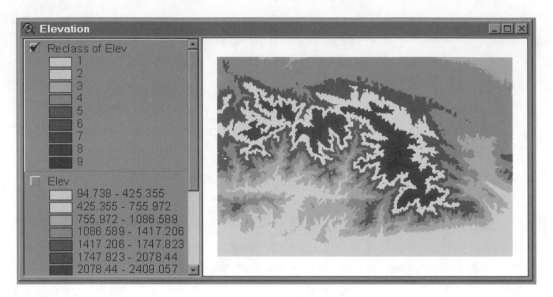

Selected cells where the Value attribute is 6.

10. One of the benefits of raster data is the ability to determine *contour* lines where cell values are the same. Create a new view called *SanFrancisco* and add a theme for the *sf_elev* grid from the *$AVEX-DATA\avdata\grids* directory. Load the *$AVEX-DATA\avdata\grids\sf_elev.avl* legend for the new theme.

11. Make the *Sf_elev* theme active. Using the Contour tool, click in the view to create a contour line graphic through the point you click. The contour may or may not correspond exactly to a legend class, depending on the granularity (resolution) of the current legend.

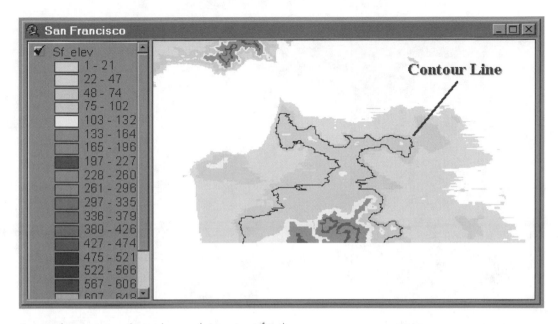

A single contour line through a specified point.

✓ **TIP:** *Capture graphics generated by the contour tool in a shapefile by first selecting New Theme from the View menu.*

12. Now you will generate a complete set of contours for the *Sf_elev* theme. Select Create Contours in the Analysis menu. You can set both a base contour and the desired interval between contours. Set a Contour Interval of *20* and close the dialog box.

13. Turn on the *Contours of Sf_elev* theme, zoom in, and examine the resulting contour lines.

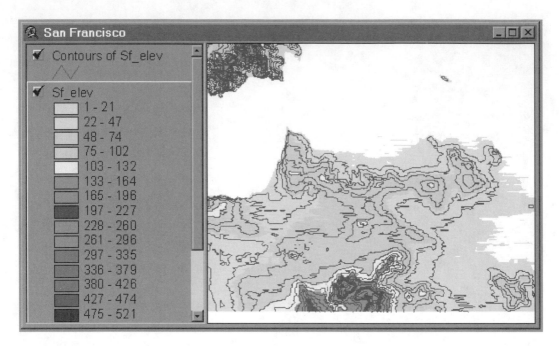

Contour lines at an interval of 20 for the Sf_elev theme.

14. Use Convert to Shapefile from the Theme menu to save the resulting temporary theme to a permanent vector data set. Add the resulting shapefile to the view and delete the temporary *Contours of Sf_elev* theme.

Displaying Grid Themes

As discussed previously, the display of grid themes is controlled by the Legend Editor. However, there are a few important differences between vector and grid theme legends. When displaying a grid theme you are restricted to solid fill patterns without outlines. Therefore, you can only set colors in the Legend Editor for grid themes.

Integer grids are frequently represented by unique value legends; floating point data are best represented by graduated colors. Integer grid themes can be classified using five different techniques: equal area, equal interval, natural breaks, quantile, and standard deviation. For floating point grids, only equal interval and standard deviation are available for classifications. Null Value symbolization is the same as for vector data.

✓ **TIP:** *Use the Statistics button in the Legend Editor for additional information about the field when setting up classifications of grid themes.*

When using grid themes, the Advanced button in the Legend Editor activates the Advanced Options dialog box, in which you can select Brightness Theme to set color vividness. This feature allows you to add depth to the display, or to see the effect of a second grid at the same time by altering the brightness of the primary grid data set.

Advanced Options dialog box.

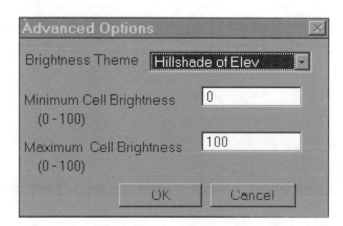

1. Create a brightness theme for the *Elev* theme by computing a hillshade. In the *Elevation* view, make the *Elev* theme active and access Compute Hillshade from the Analysis Menu.

2. In the Compute Hillshade dialog box, accept the defaults for azimuth (direction of the sun) and altitude (height of the sun in the sky) and close it. A new theme named *Hillshade of Elev* will be added to the view.

3. Turn off all themes except *Hillshade of Elev* and examine the theme.

4. Turn off all themes except the *Elev* theme. Set *Hillshade of Elev* as the brightness theme for the *Elev* theme. Accept the defaults for Minimum and Maximum cell brightness, and apply the changes. Examine the results.

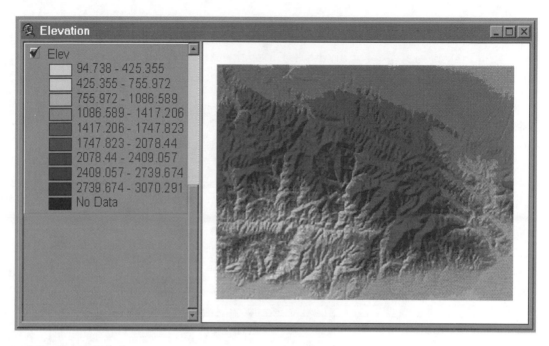

Elevation

☑ Elev
- 94.738 - 425.355
- 425.355 - 755.972
- 755.972 - 1086.589
- 1086.589 - 1417.206
- 1417.206 - 1747.823
- 1747.823 - 2078.44
- 2078.44 - 2409.057
- 2409.057 - 2739.674
- 2739.674 - 3070.291
- No Data

Hillshaded Elev theme.

Spatial Analysis

Analysis Properties

The quantity of data to be analyzed and its *resolution*, or cell size, greatly affects analysis, processing time, and output file size. For this reason, a set of grid analysis properties is maintained for each view. The parameters of spatial analysis can be complex, and options are numerous. Refer to the ArcView help system for additional detail.

For the *Elevation* view, select Analysis Properties from the Analysis menu. Set the Analysis Extent to *Same As View* to process data for the entire view extent. Set Analysis Cell Size to *Maximum of Inputs*, which will use the smallest cell size of the themes

*Analysis Properties
(Dialog Box)*

used in an analysis. Set the Analysis Mask to *No Mask Set*. Setting a mask will further restrict the data used for analysis. Close the Analysis Properties dialog box.

Analysis Properties dialog box.

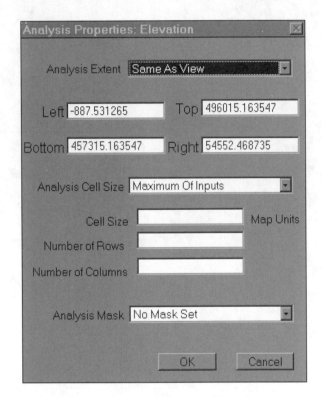

✓ **TIP:** *If you unintentionally initiate an extremely compute-intensive and time-consuming operation, use the Stop button in the lower right corner of the ArcView window to halt processing. Try altering the Analysis Properties and executing the operation again.*

Derive Slope

The Derive Slope function determines the maximum rate of change from each cell to its neighboring cells and creates an output grid.

Make the *Elev* theme active and select Derive Slope from the Analysis menu. This action will result in a new grid theme named *Slope of Elev*, which depicts the slope of the *Elev* theme. Adjust the legend of the new theme if necessary, and turn it on.

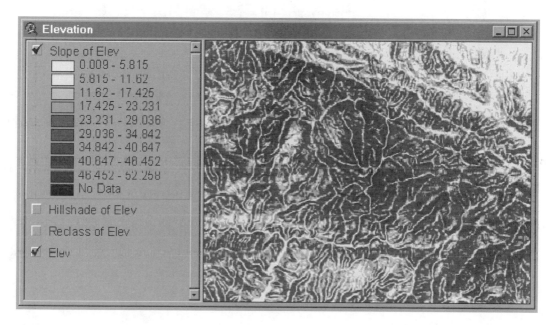

Slope of Elev theme of derived slope.

Find Distance

The Find Distance function creates an output grid whose cells contain the distance to the nearest feature of the input theme.

1. Create a new view and name it *Cellular.* Set the Map Units and Distance Units to *Miles,* and the projection to *Projections of the United States - Albers Equal Area (Conterminous U.S.).* Set the analysis properties in the same way as executed for the *Elevation* view. In this view you will investigate several types of analysis using fictitious cellular telephone antenna data.

⇨ **NOTE:** *Because a projection has been set, grid data created in this view will be in projected coordinates.*

2. Add a Feature theme for *$AVEXDATA\avdata\ grids\cellular.shp.* Name it *Towers,* and load the *$AVEXDATA\avdata\grids\cellular.avl* legend.

3. Select Find Distance from the Analysis menu. In the Output Grid Specification dialog box, set Output Grid Extent to *Same as View* and accept the other defaults. Close the dialog box to begin processing.

4. The new grid theme, *Distance to Towers,* will be added to the top of the Table of Contents. Turn on the *Distance to Towers* theme to view it. Identify several cells. Use the Measure tool to measure the distance to the nearest tower. The value of every cell in the new theme is the distance to the nearest tower.

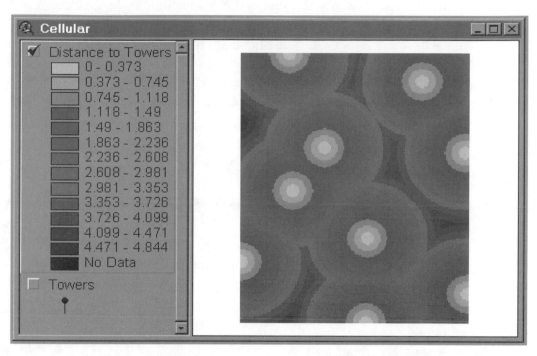

Distance to Towers grid theme.

Assign Proximity

The Assign Proximity function also creates a new output grid. Each cell in the new grid is *assigned* to the nearest feature in the input theme. The information about the nearest feature is stored in the *Value* field of the new grid.

You will analyze the cellular towers and create a grid theme that identifies the nearest tower for every grid cell location. Although cellular towers serve distinct areas, it may be useful to identify the *closest* tower, regardless of cellular service pattern. To locate the closest tower, take the following steps.

1. Make *Towers* the active theme, and select Assign Proximity from the Analysis menu. In the Output Grid Specification dialog box, set Output Grid Extent to *Same as View*, accept the other defaults, and close the dialog box. In the Proximity Field dialog box, select *ID_number* as the field from the point theme to be carried over to the new grid theme. Close the Proximity Field dialog box to begin processing.

2. Turn on the new *Proximity to Towers* theme. Examine the resulting grid theme. Move the *Towers* theme to the top of the Table of Contents and turn it on so that you can see it "on top of" the proximity theme. Can you recognize patterns? Do they seem reasonable?

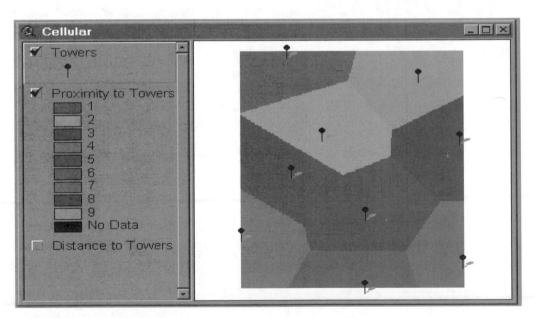

Proximity to Towers theme with cellular towers shown.

Interpolate Surface

The Interpolate Surface function creates an output grid wherein each cell contains an estimated or interpolated value based on an input theme with known values. Because the procedure yields a continuous set of data, the results are referred to as a *surface.* Several algorithms, or methods, are available for surface interpolation. Refer to the ArcView help system for more detail.

Interpolate Surface (Dialog Box)

1. Turn off all themes in the *Cellular* view. Add a new feature theme for *$AVEXDATA\avdata\grids\signal.shp.* Name it *Signal Strength* and turn it on. Examine its attribute table to familiarize yourself with the data it contains.

2. With the *Signal Strength* theme active, select Interpolate Surface from the Analysis menu. Set Output Grid Extent to *Same as View* and close the dialog box.

Interpolate Surface dialog box.

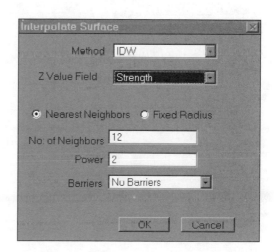

3. In the Interpolate Surface dialog box, set Method to *IDW* and Z Value Field to *Strength.* Accept the other defaults and close the dialog box.

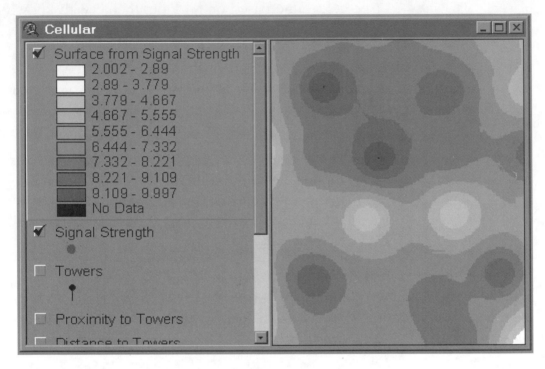

Interpolated surface grid of signal strength.

4. Load the *$AVEXDATA\avdata\grids\strength.avl* legend and turn the new theme on.

5. Identify several cells, exploring the results of the analysis. Compare the output to the values of the input theme.

Map Query

The true power of spatial analysis is realized for solving problems or answering questions. After you have created the various data sets that model the study conditions and factors, it is usually advantageous to locate areas where certain interrelated conditions exist.

The Map Query functionality allows you to construct a complex Boolean query on the values of multiple grid themes. The output grid cells will have values of 1 if the conditions specified in the query are True, and 0 if the conditions evaluate to False. A Map query theme will be added to the view depicting the results of the query.

With the *Cellular* view still active, select Map Query from the Analysis menu.

Map Query dialog box.

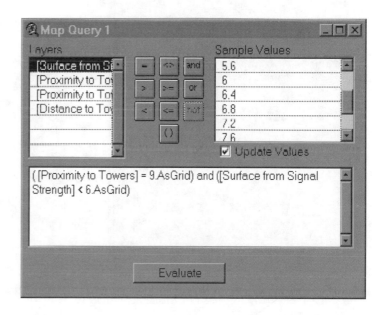

In the Map Query dialog box, build a query where Proximity to Towers is equal to 9 and Surface from Signal is less than 6. Click the Evaluate button to process the query. Turn on the *Map Query 1* theme to view the results. The display shows the cells closest to tower 9 where signal strength is less than 6.

✓ **TIP:** *Prior to closing the Map Query dialog box, you can modify the query expression and click the Evaluate button again. This can be done repeatedly. Every time you click the Evaluate button, the existing Map Query is modified; a new outpost theme will not be created.*

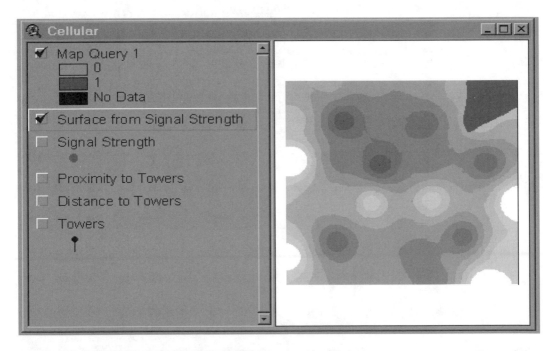

Results of the Map Query on multiple grids where the nearest tower is 9 and the signal strength is less than 6.

Optional

Practice your Spatial Analyst skills by performing the following steps.

1. Modify the legends for the *Elev* and *Slope of Elev* themes. Try to find the legend that visually represents the data.

2. Use the Map Calculator in the *Cellular* view to create a new grid for which each cell value is equal to the Signal Strength divided by two.

Visibility Tools

3. Add the Visibility tool extension from the sample extensions in the same way you loaded other sample extensions previously. Use the tool to determine line-of-sight visibility between two points on the *Elev* grid.

Summary

In this exercise you used the Spatial Analyst extension to perform, examine, view, and analyze raster data. Geographic regions were located where specific conditions existed. Many other forms of analysis can be accomplished with Spatial Analyst functionality, some of which must be accessed using the Avenue programming language.

Discussion Topics

❏ What types of real world situations would be best modeled with grids?

❏ How does the size of grid cells affect the quality and complexity of raster analysis?

❑ You used a brightness theme to depict hillshading. Under what other circumstances would you opt to use a brightness theme?

❑ How could you use a histogram to optimize the legend for a grid theme?

Glossary

Address Events

An address event is a feature located by a unique address. ArcView-supported addresses include street addresses (the most common) as well as polygon and point addresses, such as zip codes or land parcel numbers, respectively. (See also: *Event Table, Polygon Features.*)

Address Matching

Address matching involves assigning an absolute location through X,Y coordinates to each address in an address event table. This process occurs through interpolating specific address locations against a geocoded street theme coded with address ranges. (See also: *Event Table.*)

Alias Table

ArcView allows an alias table to be used for address geocoding. In an alias table, you use place name aliases in which a place name, such as Madison County Hospital, is assigned a street address. To facilitate locating addresses in a view, the alias table is associated with a matchable theme or with an address event table in address geocoding. (See also: *Event Table.*)

Annotation

Annotation is made up of text used to label features on a map. In the context of ARC/INFO data sets, annotation refers to text elements stored as part of an ARC/INFO coverage. Annotation contains not only a text string, but additional properties that define the font, color, size, and angle of the annotation. Annotation from an ARC/INFO coverage can be added as a separate feature class to an ArcView view.

Attribute Data/Table

Attribute data, also known as tabular data, are linked to themes. ArcView shapefiles (and ARC/INFO coverages) contain spatial data and attribute tables. The attribute tables linked to a particular theme may contain geographic information (e.g., addresses or zip codes). Attribute tables can also contain information associated with features in a theme, such as soil properties or land use descriptions.

A one-to-one relationship exists between features in a shapefile (or coverage) and records in the theme attribute table. At a minimum, the theme attribute table contains a shape field. In addition, theme attribute tables derived from coverages contain an additional field of a unique numeric identifier for each feature. Fields can be added to the theme attribute table to identify additional characteristics of features. For example, a block group number could be associated with each polygon of a census geography theme. Fields can also be used to join additional attribute data to a theme attribute table. (See also: *Field, Join, Record,* and *Table.*)

CAD (computer-aided design)

CAD software is designed for drafting and for the manipulation of graphic elements. CAD software is commonly used in engineering, surveying, and mapping applications.

CAD Drawing

A CAD drawing is a file created by CAD software containing the graphic elements that comprise the drawing. These drawing files include lines, polylines, text, and other elements. In ArcView 3.0, a theme can be created directly from an AutoCAD (*.dwg*) or MicroStation (*.dgn*) drawing file.

Chart

A chart is a graphic representation of attribute or tabular data. In ArcView, a chart references the data from a project table in one of six formats: area chart, bar chart, column chart, line chart, pie chart, and XY scatter chart. An ArcView chart is dynamic; that is, it represents the current status of the data in the table. Changes to either data values or the selected records in the table are immediately reflected in the corresponding chart. (See also: *Dynamic.*)

Classification

To classify is to assign features in a theme to classes according to attribute values. Symbols are then assigned to each class so that the distribution of features in each class may be viewed on a map. Within ArcView, classification methods include unique values, natural breaks, quantile, equal area, equal interval, standard deviation, and dot density. The type of classification appropriate for each field depends on the nature of the data.

Continuous Events

A continuous event is a type of route event whose features are located in a continuous fashion. Assume the route system is a natural gas distribution network. The continuous event might be pipeline age organized into categories such as very old (installed before 1965), old (1966 to 1975), moderate (1976 to 1985), and new (1986 to the present). The gas distribution network could then be coded according to locations where pipeline age category changes. (See also: *Route Events*.)

Coordinate System

A coordinate system is a map reference system in which precise geographic position can be referred to by means of a rectangular grid. The use of a rectangular grid allows features to be located using X,Y coordinates. This system facilitates the integration of regional survey data into a larger national grid.

Each coordinate system is derived from a specific map projection. The Universal Transverse Mercator System is derived from the Transverse Mercator projection. This system divides the world into 60 north-south zones and 20 east-west zones, for a total of 1,200 unique grid zones.

The State Plane Coordinate System is used in the United States. In this system, each state is divided into one or more zones extending north-south or east-west. Zones extending north-south are based on the Transverse Mercator projection; zones extending east-west are based on the Lambert Conformal Conic projection. (See also: *Geographic Coordinates, Map Projection*.)

Coverage

In the context of this book, a coverage refers to an ARC/INFO coverage. An ARC/INFO coverage is a database that stores geographic and tabular data in a set of files. These data files are organized within a common directory. An ARC/INFO coverage can serve as a spatial data source for a theme in ArcView.

Data Group

A data group is the aggregating unit of a chart. It consists of a set of related elements that describe the same variable. If the data series is formed from records, the data group is aggregated by fields. If the series is formed from fields, the data group is aggregated by record. (See also: *Chart, Field, Record,* and *Table.*)

Data Marker

A data marker is an element of one of the following types of chart: column, bar, area, pie slice, or point symbol. This element represents the value of a particular field for a specific record in a table. Data markers are analogous to cells in a spreadsheet. In other words, a data marker in a chart represents the intersection of a field and record in a table, also known as a field value. (See also: *Chart, Field, Record,* and *Table.*)

Data Series

A data series is a set of values compared in a chart. The individual elements of the data series, which may be formed from the records or fields in a table, are displayed in the chart legend. (See also: *Chart, Field, Record,* and *Table.*)

Database Theme

A database theme is a theme within a view. In ArcView 3.0, a database theme is based on spatial data stored in an RDBMS, such as Oracle or Informix, using the Spatial Database Engine (SDE). The ability to add a database theme from an SDE database is enabled by loading the SDE Themes extension from the ArcView project window. Database themes allow you to efficiently display and query spatial data comprised of hundreds of thousands of features.

Datum

A datum is a reference system used to describe the Earth's surface. Coordinate systems that are used when surveying point locations on Earth, such as the State Plane Coordinate System or the Universal Transverse Mercator Grid, are linked to a specific datum. For North America, there are two: the North American datum of 1927, and the North American datum of 1983. (See also: *Geodetic Control.*)

DOS (MS-DOS) 8.3 Convention

Under MS-DOS, file names are limited to a maximum of eight characters, followed by an extension comprising a maximum of three characters. The field name and extension are separated by a period. Examples of the convention are *highways.dbf,* and *marker.ai.* Directory names in MS-DOS are also restricted to the same naming convention.

Dynamic

In ArcView, *dynamic* refers to a document (table, chart, or layout) that reflects the current status of the source data it is based on. As the source data changes, the document associated with the source data changes accordingly.

DXF (Drawing Interchange Format)

A format used for exchanging vector data across CAD software, such as between AutoCAD and MicroStation. Dxf files can be in either ASCII or binary in format. ArcView 3.0 lets you create a theme in a view directly from a *.dxf* file.

Event Table

An event table contains geographic locations ("events"); however, the table is not in a spatial data format. The geographic locations may be absolute (e.g., latitude and longitude coordinates) or relative (e.g., street addresses). Event tables contain of one of three general types of event: X,Y; route; or address. (See also: *Address Events, Route Events,* and *X,Y Events.*)

Event Theme

An event theme is a theme based on an event table. Event themes are based on X,Y events, address events, or route events. When the geographic locations are absolute, as in the case of X,Y events, points are created in a theme directly from the X,Y coordinate values. When the geographic locations are relative, feature locations are translated from relative to absolute locations, and the resultant features are stored in the

ArcView shapefile format. A theme referencing this shapefile is subsequently added to the active view. (See also: *Event Table.*)

Export

This term is used in both a general and very specific sense in this book. The general definition is simply the process of moving a file that has been prepared in ArcView to another application. Specifically, Export is a utility provided with PC or UNIX ARC/ INFO. This utility creates an ARC/INFO interchange format file. The ARC/INFO interchange format file is given the suffix E*nn* (where *nn* is a number from 00 to 99) for each successive volume created.

Field

A field is a unique descriptor or characteristic of a record (instance) in a database. Fields are also called columns or items. For a customer database, examples of fields could be name, address, city, and zip code. ArcView supports four field types: Number, String, Boolean, and Date. (See also: *Record, Table.*)

Geocoding

Geocoding is the process of assigning an absolute location (X,Y coordinates) to a geographic feature referenced by a relative location, such as a street address or zip code.

Geodetic Control

A geodetic control consists of a correlated network of points for which accurate elevation and position locations have been determined. Local surveys are subsequently adjusted to such a correlated network of points. Control points are tied into existing horizontal and vertical control networks and then adjusted to the appropriate datum. The appropriate datum for North America is either the 1927 datum or the 1983 datum. (See also: *Datum, Map Projection.*)

Geographic Coordinates (Latitude/Longitude)

Geographic coordinates refer to the geographic reference system of latitude and longitude in which Earth is treated as a sphere and divided into 360 equal parts (degrees). This division is performed along two axes, one running east-west along the equator and the other running north-south along the Greenwich Prime Meridian. Using this coordinate system, any location on Earth can be identified with a unique X,Y coordinate pair. Geographic coordinates are commonly measured in degrees, minutes, and seconds, but can also be formatted as decimal degrees. The format used by ArcView is decimal degrees. (See also: *Coordinate System, Map Projection,* and *Map Units.*)

GIS (Geographic Information System)

A GIS is a geographic database manager. In other words, a GIS treats all geographic (spatial) features as records in a database, not simply as graphics. Nearly all concepts in traditional relational databases apply to a GIS, but with the added dimension of geography.

A GIS builds a bridge between geography and descriptive information through a georelational model. This model provides a one-to-one relationship between a spatial data set and an attribute table. Some database fields are predefined in attribute tables, but you can add any fields you desire. The georelational model also permits you to connect to other tabular databases, whether internal or external to the GIS software.

Grid

A grid is a spatial data set comprised of a regular array of equally spaced cells. Grid data is also known as raster data. Each grid cell is of uniform size and is referenced by a row and column location that precisely locates the cell within the grid. The grid is referenced to Earth by means of a world file which ties the origin point of the grid to a specific X,Y location on Earth.

Hot Link

A hot link causes a predefined action to occur when you select the Hot Link tool from the button bar and click on an appropriate feature in a theme. A user defines the action executed at this point by specifying a field value from a theme attribute table and an action to be performed. Examples of hot link actions are displaying an image or opening another view.

Image Data

Image data are a type of raster data whose features have been converted to a series of cell values by an optical or electronic device. Image data typically refer to satellite imagery or scanned aerial photographs in which each grid cell contains a brightness value representative of the portion of the light spectrum being measured. Imagery may be single band (grayscale) or multiple band (multispectral). ArcView supports the display of both single band and multiple band imagery. (See also: *Raster Data.*)

Import

This term is used in both a general and very specific sense in this book. The general sense is simply the process of loading or retrieving data into ArcView. Examples include importing dBase or delimited text files into ArcView. Both of these file types are created outside of ArcView and then incorporated (imported) into the program.

Import is also a standalone utility—one that is supplied with ArcView—that allows an ARC/INFO interchange file to be converted to an ARC/INFO coverage or database data file. The Import utility allows ARC/INFO interchange format data to be added to an ArcView project by creating a PC ARC/INFO format coverage (under the Windows platform) or a workstation ARC/INFO coverage (under UNIX). The Import utility also allows project files created under ArcView Version 1 (.av files) to be imported into an ArcView 2.*x* or 3.0 project.

Join

Joining is a process by which two or more tables are merged into a virtual table through a common field. The resultant table appears as a single table in ArcView, despite being formed from two or more separate data source files.

Join is used when there is a one-to-one or one-to-many relationship between records in a source table and records in a destination table. In the case of a many-to-one relationship between records in a source table and records in a destination table, the Link feature should be used instead of Join. (See also: *Field, Link, Table.*)

Layout

A layout is a map composition document used to prepare output from ArcView. A layout allows you to define a page and place ArcView documents (views, charts, and tables), imported graphics, and graphic primitives on the page. A layout is dynamic; that is, graphics linked to ArcView documents can immediately reflect changes made in those documents. Dynamic layouts are live-linked. (See also: *Live Link* and *Dynamic.*)

Line Features

Line features are used to represent linear entities, such as highways or streams. Other important uses for lines are to delineate perimeters of polygons and to lay down the positions of route systems and regions. Lines are located and defined through the assignment of a unique series of X,Y coordinate pairs.

Lines (also known as arcs) are made up of connected strings of line segments. Each line segment is delineated by a vertex. The vertices at the endpoints of lines are called nodes. (See also: *Vertex.*)

Linear Events

A linear event is a type of route event. Linear events are features located along a specific segment of a route. Assume the route system is a road network. A linear event could be a pothole repair segment occurring from milepost 10.5 to 10.8 on County Road 41. (See also: *Route Events.*)

Link

Linking is used in the case of a many-to-one relationship between records in a source table and records in a destination table. A link defines the relationship between the two tables, but does not combine the tables into a single virtual table. Linking displays all candidate records in the source table that match each unique value in the destination table. For example, a table that identifies apartment complexes by parcel number could be linked to a second (source) table that lists all the tenants in each apartment complex. (See also: *Join.*)

Live Link

A live link is a dynamic link between a layout frame and the corresponding ArcView document or element. Chart and table frames are always live-linked to respective chart and table documents. View, legend, and scale bar frames can be either live-linked or static. (See also: *Dynamic, Layout,* and *Static Link.*)

Look-up Table

A look-up table is a secondary table that contains additional information about features identified in a specific field of a primary table. For example, a primary table could contain a list of soil mapping units and a field that holds a symbol for each mapping unit. A look-up table could then be prepared that identifies the soil drainage class for each soil mapping unit.

A one-to-one or many-to-one relationship exists between records in a primary table and records in a secondary table. In ArcView, the Join function can be used to create a virtual table in which the records of the look-up table are associated with records in the primary table, based on values for a common field.

Map Projection

A map projection is a system by which the curved surface of Earth is represented on the flat surface of a map. The challenge inherent in all map projections is to preserve the properties of area, shape, elevation, distance, and direction present on Earth's surface through the transformation to a map surface. Because it is impossible to preserve all properties simultaneously, you need to select a map projection optimized to preserve the property you most desire.

Map Units

Map units are the units in which spatial data coordinates are stored. Map units are used in ArcView to set the scale of the view. By default, map units are set to Unknown. The map units for a view are set from the View Properties dialog window, which is accessed from the View menu.

Map units are differentiated in ArcView from distance units. Distance units are used to display measurements and dimensions within a view.

Matchable Theme

A theme becomes matchable after geocoding indexes have been built on it that conform to an ArcView-supported address style. A matchable theme is used to create an Address Event Theme by address matching from a table that contains address information. (See also: *Event Theme.*)

Normalize

When applied to thematic classification, normalize refers to expressing the values for one field relative to the values for a second field. Some data, such as those expressed by percentages, may already be normalized.

Point Events

A point event is a type of route event. Point events are located at a specific point along a route. Assume the route is a highway system coded by route (e.g., Route 41 linking Tijeras Canyon to the town of Milbank) and mile post. Point events could be accident locations identified by a specific mile post on the route system. (See also: *Route Events.*)

Point Features

Point features represent entities found at discrete locations, such as well sites, transformer sites, or customer locations. Each point feature is located using a single X,Y coordinate pair.

Polygon Features

Polygon features are used to represent entities of a real extent, such as land parcels, geologic zones, or islands. Polygon features are defined by a series of X,Y coordinate pairs that identify the polygon's perimeter.

Imagine four discrete points (X,Y coordinate pairs) and four lines (arcs) connecting the points in a closed system. The points and lines define the polygon's perimeter. The entity (area) thus defined is a polygon feature.

When polygon features are derived from an ARC/INFO coverage, a special type of point feature known as a *labelpoint* may be associated with each polygon. The labelpoint contains the same attributes as the polygon and allows the polygons to be modeled alternately by using point features.

Project

A project is the overall structure used in ArcView to organize component documents such as views, tables, charts, layouts, and scripts. A project maintains the current state of all component ArcView documents, as well as the configuration of the graphical user interface. This information is stored in an ASCII file with an *.apr* extension.

Raster Data

Raster data is also referred to as grid cell data. Raster data sets store spatial data as cells within a two-dimensional matrix. This matrix is a gridded area of uniformly spaced rows and columns in which each grid cell contains a value that represents part of the feature being depicted. Grid cell values may be continuous, as in elevation data, or discrete, as in land use data, for which each grid cell value is associated with a specific land use. The resolution of raster data is dependent on the size of the grid cell.

Record

A record is a specific instance or member of a database. Records are also called rows. In a customer database, records could be individual customers. (See also: *Table.*)

Relational Join

A relational join is the merging of two attribute tables to produce a single output table based on equivalent values of a common attribute field. For example, the feature attribute table for a theme comprised of land parcels, each identified by an assessor's unqiue parcel number, can be joined to a second table containing additional attributes for each parcel by using the common field of assessor's parcel number in the two tables. In ArcView, the result of a relational join is the creation of a single virtual table within the ArcView project. The underlying source tables are still maintained separately on the system's hard drive.

Route Events

Route events are relative locations of features along a route system, such as a road network or power lines. In this case, locations are relative because they are referenced as distances from a known starting point, such as 1.2 miles from the Salt Creek substation. Route events come in three forms: point, linear, and continuous. (See also: *Continuous Events, Event Table, Linear Events,* and *Point Events.*)

Script

An ArcView script is a macro written in Avenue (ArcView's programming language) in order to customize the ArcView environment. Avenue scripts are stored and executed within a project.

Shapefile

A shapefile is the native ArcView spatial data format. In contrast to an ARC/INFO coverage, a shapefile is a simpler, non-topological format that offers the advantages of faster display and the ability to be created or edited within ArcView. An ArcView shapefile also serves as an effective interchange format for moving data in and out of ARC/INFO or other supporting software.

Static Link

A static link is a non-dynamic link between a layout frame and the corresponding ArcView document or element. If a view, legend, or scale bar frame is static, the frame represents a snapshot of the view at the time the frame was created. (See also: *Layout, Live Link* and *Dynamic.*)

Street Net

A street net (or network) is a spatial data set that represents streets as a connected series of line segments. Each line segment is typically coded with the address range of the street represented, thereby allowing the theme resulting from the street net to be used for geocoding.

Table

A table is the basic unit of storage in a database management system. It is a two-dimensional matrix of attribute values. ArcView, ARC/INFO, and SQL (Structured Query Language) share this term.

Fields are the vertical components in a table. In SQL, fields are also called columns. Another common term used for a field is *item*. Records are the horizontal components in a table. In SQL, they are called rows. The intersection of a field and a record is a single, discrete entity called a field value or item value. In SQL, the intersection is called a datum.

In ArcView, a table references tabular data from several sources—dBASE, INFO, or delimited text files—in a uniform display format composed of fields and records. ArcView tables are dynamic; that is, they reference the source data rather than contain the data itself. Consequently, an ArcView table represents the current state of data at the time the project is opened, including all changes made to the data after the last time the project was accessed.

Tables can be displayed, queried, and analyzed. In addition, tables joined to a theme can be queried and analyzed spatially. Tables can also be joined based on sharing equivalent values of a common field, even if the underlying format for the source data differs (such as dBASE and INFO).

Thematic Classification

Thematic classification refers to the assignment of symbols to a theme's features based on field values in the theme's attribute table, including tables that have been joined to the theme attribute table. A classification may be applied to a theme based on either a range of values or unique values for the field. In ArcView, the maximum number of classes, regardless of the classification type, is 64.

Thematic Map

A thematic map is a map that displays a set of related geographic features. Typically, a classification has been applied so that the map displays attribute information associated with the geographic features. Examples include maps that display land use or soil drainage classes.

Theme

A theme is a spatial data set (geography) linked with attribute data that contain a locational component. Imagine a map of a census tract, upon which you superimpose two other maps. The other two maps represent streets and stores in a pizza chain. Each of these maps would be a separate theme.

A theme is a group of similar geographic features in a view. A theme is based on a set of features taken from a specific feature class which is, in turn, derived from a spatial data source. Feature classes include regions, routes, polygons, arcs, points, annotation, labels, and nodes. Certain feature classes, such as regions or routes, are complex classes made up of more basic feature types. The three basic feature types are points, lines (arcs), and polygons.

A theme can be comprised of all features within a specific feature class from a spatial data source, such as all land use polygons, or it can be a subset of features from a spatial data source, such as all commercial land use polygons.

A spatial data source may contain more than one feature class. For example, a census geography may contain both lines representing streets and polygons representing census tracts.

Vector Data

Vector data sets, also referred to as arc node data, contain features with discrete positions. These positions are stored as X,Y coordinate pairs. Vector data consist of a series of nodes that define line segments, which are in turn joined to form more complex features, such as line networks and polygons. ARC/INFO coverages and ArcView shapefiles are both examples of vector data. (See also: *Line Features, Polygon Features.*)

Vertex

A vertex is a specific X,Y coordinate pair that forms a line. Vertices are often referred to as shape points. The more vertices or shape points making up the line, the more accurate the representation of the feature. (See also: *Line Features.*)

View

Essentially, a view is a collection of themes. Assume you are examining the market for home improvement products in a three-county area (Bernalillo, Sandoval, and Valencia) in the state of New Mexico. You want geographic detail, including streets, roads, and zip code areas. You also want lifestyle characteristics of the people who live in specific locales and neighborhoods in the tri-county area.

One of your views could consist of four themes: a map of the tri-county area, the street net, zip code areas, and a market segmentation overlay that defines market segments by zip code area. You could choose to display all themes in the view simultaneously, with the tri-county land map on the bottom and the market segment theme on top, or you could choose to display only two themes in the view simultaneously, and so on.

In ArcView, views organize themes. A view window contains a graphics display area and a table of contents that lists all themes present in the view. You select which theme or themes will be drawn in the view.

More specifically, a view is an interactive map. All themes present in a view share a common geographic coordinate system, and most share a coincident geographic extent (area) as well.

Views are the primary document type in ArcView. Other ArcView documents (tables, charts, and layouts) are typically linked to themes contained in views. A view imposes an organizational structure on themes derived from spatial data, and it provides a means for displaying, querying, and analyzing the data. This is accomplished through the interaction of the three primary components of a view: the map display, the table of contents, and the view's graphical user interface. (See also: *Theme.*)

X,Y Coordinates

X,Y coordinates are used to refer to the unique geographic location of a spatial feature. All spatial data is maintained in some form of map coordinate system, the most widely used being the geographic coordinates of latitude and longitude.

X,Y Events

In GIS, X,Y events are the exact locations of features that have been pinpointed on a map by X,Y coordinates. Commonly used map coordinate systems are latitude/longitude, UTM, and State Plane Coordinates. (See also: *Event Table.*)

World File

A world file is a text file used to tie the location of a raster data set, such as an image or a grid, to a location on Earth. A world file contains the X and Y coordinates for the origin of the grid and, optionally, the grid cell size and rotation of the grid.

Functionality Quick Reference

This appendix serves as a reference for the functionality available through the ArcView menu, button, and tool bars. It is designed to be a quick reference to the main functionality available in ArcView

Add Event Theme

Access: View menu bar—View menu

Purpose: Adds a new theme to a view using an event table. An event table contains a locatable field such as an address; X,Y coordinates; or a route location.

Associated with: Add Theme, Event Tables, Address Geocoding

Add Field

Access: Table menu bar—Edit menu

Purpose: Adds a new field to the active table. The table must be in dBASE or INFO format.

Associated with: Start/Stop Editing, Add Record, Delete Field

Add Record

Access: Table menu bar—Edit menu

Purpose: Adds a new record to the active table, which has been opened to allow editing.

Associated with: Start/Stop Editing, Add Field, Delete Record

Add Table

Access: Project menu bar—Project menu

Purpose: Imports a dBASE, INFO, or delimited text file into the active project.

Associated with: Import Project, SQL Connect

Add Theme

Access: View menu bar—View menu; View button bar

Purpose: Adds a theme to a view from a spatial data source, such as an Arc-View shapefile, ARC/INFO coverage, or supported image source.

Associated with: Delete Themes, New Theme

Align

Access: View menu bar—Graphics menu; Layout menu bar—Graphics menu

Purpose: Aligns selected graphics vertically or horizontally in a view or layout.

Associated with: Pointer

Area Chart Gallery

Access: Chart menu bar—Gallery menu; Chart button bar

Purpose: Displays format options and changes an active chart to Area chart format.

Associated with: Create Chart, Bar Chart Gallery, Column Chart Gallery, Line Chart Gallery, Pie Chart Gallery, XY Scatter Chart Gallery

Area of Interest

Access: View tool bar

Purpose: Sets the Area of Interest for library-based themes in a view.

Associated with: Theme Properties

Attach Graphics

Access: View menu bar—Theme menu

Purpose: Attaches the selected graphics to the active theme; attached graphics will display only when the theme is turned on.

Associated with: Detach Graphics, Label Features, Auto-label

Auto-label

> **Access:** View menu bar—Theme menu
>
> **Purpose:** Labels selected features in the active themes using a specified label field. The resultant text graphics are attached to the active themes.
>
> **Associated with:** Label Features, Text

Bar Chart Gallery

> **Access:** Chart menu bar—Gallery menu; Chart button bar
>
> **Purpose:** Displays format options and changes an active chart to Bar Chart format.
>
> **Associated with:** Create Chart, Area Chart Gallery, Column Chart Gallery, Line Chart Gallery, Pie Chart Gallery, XY Scatter Chart Gallery

Bring to Front

> **Access:** View menu bar—Graphics menu; Layout menu bar—Graphics menu; Layout button bar
>
> **Purpose:** Brings selected graphics to the front of remaining graphics.
>
> **Associated with:** Send to Back, Pointer

Calculate

> **Access:** Table menu bar—Field menu; Table button bar
>
> **Purpose:** Performs calculations on all, or selected, records in the active field of a table for which editing has been enabled.
>
> **Associated with:** Start/Stop Editing

Chart Color

> **Access:** Chart tool bar
>
> **Purpose:** Changes the color of any chart element.
>
> **Associated with:** Show Symbol Palette

Chart Element Properties

> **Access:** Chart tool bar
>
> **Purpose:** Sets properties of the chart elements of the active chart.
>
> **Associated with:** Chart Axis Properties, Chart Legend Properties, Chart Title Properties

Chart Properties

Access: Chart menu bar—Chart menu; Chart button bar

Purpose: Sets the properties of the active chart by adding/deleting data series or groups, selecting the fields for labeling data series/groups, and setting the order of displaying data series/groups.

Associated with: Create Chart, Table Properties

Clear All Breakpoints

Access: Script menu bar—Script menu

Purpose: Clears all breakpoints in the active script.

Associated with: Toggle Breakpoint, Compile, Step, Run

Clear Selected Features

Access: View menu bar—Theme menu; View button bar; View popup menu

Purpose: Deselects any selected features in the active themes.

Associated with: Select Features, Select Features Using Shape, Switch Selection

Close

Access: View, Table, Chart, Layout, and Script menu bars—File menu

Purpose: Closes the active component of a project.

Associated with: Close All

Close All

Access: View, Table, Chart, Layout, and Script menu bars—File menu

Purpose: Closes all project components currently open.

Associated with: Close

Close Project

Access: Project menu bar—File menu

Purpose: Closes the active project and all components.

Associated with: Close, Close All, Exit

Column Chart Gallery

Access: Chart menu bar—Gallery menu; Chart button bar

Purpose: Displays format options and changes an active chart to Column Chart format.

Associated with: Create Chart, Area Chart Gallery, Bar Chart Gallery, Line Chart Gallery, Pie Chart Gallery, XY Scatter Chart Gallery

Combine Graphics

Access: View menu bar—Edit menu

Purpose: Combines selected graphics in a view into one graphic element.

Associated with: Select All Graphics, Union Graphics, Subtract Graphics, Intersect Graphics

Comment

Access: Script menu bar—Edit menu

Purpose: Changes selected text in a script to a non-executing comment line.

Associated with: Remove Comment

Compile

Access: Script menu bar—Script menu; Script button bar

Purpose: Compiles the script in the active script window.

Associated with: Run, Step

Convert Overlapping Labels

Access: View Menu Bar—Theme menu

Purpose: Converts labels that overlap as a result of the Auto-label function (drawn in green) to the same text symbol and color as the "good" labels.

Associated with: Remove Labels, Remove Overlapping Labels

Convert to Shapefile

Access: View menu bar—Theme menu

Purpose: Converts a theme derived from an ARC/INFO coverage to ArcView shapefile format, either for the entire theme or for a selected set of features.

Associated with: New Theme, Add Theme

Copy

Access: Table, Layout, and Script menu bars—Edit menu; Table, Layout, and Script button bars

Purpose: Copies selected features to the clipboard. For tables, the selected feature is the data in the active cell; for layouts, graphics, and scripts, it is text.

Associated with: Cut, Paste

Copy Graphics

Access: View menu bar—Edit menu

Purpose: Copies the selected graphics in a view to the clipboard.

Associated with: Cut, Paste

Copy Themes

Access: View menu bar—Edit menu

Purpose: Copies the active themes to the clipboard.

Associated with: Cut, Paste

Create Chart

Access: Table menu bar—Table menu; Table button bar

Purpose: Creates a chart from the selected records of the active table, or from the entire table if no records are selected.

Associated with: Chart Properties

Create/Remove Index

Access: Table menu bar—Field menu

Purpose: Creates or removes an ArcView index for the active field. If the active field is the Shape field, a spatial index will be created or deleted.

Associated with: Open Theme Table

Customize

Access: Project menu bar—Project menu

Purpose: Accesses the dialog window for customizing the ArcView interface; accessible only if Avenue has been installed.

Associated with: Control Properties, Project Properties

Cut

Access: Table, Layout, and Script menu bars—Edit menu; Table, Layout, and Script button bars

Purpose: Cuts the selection and places it on the clipboard. For tables, the selection is the data in the active cell; for layouts, selected graphics, and scripts, it is text.

Associated with: Copy, Paste

Cut Graphics

Access: View menu bar—Edit menu

Purpose: Cuts the selected graphics from a view and places them on the clipboard.

Associated with: Cut, Copy, Paste, Delete Graphics

Cut Themes

Access: View menu bar—Edit menu

Purpose: Cuts the active themes from a view and places them on the clipboard.

Associated with: Copy Themes, Paste, Delete Themes

Delete

Access: Layout menu bar—Edit menu

Purpose: Deletes the selected graphics in the active layout.

Associated with: Delete Graphics, Cut, Cut Graphics

Delete Field

Access: Table menu bar—Edit menu

Purpose: Deletes the active field from a table for which editing has been enabled.

Associated with: Add Field, Start/Stop Editing

Delete Graphics

Access: View menu bar—Graphics menu

Purpose: Deletes selected graphics from a view.

Associated with: Cut Graphics, Copy Graphics

Delete Last Point

Access: View popup menu

Purpose: Deletes the last point added to the line or polygon currently being drawn.

Associated with: Undo Edit, Redo Edit

Delete Left

Access: Script menu bar—Edit menu

Purpose: Deletes text from the location cursor to left margin.

Associated with: Shift Left, Shift Right, Cut

Delete Records

Access: Table menu bar—Edit menu

Purpose: Deletes the selected records for the active table, providing editing has been enabled.

Associated with: Cut, Copy, Paste, Add Records

Delete Themes

Access: View menu bar—Edit menu

Purpose: Deletes the active themes from a view.

Associated with: Cut Themes, Copy Themes

Detach Graphics

Access: View menu bar—Theme menu

Purpose: Detaches graphics from the active themes in the view.

Associated with: Attach Graphics

Draw

Access: View tool bar; Layout tool bar

Purpose: Allows graphics (points, lines, polylines, rectangles, circles, and polygons) to be added to a view or layout. Also allows existing point and line features to be split, and polygons to be appended to existing polygons.

Associated with: Text, Label, Pointer

Edit

Access: Table tool bar

Purpose: Selects cell data for editing in an active table for which editing has been enabled.

Associated with: Start/Stop Editing

Edit Legend

Access: View menu bar—Theme menu; View button bar

Purpose: Accesses the Legend Editor for changing the symbols and/or classification of the active theme.

Associated with: Theme Properties

Embed Script

Access: Script menu bar—Script menu

Purpose: Embeds a script in the project.

Associated with: Unembed Script

Erase

Access: Chart tool bar

Purpose: Removes data markers from a chart and deselects the records from the associated table.

Associated with: Erase with Polygon, Undo Erase

Erase with Polygon

Access: Chart tool bar

Purpose: Removes one or more data markers from an XY Scatter chart by defining a polygon around the markers.

Associated with: Erase, Undo Erase

Examine Variables

Access: Script menu bar—Script menu; Script button bar

Purpose: Displays current values of local and global variables.

Associated with: Compile, Step, Run

Exit

Access: Project, View, Table, Chart, Layout, and Script menu bars—File menu

Purpose: Ends the ArcView session.

Associated with: Close Project, Save Project, Save Project As

Export

Access: View and Layout menu bars—File menu

Purpose: Exports a view or layout to a file. Supported output formats include Encapsulated PostScript, Adobe Illustrator, and CGM on all platforms, as well as Windows Metafile and Windows Bitmap, and Macintosh PICT.

Associated with: Print, Print Setup

Export Table

Access: Table menu bar—File menu

Purpose: Exports a table to a file. Supported file types include dBASE, INFO, and delimited text.

Associated with: Print, Print Setup

Extensions

Access: Project menu bar—File menu

Purpose: Loads or removes available ArcView extensions.

Associated with: Open Project

Find

Access: View menu bar—View menu; Table menu bar—Table menu; Chart menu bar—Chart menu; Script menu bar—Edit menu; View, Table, and Chart button bars

Purpose: Finds a particular feature in an active theme, table, or chart, based on an entered text string; or finds selected text in a script.

Associated with: Locate, Query, Find Next, Replace

Find Next

Access: Script menu bar—Edit menu

Purpose: Finds next occurrence of selected text in a script.

Associated with: Find, Replace

Frame

Access: Layout tool bar

Purpose: Adds a view frame, legend frame, scale bar frame, north arrow frame, chart frame, table frame, or picture frame to a layout.

Associated with: Draw, Text

Full Extent

Access: View menu bar—View menu

Purpose: Zooms to the full extent of all themes in a view.

Associated with: Zoom In, Zoom Out, Zoom to Selected, Zoom to Themes, Zoom Previous

General Snapping On/Off

Access: View popup menu

Purpose: Toggles general snapping on or off during theme editing.

Associated with: Interactive Snapping On/Off

Geocode Addresses

Access: View menu bar—View menu

Purpose: Begins geocoding addresses against a theme for which a geo-coding index has been built.

Associated with: Add Event Theme, Locate, Rematch

Group

Access: View menu bar and Layout menu bars—Graphics menu; Layout button bar

Purpose: Groups selected graphics as a single graphic.

Associated with: Ungroup, Pointer

Hide/Show Grid

Access: Layout menu bar—Layout menu

Purpose: Toggles the display of the layout grid on the active layout.

Associated with: Layout Properties, Show/Hide Margins

Hide/Show Legend

Access: View menu bar—Theme menu

Purpose: Hides or shows the legend of the active themes in the Table of Contents.

Associated with: Edit Legend

Hide/Show Margins

Access: Layout menu bar—Layout menu

Purpose: Toggles the display of the layout page margins on the active layout.

Associated with: Layout Properties, Show/Hide Grid

Hot Link

Access: View tool bar

Purpose: Invokes the defined hot link for an active theme on a view.

Associated with: Open View, Open Project

Identify

Access: View, Table, and Chart tool bars

Purpose: Displays the attributes of a feature in an active theme, table, or chart.

Associated with: Select Feature, Select, Select Features Using Shape

Import

Access: Project menu bar—Project menu

Purpose: Imports components of another ArcView project, including ArcView 1.0 projects, into the active project.

Associated with: Open Project

Interactive Snap

Access: View tool bar

Purpose: Sets the interactive tolerance for snapping vertices on an editable theme.

Associated with: Snap, Start/Stop Editing, Draw, Pointer

Interactive Snapping On/Off

Access: View popup menu

Purpose: Toggles interactive snapping on or off during theme editing.

Associated with: General Snapping On/Off

Intersect Graphics

Access: View menu bar—Edit menu

Purpose: Creates an output graphic formed from the area held in common by all selected graphics.

Associated with: Select All Graphics, Combine Graphics, Union Graphics, Subtract Graphics

Join

Access: Table menu bar—Table menu; Table button bar

Purpose: Joins a table to the active table based on the values of a common field.

Associated with: Link, Remove All Joins

Label

Access: View tool bar

Purpose: Labels a feature in the active theme with the attribute from the field specified in that theme's properties.

Associated with: Auto-label, Text

Layout

Access: View menu bar—View menu

Purpose: Creates a layout using a specified template.

Associated with: Use Template, Store as Template

Line Chart Gallery

Access: Chart menu bar—Gallery menu; Chart button bar

Purpose: Displays format options and changes an active chart to Line Chart format.

Associated with: Create Chart, Area Chart Gallery, Bar Chart Gallery, Column Chart Gallery, Pie Chart Gallery, XY Scatter Chart Gallery

Link

Access: Table menu bar—Table menu

Purpose: Establishes a one-to-many relationship between the source table and the active table, based on the values of a common field.

Associated with: Join, Remove All Links

Load System Script

Access: Script menu bar—script menu; Script button bar

Purpose: Inserts the source code of a system script.

Associated with: Load Text File, Write Text File

Load Text File

Access: Script menu bar—Script menu; Script button bar

Purpose: Inserts the contents of a text file into the active script.

Associated with: Load System Script, Write Text File

Locate

Access: View menu bar—View menu; View button bar

Purpose: Locates a specific address on an active theme for which geocoding properties have been set.

Associated with: Find

Measure

Access: View tool bar

Purpose: Measures distance on a view.

Associated with: Draw

Merge Graphics

Access: View menu bar—Edit menu

Purpose: Combines or aggregates selected features from an ArcView shapefile into a single shape.

Associated with: Select Feature, Summarize

New Project

Access: Project menu bar—File menu
Purpose: Creates a new ArcView project.
Associated with: Save Project As

New Theme

Access: View menu bar—View menu
Purpose: Creates a new theme based on the ArcView shapefile format.
Associated with: Edit, Copy Theme

Open Project

Access: Project menu bar—File menu
Purpose: Opens an existing ArcView project.
Associated with: New Project, Save Project, Save Project As

Open Theme Table

Access: View menu bar—Theme menu; View button bar
Purpose: Opens the attribute tables for those themes that are active in a particular view.
Associated with: Add Table

Page Setup

Access: Layout menu bar—Layout menu
Purpose: Defines the characteristics of the layout page.
Associated with: Layout Properties, Use Template, Show/Hide Grid, Show/Hide Margins

Pan

Access: View and Layout tool bars; View popup menu
Purpose: By dragging the mouse, pans across the currently displayed view or layout.
Associated with: Zoom In, Zoom Out

Paste

Access: View, Table, Layout, and Script menu bars—Edit menu; Table, Layout, and Script button bars

Purpose: Pastes the contents of the clipboard into the active document.

Associated with: Copy, Cut

Pie Chart Gallery

Access: Chart menu bar—Gallery menu; Chart button bar

Purpose: Displays format options and changes an active chart to Pie Chart format.

Associated with: Create Chart, Area Chart Gallery, Bar Chart Gallery, Column Chart Gallery, Line Chart Gallery, XY Scatter Chart Gallery

Pointer

Access: View and Layout tool bars

Purpose: Selects graphics in a view or layout for subsequent editing and manipulation.

Associated with: Select All, Select All Graphics

Print

Access: View, Table, Chart, Layout, and Script menu bars—File menu; Layout button bar

Purpose: Prints the active project component.

Associated with: Print Setup

Print Setup

Access: View, Table, Chart, Layout, and Script menu bars—File menu

Purpose: Controls the output format and printing environment.

Associated with: Print

Promote

Access: Table menu bar—Table menu; Table button bar

Purpose: Displays selected records at the top of the table.

Associated with: Select, Sort Ascending, Sort Descending

Properties—Graphic

Access: View and Layout menu bars—Graphics menu

Purpose: Displays and edits graphics properties for graphic primitives, text, and frames.

Associated with: View Properties, Layout Properties, Pointer, Text

Properties—Layout

Access: Layout menu bar—Layout menu; Layout button bar

Purpose: Displays and edits layout properties, including name, grid spacing, and snapping to grid.

Associated with: Graphics Properties, View Properties, Table Properties, Chart Properties

Properties—Project

Access: Project menu bar—Project menu

Purpose: Displays and edits project properties, including start-up and shut-down scripts, work directory, name of creator and creation date, and selection color.

Associated with: View Properties, Table Properties, Chart Properties, Layout Properties

Properties—Script

Access: Script menu bar—Script menu

Purpose: Displays and edits script properties such as name, creator, creation date, comments, and behavior (i.e., whether the script will remain active during execution).

Associated with: View Properties, Table Properties, Chart Properties, Layout Properties

Properties—Table

Access: Table menu bar—Table menu

Purpose: Displays and edits properties of the active table, including name, creator, visible fields, and field alias names.

Associated with: View Properties, Chart Properties, Layout Properties

Properties—View

Access: View menu bar—View menu

Purpose: Displays and edits the properties of the current view, including name, creation date, creator, map units, distance units, and projection.

Associated with: Table Properties, Chart Properties, Layout Properties

Query

Access: View menu bar—Theme menu; Table menu bar—Table menu; View and Table button bars

Purpose: Opens the Query Builder dialog window, which allows feature(s) in a view or records in a table to be selected by a logical expression based on attribute values.

Associated with: Find, Locate, Theme Properties

Redo Edit

Access: Table menu bar—Edit menu; View popup menu

Purpose: Restores the last "undo" edit on a shapefile or table.

Associated with: Undo Edit, Delete Last Point

Refresh

Access: Table menu bar—Table menu

Purpose: Causes ArcView to reread source data for the active table.

Associated with: Open, Add Table, Join, Link

Rematch

Access: View menu bar—Theme menu

Purpose: Opens the Geocoding Editor dialog window, allowing features to be rematched in the geocoded theme.

Associated with: Add Event Theme

Remove All Joins

Access: Table menu bar—Table menu

Purpose: Removes all joins from the active table.

Associated with: Join, Remove All Links

Remove All Links

Access: Table menu bar—Table menu

Purpose: Removes all links to other tables for the active table.

Associated with: Link, Remove All Joins

Remove Comment

Access: Script menu bar—Edit menu

Purpose: Converts selected commented text in a script to executable code.

Associated with: Comment

Remove Labels

Access: View menu bar—Theme menu

Purpose: Removes all labels attached to the active theme.

Associated with: Remove Overlapping Labels, Convert Overlapping Labels

Remove Overlapping Labels

Access: View menu bar—Theme menu

Purpose: Removes all overlapping labels attached to the active theme. Overlapping labels result from the Auto-label function, and they appear in green in the view.

Associated with: Remove Labels, Convert Overlapping Labels

Rename

Access: Project menu bar—Project menu

Purpose: Renames the selected project component.

Associated with: Properties

Replace

Access: Script menu bar—Edit menu

Purpose: Replaces the selected string in a script.

Associated with: Find, Find Next

Run

Access: Script menu bar—Script menu; Script button bar

Purpose: Runs the compiled script.

Associated with: Compile, Step

Save Edits

Access: View menu bar—Theme menu; Table menu bar—Table menu

Purpose: Saves all current edits to the theme or table being edited.

Associated with: Save Edits As, Start Editing, Stop Editing

Save Edits As

Access: View menu bar—Theme menu; Table menu bar—Table menu

Purpose: Saves the current theme or table, including all edits, to a new shapefile or table.

Associated with: Save Edits, Start Editing, Stop Editing

Save Project

 Access: Project, View, Table, Chart, Layout, and Script menu bars—File menu; Project, View, Table, Chart, Layout, and Script button bars

Purpose: Saves the active project.

Associated with: Save Project As

Save Project As

Access: Project menu bar—File menu

Purpose: Saves the active project to a new name and/or directory.

Associated with: Save Project

Select

 Access: Table tool bar

Purpose: Selects records in the active table.

Associated with: Select All, Select None, Switch Selection

Select All

 Access: Table, Layout, and Script menu bars—Edit menu; Table button bar

Purpose: Selects all records in the active table, all graphics drawn in the active layout, or all text in the active script.

Associated with: Pointer, Select, Select Name, Switch Selection

Select All Graphics

Access: View menu bar—Edit menu
Purpose: Selects all graphics drawn in the view.
Associated with: Pointer

Select by Theme

Access: View menu bar—Theme menu
Purpose: Selects features from active themes based on features chosen in the selector theme.
Associated with: Select Feature, Select Features Using Shape

Select Feature

Access: View tool bar
Purpose: Selects features in the active theme using the mouse.
Associated with: Select Features Using Shape, Select by Theme

Select Features Using Shape

Access: View button bar
Purpose: Selects features in the active theme using selected graphics in the view.
Associated with: Select Feature, Select by Theme, Pointer

Select None

Access: Table menu bar—Edit menu; Table button bar
Purpose: Clears the selected set in the active table.
Associated with: Select, Select All, Switch Selected

Send to Back

Access: View and Layout menu bars—Graphics menu; Layout button bar
Purpose: Places the selected graphics behind the remaining graphics.
Associated with: Bring to Front, Pointer

Series from Records/Fields

Access: Chart menu bar—Chart menu; Chart button bar

Purpose: Toggles between using records and using fields for plotting the data series in a chart.

Associated with: Create Chart, Chart Properties

Set Work Directory

Access: View menu bar—File menu

Purpose: Sets or changes the current working directory.

Associated with: Project Properties

Shift Left

Access: Script button bar

Purpose: Shifts the currently selected line (or lines) two spaces to the left.

Associated with: Shift Right

Shift Right

Access: Script button bar

Purpose: Shifts the currently selected line (or lines) two spaces to the right.

Associated with: Shift Left

Show/Hide Grid

Access: Layout menu bar—Layout menu

Purpose: Toggles the display of the active layout's grid on and off.

Associated with: Layout Properties, Show/Hide Margins

Show/Hide Legend

Access: Chart menu bar—Chart menu

Purpose: Toggles the display of the active chart's legend on and off.

Associated with: Chart Properties, Show/Hide X Axis, Show/Hide Y Axis, Show/Hide Title

Show/Hide Margins

Access: Layout menu bar—Layout menu

Purpose: Toggles the display of the active layout's page margins on and off.

Associated with: Layout Properties, Show/Hide Grid

Show/Hide Title

Access: Chart menu bar—Chart menu

Purpose: Toggles the display of the active chart's title on and off.

Associated with: Chart Properties, Show/Hide Legend, Show/Hide X Axis, Show/Hide Y Axis

Show/Hide X Axis

Access: Chart menu bar—Chart menu

Purpose: Toggles the display of the active chart's X axis (with tick marks) on and off.

Associated with: Chart Properties, Show/Hide Y Axis, Show/Hide Legend, Show/Hide Title

Show/Hide Y Axis

Access: Chart menu bar—Chart menu

Purpose: Toggles the display of the active chart's Y axis (with tick marks) on and off.

Associated with: Chart Properties, Show/Hide X Axis, Show/Hide Legend, Show/Hide Title

Show Symbol Palette

Access: View, Table, Chart, and Layout menu bars—Window menu

Purpose: Displays the symbol palette.

Associated with: Legend Editor

Simplify

Access: Layout menu bar—Graphics menu

Purpose: Explodes the selected graphics, including legends and scale bars, into component graphic elements.

Associated with: Frame, Group

Size and Position

Access: View and Layout menu bars—Graphics menu

Purpose: Displays the dialog window for controlling the size and position of the selected graphics.

Associated with: Graphics Properties, Pointer

Snap

Access: View tool bar

Purpose: Sets the general tolerance of snapping vertices for an editable theme.

Associated with: Snap Feature, Start/Stop Editing, Draw, Pointer

Snap to Boundary

Access: View popup menu

Purpose: Snaps the next entered point to the nearest line segment within the interactive snapping tolerance.

Associated with: Snap to Endpoint, Snap to Intersection, Snap to Vertex

Snap to Endpoint

Access: View popup menu

Purpose: Snaps the next entered point to the nearest node held in common by two or more features within the interactive snapping tolerance.

Associated with: Snap to Boundary, Snap to Intersection, Snap to Vertex

Snap to Intersection

Access: View popup menu

Purpose: Snaps the next entered point to the nearest line endpoint within the interactive snapping tolerance.

Associated with: Snap to Boundary, Snap to Endpoint, Snap to Vertex

Snap to Vertex

Access: View popup menu

Purpose: Snaps the next entered point to the nearest vertex within the interactive snapping tolerance.

Associated with: Snap to Boundary, Snap to Endpoint, Snap to Intersection

Sort Ascending/Sort Descending

Access: Table menu bar—Field menu; Table button bar

Purpose: Sorts all records in the active table on the active field.

Associated with: Promote

SQL Connect

Access: Project menu bar—Project menu

Purpose: Opens the SQL Connect dialog window to enable connection to a database server and subsequent retrieval of records based on an SQL query.

Associated with: Export

Start/Stop Editing

Access: Table menu bar—Table menu; View menu bar—Theme menu

Purpose: Controls the enabling of editing on a theme or table.

Associated with: Edit, Pointer

Statistics

Access: Table menu bar—Field menu

Purpose: Obtains statistics about the currently active numeric field in the active table.

Associated with: Summarize, Query

Step

Access: Script menu bar—Script menu; Script button bar

Purpose: Executes one request or object reference in the compiled script.

Associated with: Compile, Run, Toggle Breakpoint

Store As Template

Access: Layout menu bar—Layout menu

Purpose: Creates a layout template from the current layout.

Associated with: Use Template

Store North Arrows

Access: Layout menu bar—Layout menu

Purpose: Stores each graphics group in the current layout as a north arrow.

Associated with: Draw, Use Template

Subtract Graphics

Access: View menu bar—Edit menu

Purpose: Subtracts the shape of one graphic from the shape of another (the second selected one from the first selected one).

Associated with: Select All Graphics, Combine Graphics, Union Graphics, Intersect Graphics

Summarize

Access: Table menu bar—Field menu; Table button bar

Purpose: Displays the Summary Table Definition dialog window for preparing a summary table based on the active field.

Associated with: Statistics, Merge, Query

Switch Selection

Access: Table menu bar—Edit menu; Table button bar

Purpose: Switches the selected set of records in the active table to all records previously unselected.

Associated with: Select, Select All, Select None

Table

Access: View menu bar—Theme menu; View button bar

Purpose: Opens the attribute tables for the active themes in a view.

Associated with: Add Table

Text

Access: View and Layout tool bars

Purpose: Adds or edits text in the active view or layout.

Associated with: Pointer, Draw

Theme Properties

Access: View menu bar—Theme menu; View button bar

Purpose: Reviews and sets properties of the active theme, including name, logical queries, field for feature labeling, range of scales for display, hot link definition, geocoding properties, and snapping.

Associated with: View Properties, Edit Legend

Themes On/Themes Off

Access: View menu bar—View menu
Purpose: Toggles all themes in a view on or off.
Associated with: Theme Properties

Toggle Breakpoint

Access: Script menu bar—Script menu; Script button bar
Purpose: Toggles a breakpoint on or off at the cursor location.
Associated with: Compile, Step, Run, Clear All Breakpoints

Undo

Access: Script menu bar—Edit menu; Script button bar
Purpose: Undo the last change made in a script window.
Associated with: Redo

Undo Edit

Access: Table menu bar—Edit menu; View popup menu
Purpose: Undo the last edit made to a shapefile or table.
Associated with: Redo Edit, Delete Last Point

Undo Erase

Access: Chart menu bar—Edit menu; Chart button bar
Purpose: "Undeletes" the last data markers that were erased from the active chart.
Associated with: Erase, Erase with Polygon

Unembed Script

Access: Script menu bar—Script menu
Purpose: Removes the selected script so that it is no longer embedded in the project.
Associated with: Embed Script

Ungroup

Access: View and Layout menu bars—Graphics menu

Purpose: Ungroups a previously grouped graphic into its original individual pieces.

Associated with: Group, Pointer

Union Graphics

Access: View menu bar—Edit menu

Purpose: Combines the selected graphics from a view into a single graphic. For polygon graphics, only the exterior boundary is preserved in the output graphic.

Associated with: Select All Graphics, Combine Graphics, Subtract Graphics, Intersect Graphics

Use Template

Access: Layout menu bar—Layout menu; View menu bar—View menu

Purpose: Using a specified stored template, creates a new layout or updates the current layout.

Associated with: Store As Template, Layout Properties

Vertex Tool

Access: View tool bar; Layout tool bar

Purpose: Adds, moves, or deletes vertices from a selected shapefile feature or graphic element.

Associated with: Pointer Tool

Write Text File

Access: Script menu bar—Script menu; Script button bar

Purpose: Writes an entire script or selected text to a text file.

Associated with: Load Text File, Load System Script

XY Scatter Chart Gallery

Access: Chart menu bar—Gallery menu; Chart button bar

Purpose: Displays format options and changes an active chart to XY Scatter Chart format.

Associated with: Create Chart, Area Chart Gallery, Bar Chart Gallery, Column Chart Gallery, Line Chart Gallery

Zoom In (button)

Access: View menu bar—View menu; Layout menu bar—Layout menu; View and Layout button bars; View popup menu

Purpose: Zooms in on the center of the active view or layout by a factor of two.

Associated with: Zoom Out, Zoom to Full Extent, Zoom to Selected, Zoom to Themes, Zoom to Page, Zoom to Actual Size

Zoom In (tool)

Access: View and Layout tool bars

Purpose: Zooms in on the area you click on or the area you describe on a view or layout.

Associated with: Zoom Out, Zoom to Full Extent, Zoom to Selected, Zoom to Themes, Zoom to Page, Zoom to Actual Size

Zoom Out (button)

Access: View menu bar—View menu; Layout menu bar—Layout menu; View and Layout button bars; View popup menu

Purpose: Zooms out from the center of the active view or layout by a factor of two.

Associated with: Zoom In, Zoom to Full Extent, Zoom to Selected, Zoom to Themes, Zoom to Page, Zoom to Actual Size

Zoom Out (tool)

Access: View and Layout tool bars

Purpose: Zooms out from a position you click on or the area you describe on a view or layout.

Associated with: Zoom In, Zoom to Full Extent, Zoom to Selected, Zoom to Themes, Zoom to Page, Zoom to Actual Size

Zoom Previous

Access: View menu bar—View menu; View button bar

Purpose: Zooms to the previously displayed extent in the view.

Associated with: Zoom In, Zoom Out, Zoom to Full Extent, Zoom to Selected, Zoom to Themes

Zoom to Actual Size

Access: Layout menu bar—Layout menu; Layout button bar

Purpose: Zooms to the actual size (1:1) of the layout page.

Associated with: Zoom In, Zoom Out, Zoom to Page, Zoom to Selected

Zoom to Full Extent

Access: View menu bar—View menu; View button bar

Purpose: Zooms to the full extent of all themes in a view.

Associated with: Zoom In, Zoom Out, Zoom to Selected, Zoom to Themes

Zoom to Page

Access: Layout menu bar—Layout menu; Layout button bar

Purpose: Zooms to the full extent of the layout page.

Associated with: Zoom In, Zoom Out, Zoom to Actual Size, Zoom to Selected

Zoom to Selected

Access: View menu bar—View menu; Layout menu bar—Layout menu; View and Layout button bars; View popup menu

Purpose: Zooms to selected features of the active themes in a view, or to the selected graphics of a layout.

Associated with: Zoom In, Zoom Out, Zoom to Full Extent, Zoom to Themes, Zoom to Page, Zoom to Actual Size

Zoom to Themes

Access: View menu bar—View menu; View button bar

Purpose: Zooms to the extent of the active themes in a view.

Associated with: Zoom In, Zoom Out, Zoom to Full Extent, Zoom to Selected

Index

T

More OnWord Press Titles

Computing/Business

Lotus Notes for Web Workgroups
$34.95

Mapping with Microsoft Office
$29.95 Includes Disk

Geographic Information Systems (GIS)

GIS: A Visual Approach
$39.95

The GIS Book, 4E
$39.95

INSIDE MapInfo Professional
$49.95 Includes CD-ROM

MapBasic Developer's Guide
$49.95 Includes Disk

Raster Imagery in Geographic Information Systems
$59.95

INSIDE ArcView GIS, 2E
$39.95 Includes CD-ROM

ArcView GIS Exercise Book, 2E
$49.95 Includes CD-ROM

ArcView GIS/Avenue Developer's Guide, 2E
$49.95

ArcView GIS/Avenue Programmer's Reference, 2E
$49.95

101 ArcView/Avenue Scripts: The Disk
Disk $101.00

ArcView GIS/Avenue Scripts: The Disk, 2E
Disk $99.00

ARC/INFO Quick Reference
$24.95

INSIDE ARC/INFO
$59.95 Includes CD-ROM

MicroStation

INSIDE MicroStation 95, 4E
$39.95 Includes Disk

MicroStation 95 Exercise Book
$39.95 Includes Disk
Optional Instructor's Guide $14.95

MicroStation 95 Quick Reference
$24.95

MicroStation 95 Productivity Book
$49.95

Adventures in MicroStation 3D
$49.95 Includes CD-ROM

MicroStation for AutoCAD Users, 2E
$34.95

MicroStation Exercise Book 5.X
$34.95 Includes Disk
Optional Instructor's Guide $14.95

MicroStation Reference Guide 5.X
$18.95

Build Cell for 5.X
Software $69.95

101 MDL Commands (5.X and 95)
Executable Disk $101.00
Source Disks (6) $259.95

Pro/ENGINEER and Pro/JR.

*Automating Design in Pro/ENGINEER
with Pro/PROGRAM*
$59.95 Includes CD-ROM

INSIDE Pro/ENGINEER, 3E
$49.95 Includes Disk

Pro/ENGINEER Exercise Book, 2E
$39.95 Includes Disk

Pro/ENGINEER Quick Reference, 2E
$24.95

Thinking Pro/ENGINEER
$49.95

Pro/ENGINEER Tips and Techniques
$59.95

INSIDE Pro/JR.
$49.95

Softdesk

INSIDE Softdesk Architectural
$49.95 Includes Disk

*Softdesk Architecture 1 Certified
Courseware*
$34.95 Includes CD-ROM

*Softdesk Architecture 2 Certified
Courseware*
$34.95 Includes CD-ROM

INSIDE Softdesk Civil
$49.95 Includes Disk

Softdesk Civil 1 Certified Courseware
$34.95 Includes CD-ROM

Softdesk Civil 2 Certified Courseware
$34.95 Includes CD-ROM

Other CAD

*Manager's Guide to Computer-Aided
Engineering*
$49.95

Fallingwater in 3D Studio
$39.95 Includes Disk

Interleaf

INSIDE Interleaf (v. 6)
$49.95 Includes Disk

Interleaf Quick Reference (v. 6)
$24.95

Interleaf Exercise Book (v. 5)
$39.95 Includes Disk

Interleaf Tips and Tricks (v. 5)
$49.95 Includes Disk

Adventurer's Guide to Interleaf LISP
$49.95 Includes Disk

Windows NT

Windows NT for the Technical Professional
$39.95

SunSoft Solaris

SunSoft Solaris 2.* for Managers and Administrators
$34.95

SunSoft Solaris 2.* User's Guide
$29.95 Includes Disk

SunSoft Solaris 2.* Quick Reference
$18.95

Five Steps to SunSoft Solaris 2.*
$24.95 Includes Disk

SunSoft Solaris 2.* for Windows Users
$24.95

HP-UX

HP-UX User's Guide
$29.95

Five Steps to HP-UX
$24.95 Includes Disk

OnWord Press Distribution

End Users/User Groups/Corporate Sales

OnWord Press books are available worldwide to end users, user groups, and corporate accounts from local booksellers or from Softstore/CADNEWS Bookstore: call 1-800-CADNEWS (1-800-223-6397) or 505-474-5120; fax 505-474-5020; write to SoftStore, Inc., 2530 Camino Entrada, Santa Fe, NM 87505-4835, USA or e-mail orders@hmp.com. SoftStore, Inc., is a High Mountain Press Company.

Wholesale, Including Overseas Distribution

High Mountain Press distributes OnWord Press books internationally. For terms call 1-800-4-ONWORD (1-800-466-9673) or 505-474-5130; fax to 505-474-5030; e-mail orders@hmp.com; or write to High Mountain Press, 2530 Camino Entrada, Santa Fe, NM 87505-4835, USA.

On the Internet: http://www.hmp.com

OnWord Press, 2530 Camino Entrada, Santa Fe, NM 87505-4835 USA

CD-ROM Credits and Copyrights

Material herein is for installation under UNIX, DOS/Windows, Windows NT, Windows 95, and Macintosh. Contains data project files referenced throughout the accompanying book. Some of the data files are used herein with the permission of Environmental Systems Research Institute (ESRI); Geographic Data Technology, Inc.; Equifax National Decision Systems, Inc.; SPOT IMAGE, S.A.; and Vista Information Solutions, Inc. All rights reserved.

The Claritas directory herein contains a Claritas Connect software demonstration program, sample Trendline-GIS files, documentation files on Trendline-GIS files, file layouts for Trendline-GIS files, Dr. Know-It-All Help file, and a Quick Data Guide to Claritas products. All rights reserved.